Microprocessor-based Systems
Level V

Units in this series

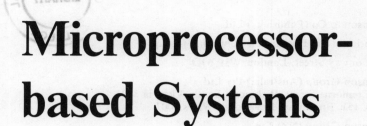

Microprocessor-based Systems

Level V

M. J. Morse

School of Electronics and Electrical Engineering,
Leicester Polytechnic

TECHNICIAN EDUCATION COUNCIL
in association with
HUTCHINSON
London Melbourne Sydney Auckland Johannesburg

Hutchinson & Co (Publishers) Ltd

An imprint of the Hutchinson Publishing Group

17–21 Conway Street, London W1P 6JD

Hutchinson Group (Australia) Pty Ltd
30–32 Cremorne Street, Richmond South, Victoria 3121
PO Box 151, Broadway, New South Wales 2007

Hutchinson Group (NZ) Ltd
32–34 View Road, PO Box 40–086, Glenfield, Auckland 10

Hutchinson Group (SA) (Pty) Ltd
PO Box 337, Bergvlei 2012, South Africa

First published 1982

Set in Times

Printed in Great Britain by The Anchor Press Ltd
and bound by Wm Brendon & Son Ltd.
both of Tiptree, Essex

British Library Cataloguing in Publication Data

Microprocessor-based systems Level V.
  1. Microprocessors
  I. Technician Education Council
  621.3819′5835   TK7895.M5

ISBN 0 09 147361 6

Contents

Preface

This book is one of a series on microelectronics/microprocessors published by Hutchinson on behalf of the Technician Education Council. The books in the series are designed for use with units associated with Technician Education Council programmes.

In June 1978 the United Kingdom Prime Minister expressed anxiety about the effect to be expected from the introduction of microprocessors on the pattern of employment in specific industries. From this stemmed an initiative through the Department of Industry and the National Enterprise Board to encourage the use and development of microprocessor technology.

An important aspect of such a development programme was seen as being the education and training of personnel for both the research, development and manufacture of microelectronics material and equipment, and the application of these in other industries. In 1979 a project was established by the Technician Education Council for the development of technician education programme units (a unit is a specification of the objectives to be attained by a student) and associated learning packages, this project being funded by the Department of Industry and managed on their behalf by the National Computing Centre Ltd.

TEC established a committee involving industry, both as producers and users of microelectronics, and educationists. In addition widespread consultations took place. Programme units were developed for technicians and technician engineers concerned with the design, manufacture and servicing aspects incorporating microelectronic devices. Five units were produced:

Microelectronic Systems	Level I
Microelectronic Systems	Level II
Microelectronic Systems	Level III
Microprocessor-based Systems	Level IV
Microprocessor-based Systems	Level V

Units were also produced for those technicians who required a general understanding of the range of applications of microelectronic devices and their potential:

Microprocessor Appreciation	Level III
Microprocessor Principles	Level IV

This phase was then followed by the development of the learning packages, involving three writing teams, the key people in these teams being:

Microelectronic Systems I, II, III — P. Cooke
Microprocessor-based Systems IV — A. Potton
Microprocessor-based Systems V — M. J. Morse
Microprocessor Appreciation III — G. Martin
Microprocessor Principles IV — G. Martin

The project director during the unit specification stage was N. Bonnett, assisted by R. Bertie. Mr Bonnett continued as consultant during the writing stage. The project manager was W. Bolton, assisted by K. Snape.

Self-learning

As an aid to self-learning, questions are included in every chapter. These appear at the end of the chapters with references in the margin of the chapter text (for example Q1.2), indicating the most appropriate position for self-learning use. Answers to each question are given at the back of the book.

The books in this series have therefore been developed for use in either the classroom teaching situation or for self-learning.

Introduction

This book was written to meet the needs of those studying the TEC Unit Microprocessor-based Systems Level V (TEC U80/675). It assumes that the student has access to a modern software development station, preferably diskette-based, and has studied previous units in the series.

The material covered in the book is broadly divided into two main sections. The first describes typical system utilities and the way in which these are used to develop microprocessor application programs. Since all the microprocessor TEC units are based on the Intel 8080, a natural choice for the program development environment is the CP/M operating system, and its utilities ED, ASM and DDT, which were originally written for 8080 systems. CP/M is now widely regarded as the standard operating system for 8-bit microprocessors.

The second main section of the book begins at Chapter 7 and covers the common application areas of data acquisition and stepping motor control. It ends with a discussion of the limitations of assembly language programming and the need for a high-level language, such as PASCAL*, to increase programming efficiency.

The choice of material in the book was dictated wholly by the need to cover the TEC syllabus and it is with gratitude that I acknowledge the help and advice of Norman Bonnett of the Bradford College, on matters concerning syllabus interpretation, and also for his critical reading of the manuscript. Needless to say, any opinions expressed are those of the author.

My thanks are also due to my wife Lesley, for typing the original manuscript, and to Leicester Polytechnic for the use of their micro-computing facilities.

Leicester, January 1982   M. J. MORSE

---

*For consistency, all programming languages have been set in capital letters, but it should be appreciated that PASCAL is named after Blaise Pascal and is not an acronym.

Chapter 1 An introduction to floppy disks and operating systems

Objectives of this chapter *When you have completed studying this chapter you should be able to:*

1 *Appreciate the need for a backing store in microprocessor development systems.*
2 *Understand why magnetic tapes and cassettes are less suitable than floppy disks.*
3 *Know the popular sizes of floppy disks, how the information is stored on the disk surface and how the surface is subdivided into tracks and sectors.*
4 *Understand the difference between hard- and soft-sectored disks.*
5 *Appreciate the reason why the bit packing density on a disk surface is greater if delay modulation is used in preference to frequency modulation, and understand the terms single-density, double-density, single-sided and double-sided in relation to disk storage systems.*
6 *Be able to explain the terms file, directory and operating system.*
7 *Be familiar with typical operating system commands to create, delete, rename and examine files stored on disk.*

1.1 Introduction

A microprocessor development system that consisted only of some hardware and a control/monitoring program would make life very difficult for the microprocessor applications engineer. Developing hardware and software that satisfies a system specification is difficult enough without having to contend with gross limitations of a development system. Fortunately there are hardware/software development aids available that provide a good deal of support. For example, if we consider only software development, earlier units in this series have discussed utility programs such as assemblers, editors and debuggers which are a minimum requirement for serious applications work. In this unit we shall deal in more detail with these and other system utilities and explain how they are stored in the system and used to develop realistic microprocessor application programs. We shall also look beyond assembly language programming to see which high-level languages are being used to develop microprocessor software and when it is beneficial to use them.

1.2 The need for backing stores

The 8080/8085 range of microprocessors, in common with all the other established 8-bit microprocessors, has a 16-bit address bus and can therefore directly address 64 Kbytes of main memory – sometimes called primary memory. It is quite possible to imagine a system in which the assembler, editor, debugger and other system utility packages are each stored in ROM and allocated address space within the total of 64 Kbytes available. You will know from studying previous units that the assembler and some of the other standard utilities need extra memory (RAM) to store such things as symbol tables, breakpoint instructions and command characters. This extra memory accounts for more of the available address space.

Continuing with this line of thought, if the program being developed is anything more than modest it will probably be developed by degrees with previously tested code segments (mainly subroutines) held in user EPROM. Address space will therefore be needed for the EPROMs. Finally the program segment being developed will have to be in RAM and so will the control program which allows the user to access the various utilities. All this can amount to a significant memory requirement and introduce some quite difficult memory organisation problems.

Nonetheless systems configured exactly as described above have been manufactured over a number of years. Quite apart from the difficulties of designing such systems, they have at least two serious drawbacks as far as the user is concerned. The first is that, because memory is limited, only so much software support can be provided without plugging-in different ROMs whenever a different program is needed; and secondly, primary memory is expensive, or at least more expensive than some of the alternatives. A less precise objection is that, conceptually, the system is untidy.

A much neater, and obvious, alternative is to use some form of backing store, or secondary memory, to hold all those extra programs which were previously held in primary memory. As a system component the backing store is just somewhere, other than primary memory, in which to store information. It should have sufficient capacity to accommodate all the system utilities and user programs and it should be non-volatile.

When one of the programs in the backing store is needed it is recalled to primary memory (RAM) and processing continues as though it had always existed in RAM. For example, when a source code program is to be assembled, the assembler program is copied into primary memory and executed. If the source code also resides in the backing store, the assembler will fetch that too into primary memory, assemble it, and then write the assembled code back out to the backing store.

See note in Preface about questions

Q1.1

Such a simplistic explanation raises a number of questions about the nature of the backing store and how the correct program is located, but the idea should be clear.

1.3 Backing stores

Almost without exception, backing stores are some form of magnetic surface. Possibilities are magnetic tapes, cassettes or, more usually in modern microprocessor development systems, magnetic disks or diskettes. Data are stored on these surfaces, and subsequently read back from them, in much the same way as music and speech are recorded and replayed on domestic recording equipment. In the simplest system, binary one is stored by passing current in one direction through the write head energising coil, and binary zero is stored by reversing the current direction. Figure 1.1 illustrates the procedure.

When stored data are read back from the surface the changes in direction of magnetisation are detected by a read head (which may be the write head reconfigured) and the voltage induced in the read head coil is amplified to reveal the sequence of ones and zeros previously recorded. The whole surface is divided into a number of tracks and data are stored as a serial pattern of magnetisation on particular tracks. This means that when the same data are read back, the access time, i.e. the time taken to locate a particular block of data, is much longer than the access time of random access memories. Note that in this connection, the term 'random access' really means that every address in memory is equally available. In other words, access time is not dependent upon which address is being accessed. Strictly speaking then, a ROM is also a random access memory device, but by common usage the term RAM has come to mean read/write memory.

The longer access times of serial access memories is particularly noticeable in magnetic tape and cassette systems because the required data may be at one end of the tape while the read head is at the other. In these systems the total access time is the time to wind-on or rewind the tape, plus the time to read off the data. In the worst case this time can be of the order of minutes.

Q1.2

For this reason tapes and cassettes are only used in systems in which access time is not important, or less important than cost. Inexpensive cassette recorders with a suitable interface are used as backing stores in some small business machines and personal computers but never in professional microprocessor development systems. They also have a use as archive stores in some mini- and mainframe computers. An archive store can hold back-up versions of any system or user program but its main function is, often, to store extensive blocks of

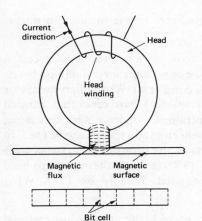

Figure 1.1 Basic principle of recording on a magnetic surface. A write current is imposed on the coil winding during recording and induced in it when replaying. Change of magnetic polarity within a bit cell and/or at its boundaries indicates the bit stored

data which may, for example, be needed for payroll calculations in a large organisation. In effect, the archive store backs up the main backing store which will almost certainly be some form of magnetic disk.

Q1.3

1.4   Floppy disks

Floppy disks are the universal backing storage medium in microprocessor development systems.

Historically, computer systems have always needed to access a backing store and pick out any one of perhaps several million bytes, all within a few hundredths of a second or so. When microprocessor systems began to appear, the conventional, hard disks that satisfied this demand in mini- and mainframe computers were too large, consumed too much power and were also too expensive to be used. In any case, the speed requirements of microprocessor systems were much less stringent. In the early 1970s cheaper alternatives to hard disks were already being investigated, notably by IBM. What emerged was the floppy disk!

Floppy disks are cut from thin sheets of Mylar, a recording material used to make ordinary magnetic tape. They are called floppy disks because they are, literally, floppy, or flexible, and disk-like. Every disk is enclosed in a plastic envelope, which keeps it flat, protects it, and inside which it is free to rotate.

When a disk is inserted into a disk-drive unit, a drive shaft engages with a centre hole in the disk and rotates it at 300 rev/min. The read/write head, which can be positioned to an accuracy of 1/50 inch, contacts the disk surface through a radial slot in the envelope. Positioning of the read/write head to locate with any one of a number of concentric recording tracks is controlled by a stepping motor (see Chapter 8). When the required track has been located, a solenoid operates and the read/write head is pressed against the disk surface as

Q1.4   illustrated in Figure 1.2. This is called 'loading' the head.

Two sizes of disk are used in microprocessor development systems (Figure 1.3). The 8 inch disk, which was developed by IBM and was the first to appear, has 77 tracks, and the smaller $5\frac{1}{4}$ inch disk, called a mini-floppy diskette, has, typically, 35 tracks. The storage capacity of these disks depends on the way information is recorded. The minimum capacity of an 8 inch disk is usually quoted as 250 Kbytes

Q1.5   and the minimum capacity of the $5\frac{1}{4}$ inch disk is about 100 Kbytes.

Apart from being divided into a prescribed number of tracks, the surface of a disk is further sub-divided into a number of sectors, as shown in Figure 1.4. A disk address is made up of a track number and a sector number and every self-contained block of data (utilities, user programs or whatever) starts in a new sector.

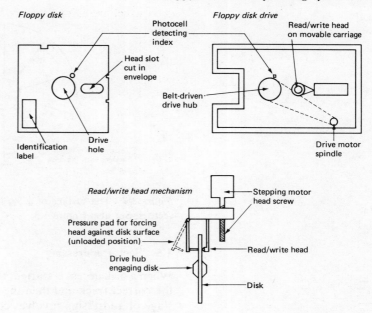

Figure 1.2 Floppy disk and floppy disk drive mechanism. The disk spins inside its protective envelope and the read/write head engages with the disk surface through the head slot cut in the envelope

Figure 1.3

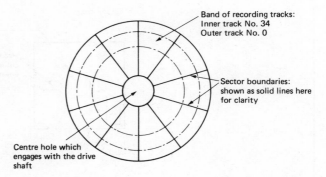

Figure 1.4   The surface of a $5\frac{1}{4}$ inch disk is divided into 35 tracks and 10 sectors. See also Figure 1.3

1.5   Sector addressing

When a disk access is started, the read/write head is first loaded onto the correct track and then the correct sector is located. This second stage of addressing involves comparing the required sector address with sector information read from the disk. Two addressing methods, known as hard and soft sectoring, are used. Hard-sectored disks have concentric sector holes, sometimes called index holes, punched out at precise angular intervals around the disk. These holes are detected by a photocell and used to mark the beginning of a sector. One extra hole is provided to mark sector 0.

Soft-sectored disks sometimes have a single index hole which marks sector 0, but the essential difference between these disks and the hard-sectored variety is that sector boundaries are marked by pre-stored information on the disk surface. Figure 1.5 shows the different

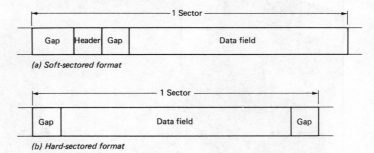

Figure 1.5   Simplified recording formats for hard- and soft-sectored diskettes. The gaps isolate various blocks of recorded information and give time for the read electronics to be synchronised with data coming from the track. The header contains address and error detection codes. Hard-sectored diskettes have 23% more storage capacity because they do not have to record headers

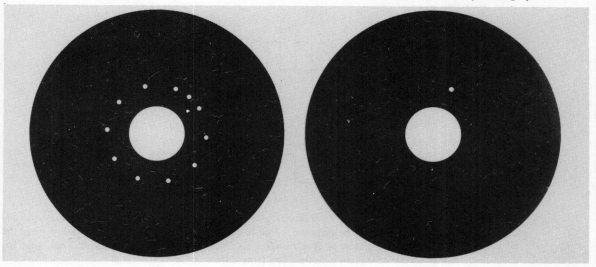

Figure 1.6   Hard- and soft-sectored discs outside their envelopes; the sector hole can be easily seen

Q1.6

recording formats and Figure 1.6 the different disks outside their envelopes. The program that stores this sector information is called a formatter and it usually does three things:

1   It stores the sector address information on the disk surface as already explained.
2   It identifies any 'bad' sectors in which, because of surface imperfections, data cannot be stored.
3   It inserts gaps between the sector address and data fields so that the read/write circuits can identify the information type in every disk access.

Programs called formatters are sometimes used on hard-sectored disks but for a different reason.

1.6   Recording methods

Having positioned the read/write head at the correct disk address, data are recorded by magnetising areas of the track to store binary 1 or binary 0. The way in which the surface is magnetised has a critical effect on the amount of information that can be stored. The first generation of floppy disk controllers used what later became known as single-density recording format. In these systems the binary data to be stored on the disk were re-coded using a technique called frequency modulation (Figure 1.7).

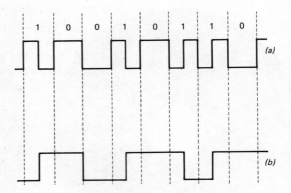

Figure 1.7   Recording waveforms for *(a)* frequency modulation and *(b)* delay modulation. Double density systems use delay modulation since the number of flux transistions for a given bit pattern is about half that for frequency modulation (single density) systems

You will appreciate that, since the disk is rotating quite independently of the read/write circuits, timing information must somehow be imbedded in the data. If this were not done then it would be almost impossible to synchronise data as it was read from the disk surface. You may further appreciate that it would be easy to lose synchronisation if, for example, a sequence of ones was stored by magnetising a length of the track in one or other direction. What is needed to maintain synchronisation are fairly regular changes in the pattern of magnetisation, because changes in magnetic flux, according to Faraday's law, produce induced voltages when detected, and voltage changes at regular intervals provide synchronisation information.

In frequency modulation encoding, a change occurs at every bit cell boundary and in the middle of a bit cell which stores a 1. Of course these changes cannot occur too closely together otherwise they will overlap when the information is read back from the disk surface. Consequently there is a limit to the bit packing density which can be achieved with this, or indeed any other, recording method.

In an attempt to increase the bit packing density, a technique known as delay, or modified frequency, modulation (d.m. or m.f.m.) was adopted. In this technique a change occurs in the middle of a bit cell when a 1 is stored, and at the end of a cell when a 0 is stored, if the 0 is followed by another 0. Figure 1.7 shows that, with delay modulation, the changes are more widely separated so that information can be more tightly packed before differentiation of consecutive bits becomes a problem. In fact it was found that the bit packing density could be doubled, so the systems which used delay modulation came

Q1.7   to be known as double-density systems.

A further development, again designed to increase storage capacity, was to use both sides of the disk where only one had been used before. Consequently, there are in existence single- and double-sided, single- and double-density systems. Not surprisingly, double-sided double-density systems have the largest capacity, which for an 8 inch disk is about 1 Mbyte and for a $5\frac{1}{4}$ inch disk 0.5 Mbytes.

1.7   Files and directories

Packages of information are stored on a floppy disk in self-contained blocks. One block could be the assembler program, another could be the debugger, and another could be just a block of data to be processed by yet another program block. If we could pick up a disk and examine these blocks they would, of course, all look the same – just different patterns of magnetisation for different binary information. So what, for example, distinguishes the assembler block from any other block?

All blocks of information are contained within files. The assembler program for example is contained within a file. A large program may extend over several sectors or even several tracks, but it is still a single entity, a single file. When a new file is written out to the disk (created), it is always started in a new, unused, sector so it has a unique disk address. It is also given a name which, from then on, is intimately linked with the start address. That link is formed by entering the name of the file and its start address in the disk directory. The directory is itself stored on disk, usually in the first sectors on the outside track, and, like a telephone directory, it contains the names and addresses of all the files stored on the disk. It may also contain such other file information as length in sectors, type (binary or ASCII, for example) and the recording density. Directory entries may also indicate when a file was created, when it was last used and whether, for example, it may be accessed for reading but not writing.

As far as the user is concerned, files are identified by name. When a particular file is required the directory is first searched to discover if the named file exists on the disk. If it does, the disk address is read from the directory, the read/write head is moved to that address and the contents of the file are copied from the disk surface to primary memory. If the file contained an executable program, the program is **Q1.8** executed.

Note that the name of a file is just an identifier. It does not necessarily give any idea about what the file contains. We may for example put our assembler program in a file called FRED. The fact that the assembler is now identified by the name FRED, and not the more usual ASM, has not changed the assembler in any way.

File names must usually be no longer than eight characters and must always be unique. Since there is a limited amount of disk space allocated for the directory, the total number of files that can exist on a disk is also limited but the limit varies widely between different systems.

1.8   The operating system

The program responsible for looking after the files and the disk directory is called the Disk Operating System (DOS), or just operating system (OS). Disk-based microprocessor development systems are normally supplied with an operating system tailored for the system hardware. This may have been written by the supplier, or their agents, and designed to work with only one set of hardware, or it may be a more general operating system such as CP/M (Control Program for Microprocessors)* which, with minor modifications, will work with a number of different microcomputers. Whichever is the case, the operating system is designed to manage rot only the disk drives but all the system resources – the computer itself, primary memory, computer peripherals and the utility programs. It does this by interpreting simple commands entered at the console keyboard.

Imagine for instance that we had previously saved a source code program called MYFILE on the disk and now wished to see what it contained. In these circumstances we may enter,

    TYPE MYFILE

The operating system recognises the character string TYPE as an allowable command, and may then,

1   Interpret MYFILE as the name of a disk file.
2   Look in the directory for the start address of MYFILE.
3   Locate MYFILE on the disk.
4   Read from MYFILE and print the ASCII equivalent of each byte read.
5   Then display a prompt character indicating that it is ready to accept another command.

A different command would be entered if, for example, the contents of MYFILE were to be displayed on the printer. The point to remember here is that the operating system is just a program that enables a user to control system resources. In effect it is a software interface between the user and the development system. The only facilities that it has are those written into it when the system was designed. Consequently it can be very powerful or very elementary, but to qualify as an operating system there are a few minimal facilities which must be provided.

Q1.9

*CP/M is a trade name of Digital Research Inc.

1.9 CP/M, the standard operating system for 8-bit systems

The TYPE command explained above is actually a CP/M facility, although most operating systems would have a similar command. In the classification of operating systems CP/M is described as a single-user, single-tasking operating system which means that it can handle only one user terminal and one task at a time. Some more powerful operating systems can support a large number of on-line terminals (multi-user) and others can dynamically reallocate system resources to allow different programs to, apparently, run concurrently (multi-tasking and foreground/background programming). Therefore in the hierarchy of operating systems CP/M ranks well down the scale, just as microcomputers, for which CP/M was designed, rank well down the scale in the hierarchy of computer systems.

CP/M was designed to run on any 8080, 8085 or Z80 microcomputer. One such microcomputer is the North Star Horizon shown in Figure 1.8. Attached to the Horizon is a Visual Display Unit (VDU), which is the system console, and a printer. The whole set-up is called a software development station and, at 1980 prices, represents an

Q1.10 investment of just less than £3,000.

The operator communicates with the operating system via the keyboard and the system responds by displaying information on the screen. Note the two disk enclosures at the front of the micro-computer. The left-hand disk drive, drive A, is for the disk containing the operating system (the system disk) and the other disk drive, drive

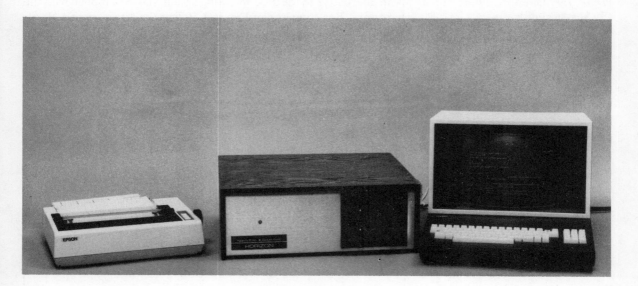

Figure 1.8 A North Star software development station comprising a computer, a printer and a VDU. The disk drives are clearly visible

B, can conveniently be used for user disks. When the microcomputer is first switched on, the operating system, or a part of it, is read from the system disk and stored in primary memory. This can take place automatically or it may be necessary to operate a reset switch to load the operating system. What happens during loading is that a short loader program contained in a ROM is executed. When loading is finished, program control is transferred to the program just read – the operating system. You will appreciate that the operating system must be stored at a disk address known to the loader.

Once loaded, the operating system signals to the user that it is in control by issuing a sign-on message. The CP/M sign-on message for our North Star system is:

```
CP/M on North Star double density disk
22K Version 1.45
Copyright (C) 1979 Lifeboat Associates

A>
```

A> is the CP/M prompt. It means that CP/M is in control and that files on disk A, the system disk, are accessible. In other words directory A is the currently active directory.

To list all the files on disk A we would issue the DIR (directory) command. The effect of doing this is shown in Figure 1.9. Recall that CP/M is an operating system that runs in a number of different microcomputer systems. It is sold as a separate software package and is an alternative to the disk operating system (DOS) supplied with the hardware. For comparison Figure 1.10 lists the directory of a North Star operating system disk. The DOS prompt is '+', and the directory listing was obtained using the DOS LI (for LIst directory) command.

Figure 1.10 contains much more information than the listing of the

```
A>DIR
A:  MOVCPM    COM
A:  CONFIG    COM
A:  ASM       COM
A:  DDT       COM
A:  DUMP      COM
A:  ED        COM
A:  LOAD      COM
A:  PIP       COM
A:  STAT      COM
A:  SUBMIT    COM
A:  SYSGEN    COM
A:  DUMP      ASM
A:  LIST      COM
A:  COPY      COM
A:  FORMAT    COM
A:  DENSITY   COM
A:  SAVEUSER  COM
A:  GENUSER   ASM
A:  IOLIB
A:  ZDT       COM
A:  DRIVE
A:  TBLSUB
A>
```

Figure 1.9 Directory listing for a CP/M system disk

```
NORTH STAR DOS 5.1DQ
+LI
HRQ-R5.1    0     8 D   0
DOS         4    12 D   0
BASIC      10    52 D   1  2D00
FPBASIC    36    50 D   1  2D00
CD         61     4 D   1  2D00
CF         63     6 D   1  2D00
CO         66     8 D   1  2D00
DT         70     4 D   1  2D00
M0000      72     8 D   1     0
M2D00      76     8 D   1  2D00
M5700      80    10 D   1  5700
M6700      85     8 D   1  6700
MF400      89     8 D   1  F400
+
```

Figure 1.10 Directory listing of a North Star Horizon system disk

CP/M directory. For example, the first column after the filename shows the disk address as a track number (0 to 34) and sector number (0 to 9). The second column gives the length of the file in multiples of 512 bytes, the D in the third column means that double density recording was used, the fourth column is a file type number (type 1 is a directly executable program) and the fifth column lists the execution address in RAM when type 1 files are loaded.

Most of the files listed in Figure 1.9 have the filename extension COM which means that they, like the North Star type 1 files, are directly executable. This means that we can execute the programs contained in these files by typing the filename followed by any additional information needed for execution. For example, typing

```
ASM  MYFILE.ASM
```

is a request to assemble the program contained in MYFILE.ASM. Of course, if we were to issue this command the system would respond by displaying an error message because MYFILE.ASM does not exist on disk A. Notice that the full name of a file is the name itself followed by the file name extension. By convention the extension is linked to the file name by a full stop. A different operating system may well adopt a different convention.

Those files which have the .ASM extension are source code files. They usually contain programs that have not yet been assembled so we could use the TYPE command if we wished to view their contents.

You may have noticed already that there is no file called TYPE.COM listed in Figure 1.9, and neither is there any reference to CP/M itself. We know, of course, that CP/M exists because we are using it. TYPE also exists as one of five built-in functions in CP/M. It is an integral part of CP/M and therefore not listed as a separate directory entry. The other four built-in functions are:

DIR   which we have already used to list directory A.
ERA   which means erase a named file from the disk.
REN   rename a file.
SAVE   which is used to save the contents of some part of primary memory in a named disk file.

We can briefly illustrate the use of these four functions using the program called DRIVE on disk A. Firstly, to verify that DRIVE exists we could type:

```
A>DIR DRIVE
A: DRIVE
A>
```

In this form the command means: 'Is there a file called DRIVE listed in the directory?'. Since the file exists the system responds by printing the directory entry.

If we now wished to change the name DRIVE to FRED, the format of the command is:

```
A>REN FRED=DRIVE
A>DIR FRED
A: FRED
A>DIR DRIVE
NOT FOUND
A>
```

Notice that we can check that the REN command has worked properly by looking in the directory for DRIVE, which does not now exist, and FRED, which is DRIVE under another name. You will recall that a file name is only for identification purposes. It does not tell us what is in the file, although it is usual to choose a file name that bears some relationship to the contents.

If we now wished to erase FRED altogether, we could issue the command:

```
A>ERA FRED
A>DIR FRED
NOT FOUND
A>
```

Finally, assume that we have a program in memory which we want to save on the disk. Under CP/M all user programs are held in memory starting at address 0100H. The SAVE command takes the contents of *n* 256-byte blocks starting at 0100H and puts them into a named disk file. For example, if we were sure that our program was completely contained in 3 blocks (768 bytes), we might issue the command:

```
A>SAVE 3 FRED.ASM
A>DIR FRED.ASM
A: FRED     ASM
A>
```

The other facilities of CP/M are listed in Figure 1.9. Some of these facilities, in particular ED (the editor), ASM (the assembler), DDT (the debugger) and LOAD (the loader) will be discussed in later chapters and used to produce working assembly language programs.

Q1.11

With two disk drives in the system, user programs are normally saved on the second disk, disk B. To access this directory we would type B: and then ask for a directory listing. Figure 1.11 lists the files that are currently stored on the author's user disk. There are only four different programs there and they all relate to the work completed for Chapter 9 of this unit. The various file name extensions will be explained in due course.

```
A>B:
B>DIR
B: STEP1    PRN
B: STEP1    HEX
B: STEP1    ASM
B: STEP1    BAK
B: STEP1    COM
B: DELAY    PRN
B: DELAY    BAK
B: DELAY    HEX
B: RAMP     PRN
B: RAMP     HEX
B: STEPON   BAK
B: STEPON   PRN
B: STEPON   HEX
B: STEPON   COM
B: STEPON   ASM
B: RAMP     BAK
B: DELAY    ASM
B: RAMP     ASM
B: RAMP     COM
B: RAMP
B>
```

Figure 1.11 Directory listing of the author's CP/M user disk

1.10 Practical considerations

Floppy disks are a reliable and convenient way of storing programs, but they do not last for ever. It is always prudent to hold back-up copies of your disks and update them at the end of every development session. Having finally developed a working program, there is nothing more frustrating than to find that the disk cannot be read when the program is next required. Of course, the life of a disk can be prolonged by careful handling. Never bend a disk or stress it in any way, and always keep it in its protective envelope, away from strong magnetic fields, when not in use. Your disks are delicate and vital system components and should always be treated with the greatest respect.

References and bibliography

1.1 D. Moralee, 'Floppy disks, the storage system for microprocessor systems', *Electronics and Power*, Vol. 24(9), pp637–41 (September 1978).

1.2 John Worden, 'Design considerations for dual-density diskette controllers', *Computer Design (USA)*, Vol. 17(6), pp103–10 (June 1978).

1.3 A. Manildi, 'Designers guide for selecting magnetic mini-media', *ibid.*, Vol. 16(9), pp120a–f (September 1977).

1.4 Staff report, 'Flexible disk drives', *Digital Design*, Vol. 10(4), pp46–60 (April 1980).

1.5 Digital Research, *CP/M FDOS and Utilities Manual, Distributed by Lifeboat Associates, 164 West 83rd Street, New York, New York 10024 (Revised edition January 1978)*.

1.6 J. Hemenway, *'EDN Software Systems Design Course', EDN* Vol. 28(21), pp251–93 (20 November 1978).

1.7 North Star Computers Inc., *North Star System Software Manual*, North Star Computer Inc., 2547 Ninth Street, Berkeley, Ca. 94710 (Revision 2.1, 1979).

1.8 B. Wilkinson and D. Horrocks, *Computer Peripherals*, Hodder & Stoughton (1980).

Questions

1.1 Explain the need for a backing store in modern microprocessor development systems.

1.2 *(a)* Define the term random access as applied to memory systems.
　　(b) Explain why serial access memories have longer access times than random access memories.
　　(c) A single track on a magnetic surface can be compared with a very long shift register with a single input/output port. The essential difference between the two is that, in the first case, the

data is stationary but the surface moves, and in the second case the shift register is stationary and the data moves. Assuming a 1,024-stage shift register, how many bytes can be stored? If the shift clock rate is 1 MHz, what is the average access time?

1.3 By considering an ordinary domestic tape or cassette recorder, list some of the factors that contribute to the total access time if a particular point on the tape is to be read.

1.4 Assuming an average time of T s to position the read head in a floppy disk drive unit over a particular track and a rotational speed of 300 rev/min, estimate the average total access time.

1.5 Consider a disk with a track separation of 1/50 inch, 35 usable tracks and 10 sectors each holding 256 bytes, what is:
(a) The width of the recording band on the disk surface?
(b) The single-sided capacity of the disk?

1.6 Explain the difference between hard- and soft-sectored disks. Would it be possible to use hard-sectored disks in a drive unit configured for soft-sectoring?

1.7 By considering the sequence 11100011, explain the difference between frequency and delay modulation as methods of recording information on a disk surface.

1.8 Define the words *file* and *directory* when used in connection with disk operating systems. What information is normally stored in a disk directory?

1.9 What is an operating system? What features must a disk operating system include if it is to properly control a floppy disk backing store?

1.10 What are the essential components of a modern software development station and what is the main function of each component?

1.11 If your microcomputer has an operating system it, almost certainly, has equivalents of the CP/M, DIR, ERA, SAVE and perhaps TYPE. Use your operating system to create, rename and erase a file, and then list the directory. Repeat this exercise as often as necessary to become familiar with the operating system. You will find this a great help when developing software.

Chapter 2 The editor

Objectives of this chapter   *When you have completed studying this chapter you should be able to:*

1   *Understand the role of the editor when developing assembly language programs.*
2   *Appreciate the difference between line-orientated, string-orientated and cursor-orientated editors.*
3   *Understand the concept of an edit buffer and how text is inserted into it.*
4   *Be familiar with some of the more common commands supported by the CP/M editor, ED and their use in editing source code programs.*
5   *Appreciate that although all editors broadly support the same range of facilities, they may use different command characters and different command line formats to invoke these facilities.*

2.1   Introduction

The conclusions to be drawn from Chapter 1 are that a software development station with disk back-up and an operating system makes the task of developing assembly programs easier by, first of all, providing somewhere to store the utility and user programs needed during development, and secondly, by allowing easy access to the programs using explicit operating system commands.

Development of usable software begins with an exhaustive analysis of the problem being tackled, followed by a formulation of a solution in terms of a list of instructions – a program – and supporting documentation. After that we have to 'put the program into the computer'. The utility that enables us to do this is the editor. Apart from allowing us to enter program, the editor also provides us with a number of edit commands to correct the source code of any obvious errors and save it in a named disk file. The next step is to assemble the source code using the assembler program.

Assembly involves translating the opcode mnemonics, operands and data into object code. This, too, is saved in a disk file called the object code file. Any previously undetected errors such as the omission of essential punctuation marks, unrecognisable opcode mnemonics and the like, will cause the assembler to issue error messages. If this happens the editor is recalled and the source code is corrected so that it assembles without any error messages.

What happens after that depends upon the system software. If the CP/M assembler, ASM, is used, the object code is converted to an executable program module with the CP/M loader program, LOAD. This .COM file is also saved on the disk and, if it is a complete program rather than a subroutine which needs a calling program, it can be recalled and executed whenever the CP/M prompt is displayed by typing the .COM file name. When executing a program for the first time, however, the more usual procedure is to load the program into the debugger and use debug commands to test it comprehensively.

The CP/M debugger is called DDT (for dynamic debugging tool) and its commands allow the user to verify that the program being tested is logically correct. You should realise that assembler error messages only refer to the program syntax. Because a program assembles without error does not mean that it will work as intended. If logical mistakes are detected when the program runs in the debugger, corrections can be made, but ultimately the editor and assembler will have to be recalled for the source and object code to be corrected. Program development is finished only when the source code and documentation describe the latest edition of the program, and the program logic has been thoroughly tested and found to be correct.

Figure 2.1 summarises the complete software development procedure for CP/M users. Other systems have extra, or at least different, facilities which means that the development cycle is not exactly the same in every case. Some of these differences will be explained in due course but, in the main, we shall concentrate on program develop-

Q2.1, 2.2 ment using CP/M utilities.

2.2 Editors in general

The editor is a program that is used to enter source code and correct it of errors using the available edit commands. For a new program, the source code is typed at the keyboard and goes into an area of primary memory identified as the edit buffer. The most usual edit command for this is Insert (I). The size of the edit buffer depends partly on how the editor is written. In some cases an editor will determine how much primary memory is available to receive the user programs by 'sizing' memory. Any program that needs more than that amount of memory has to be edited in blocks, or pages, which will fit into the available space. Other editors have a fixed page size, regardless of memory capacity.

There are three basic types of editor which differ in the way they interpret and display program text. The most common in software development systems seem to be line-orientated and string-orientated editors. The third kind is called a cursor-orientated editor.

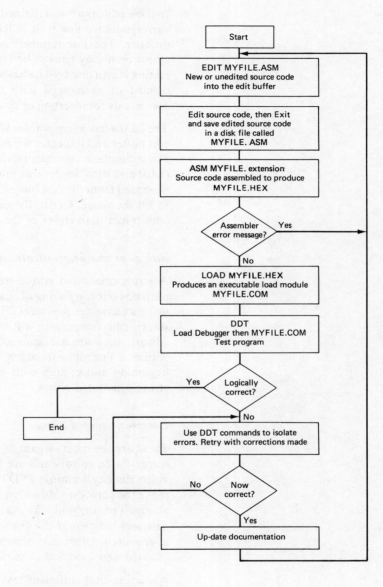

```
                    ┌──────────────┐
                    │    Start     │◄────────────────┐
                    └──────┬───────┘                 │
                           │                         │
          ┌────────────────▼────────────────┐        │
          │        EDIT MYFILE.ASM           │        │
          │   New or unedited source code    │        │
          │        into the edit buffer      │        │
          └────────────────┬────────────────┘        │
                           │                         │
          ┌────────────────▼────────────────┐        │
          │   Edit source code, then Exit    │        │
          │   and save edited source code    │        │
          │        in a disk file called     │        │
          │           MYFILE. ASM            │        │
          └────────────────┬────────────────┘        │
                           │                         │
          ┌────────────────▼────────────────┐        │
          │      ASM MYFILE. extension       │        │
          │  Source code assembled to produce│        │
          │           MYFILE.HEX             │        │
          └────────────────┬────────────────┘        │
                           │                         │
                     ◄─── Assembler ───► Yes          │
                         error message? ──────────────┤
                           │                         │
                           │ No                       │
          ┌────────────────▼────────────────┐        │
          │       LOAD MYFILE.HEX            │        │
          │  Produces an executable load module      │
          │           MYFILE.COM             │        │
          └────────────────┬────────────────┘        │
                           │                         │
          ┌────────────────▼────────────────┐        │
          │            DDT                   │        │
          │  Load Debugger then MYFILE.COM   │        │
          │         Test program             │        │
          └────────────────┬────────────────┘        │
                           │                         │
              Yes   ◄─── Logically ───►               │
          ┌────────────    correct?                   │
          │                  │ No                      │
    ┌─────▼────┐   ┌──────────▼───────────────────┐   │
    │   End    │   │  Use DDT commands to isolate  │   │
    └──────────┘   │  errors. Retry with corrections made │
                   └──────────┬───────────────────┘   │
                              │                        │
                         ◄─── Now ───► No               │
                             correct? ─────────────────┤
                              │ Yes                     │
                   ┌──────────▼───────────────┐        │
                   │   Up-date documentation   │────────┘
                   └───────────────────────────┘
```

Figure 2.1   Development procedure for assembly language programs under CP/M

Line-orientated editors

In these editors a line is defined as a sequence of characters ending in a carriage-return-line feed (CRLF) and beginning, usually, in a line number. The line number may be supplied automatically by the editor or it may have to be typed at the beginning of every line. All editing is on a line-by-line basis. For example, lines may be inserted or deleted or exchanged with other lines but there are no specific commands for inserting or deleting characters within an existing line.

The editor has a line pointer which can be moved up and down in the edit buffer and indicates the point at which edit activity is referenced. For example, a command sequence that moves the pointer to line 63 (L63) and then deletes one line (D1), causes line 63, and no other, to be erased from the edit buffer. All the lines after 63 will move up one to fill the space. Generally speaking, line-orientated editors are less convenient than either of the other two types.

String- or character-orientated editors

A string-orientated editor treats everything inserted into the edit buffer as one long string of characters. Once entered, the text is edited using a character pointer (CP), or current activity pointer, to indicate where edit commands will take effect. Unlike the line-orientated editor, there are commands for inserting and deleting characters within a line of text which is now defined as a character string beginning and ending with a CRLF. The CP/M editor, ED, is a string-orientated editor.

Cursor-orientated editors

These are the most elegant of the editors. They are sometimes called screen-based editors and are found mainly in systems which have a video display terminal (VDT) with a flashing cursor and keys to move the cursor up, down, right and left. The cursor marks the point at which editing will take place. When it is correctly positioned, the new text is typed at the keyboard and the old text is automatically overwritten. Other commands enable previously omitted text to be inserted and modified in various ways.

Q2.3 Assuming that sufficient text has been entered, the VDT screen is always filled by a block of text (typically 25 lines of 80 characters/line) with the cursor somewhere in the middle. In many ways cursor-orientated editors are similar to those used in commercial word-processing systems.

2.3 Using an editor

Text stored in the edit buffer is just a sequence of characters which may be a source code program, a nursery rhyme or a jumble of random alphanumeric symbols. Since in most cases the editor will be used to prepare source code programs, it must provide a range of easy-to-use commands so that the eventual source code format and content is acceptable to the assembler.

In CP/M systems, source code is usually held in files with the .ASM extension. An edit session begins when the command line,

```
A>ED MYFILE.ASM
```

is typed at the console. The system responds in three ways:

1   It loads the editor into memory and the edit buffer is established.
2   A channel is opened to the file MYFILE.ASM, if it exists.
3   A temporary file called MYFILE.£££ is created.

MYFILE.ASM is the input file that contains unedited source code and MYFILE.£££ is a new, temporary output file which will receive edited source code.

The advantage of having separate input and output files is that manageable blocks of text can be read from the input file into the edit buffer, edited and written to the output file, no matter how large the program or how limited the capacity of the edit buffer. The movement of text in this way is controlled by a series of pointers which keep track of text in the source file, edit buffer and temporary output file.

Unedited source code is moved to the edit buffer using the A (append) command. Responding to the edit prompt with 100A for example, causes 100 lines of source code to be moved from the input file to the edit buffer. The source file pointer (SP) is then moved on 100 lines so that any future append command will append the next block of source code to that already existing in the edit buffer. The edit buffer pointer, MP (for memory pointer), is also moved on so that it marks where any further appended source code will go.

When large programs are being edited it may be necessary to make space in the edit buffer before any further append commands are issued. This involves transferring lines from the edit buffer to the temporary output file. For example, the command 100W does the following:

1   The first 100 lines in the edit buffer are written to the output file.
2   The temporary output file pointer, TP, is updated.
3   In the edit buffer, lines 101 and greater are moved to the top of the edit buffer and MP is updated.

Very often the existence of these file pointers is of no concern to the user. In a minimum 16K system the edit buffer can hold about 6,000 characters. If a line of source code, including comments, contains an average of 35 characters, this amounts to about 170 lines of source code, or about three A4 pages of program text. At this stage of the learning process most of our programs will be easily contained within an edit buffer of this size. Larger systems have larger edit buffers of course. For example, the 22K version of CP/M maintains an edit buffer of 8864 bytes which is equivalent to about five pages of source text.

At the end of an edit session when all the source code is apparently correct, the editor is dismissed by typing E (for exit or end). Any remaining text in the input file is copied directly to the temporary output file, the input file is automatically renamed MYFILE.BAK and the output file renamed MYFILE.ASM. The .BAK file contains a back-up version of the source code without the latest corrections, whereas the .ASM file contains the latest revision of the source code. In the event that the .ASM file becomes corrupted, or it turns out that the corrections made were unnecessary or themselves incorrect, the .ASM file could be deleted and the .BAK file renamed .ASM. The

Q2.5   whole edit procedure could then start again.

When entering a new program, the I (insert) command is used. In this case there is no existing .ASM file so the A (append) command cannot be used. At the end of the session the temporary output file will be renamed MYFILE.ASM as before, but there will be no back-up file.

2.4   A typical editing session

The best way of describing how to use an editor is with an example. The same example will be used when we consider the assembler and the debugger so we have deliberately introduced syntax and logical errors in order to demonstrate how they can be located and corrected.

The main program, which we will not consider at this stage, reads the output of an analogue-to-digital converter (ADC) and stores the number in an address labelled VALUE. Our subroutine is required to compare the contents of VALUE with an upper and lower limit and return a different number in one of the 8080 registers if the measured value is greater than the high limit or less than the low limit or within limits – three different numbers. Figure 2.2 shows the program flowchart. From this you will see that if register B contains 02 when control passes back to the main program, the high limit has been exceeded, if B contains 01 we have a low alarm condition and if it contains 00 the measured value is within limits. The first few instructions back in the main program will determine which, if any, limit has been exceeded and initiate appropriate action. Note that there are no errors in the flowchart. It accurately describes how the subroutine should work.

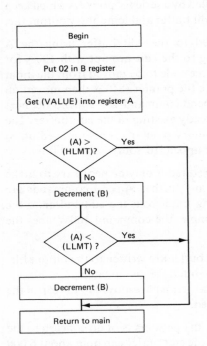

Figure 2.2   Flowchart for example program

At the end of the first edit session the subroutine (with errors) appeared as shown in Figure 2.3. Before this stage was reached the

```
**********************************************************
*    PROGRAM NAME : COMP                                 *
*                                                        *
*    PROGRAMMER : M.J.MORSE                              *
*    DATE : 3 2 81                                       *
*                                                        *
*    PROGRAM TO COMPARE A MEASURED TEMPERATURE STORED IN.*
*    ADDRESS 'VALUE' WITH UPPER AND LOWER LIMITS STORED  *
*    IN ADDRESSES 'HLMT' AND 'LLMT'. WHEN TESTING, THE   *
*    CONTENTS OF 'VALUE' SHOULD BE CHANGED IN THE        *
*    DEBUGGER, DDT, AND THE NUMBER IN REGISTER B CHECKED *
*    AT THE END OF THE PROGRAM.                          *
*                                                        *
*    IF THE (VALUE) > (HLMT) THEN (B) SHOULD BE 02       *
*    IF THE (VALUE) < (LLMT) THEN (B) SHOULD BE 01       *
*    OTHERWISE (B) SHOULD BE 00.                         *
*                                                        *
*                 STRUCTURE.                             *
*                 '''''''''                              *
*    BEGIN                                               *
*        FLAG := 2;                                      *
*        HLMT := A0H;                                    *
*        LLMT := 10H;                                    *
*        IF (VALUE) > (HLMT) THEN                        *
*            CONTINUE    (* TO THE END WITH FLAG = 2*)   *
*        ELSE                                            *
*            FLAG := FLAG -1;                            *
*            IF (VALUE) < (LLMT) THEN                    *
*                CONTINUE (* TO THE END WITH FLAG = 1*)  *
*            ELSE                                        *
*                FLAG := FLAG - 1;                       *
*            ENDIF                                       *
*        ENDIF                                           *
*    END.                                                *
*                                                        *
*    NOTE, REGISTERS A, B, H AND L CORRUPTED.            *
**********************************************************
*
COMP:   MVI     B,02H           ;FLAG CONTAINED IN B
        LXI     H,VALUE         ;POINT (H,L) AT VALUE
        MOV     A,M             ;GET VALUE
        INR     H               ;POINT AT HLMT
        CMP     M               ;(VALUE) > (HLMT)
        JC      BACK            ;CY SET MEANS VALUE HIGH
        INR     H               ;POINT AT LLMT
        DEC     B               ;FLAG := FLAG -1
        CMP     M               ;(VALUE) < (LLMT)
        JNC     BACK            ;CY = 0 MEANS VALUE LOW
        DEC     B               ;FLAG NOW ZERO
BACK:   RET                     ;RETURN TO MAIN
*
*   DATA AREA
*
VALUE:  DEFB    40H             ;INITIAL TRIAL VALUE
HLMT:   DEFB    A0H             ;HIGH LIMIT
LLMT:   DEFB    10H             ;LOW LIMIT
*
        END

B>
```

Figure 2.3 The contents of the edit buffer after editing

```
*********************************************************
*   PROGRAM NAME : COMP                                 *
*                                                       *
*   PROGRAMMER : M.J.MORSE                              *
*   DATE : 3 2 81                                       *
*                                                       *
*   PROGRAM TO COMPARE A MEASURED TEMPARATURE STORED IN *
*   ADDRESS 'VALUE' WITH UPPER AND LOWER LIMITS STORED  *
*   IN ADDRESSES 'HLMT' AND 'LLMT'. WHEN TESTING, THE   *
*   CONTENTS OF 'VALUE' SHOULD BE CHANGED IN THE        *
* DEBUGGER, DDT, AND THE NUMBER IN REGISTRE B CHECKED   *
*   AT THE END OF THE PROGRAM.                          *
*                                          *            *
*   IF THE (VALUE) > (HLMT) THEN (B)  SHOULD BE 02      *
*   IF THE (VALUE) < (LLMT) THEN (B)  SHOULD BE 01      *
*   OTHERWISE (B) SHOULD BE 00.                         *
*                                                       *
*                 STRUCTURE                             *
*                 '''''''''                             *
*   BEGIN                                               *
*       FLAG := 2;                                      *
*       HLMT := A0H;                         *          *
*       LLMT := 10H;                                    *
*       IF (VALUE) > (HLMT) THEN                        *
*         CONTINUE   (* TO THE END WITH FLAG = 2*)      *
*       ELSE                                            *
*           FLAG := FLAG -1;                            *
*           IF (VALUE) < (LLMT) THEN                    *
*               CONTINUE (* TO THE END WITH FLAG = 1*)  *
*           ELSE                                        *
*               FLAG := FLAG - 1;                       *
*           ENDIF                                       *
*       ENDIF                            *              *
*   END.                                                *
*                                                       *
*   NOTE, REGISTERSA, B, H AND L CORRUPTED.             *
*********************************************************
*
COMP:    MVI     B,02H                ;FLAG CONTAINED IN B
         LXI     H,VALEU              ;POINT (H,L) AT VALUE
         MOV     A,M1                 ;GET VALUE
         INR     H                    POINT AT HLMT
         CMP     M                    ; (VALUE) > (HLMT)
         JC      BACK                 ;CY SET MEANS VALUE HIGH
         INR     H                    ;POINT AT LLMT
         DEC     B          ;FLAG := FLAG -1
         CMP     M                    ;(VALUE) < (LLMT)
         DEC     B                    ;FLAG NOW ZERO
BACK:    RET                          ;RETIRN TO MAIN
*
*
*   DATA AREA
*
VALUE:   DEFB    40                   ;INITIAL TRIAL VALUE
HLMT:    DEFB    A0                   ;HIGH LIMIT
LLMT:    DEFB    10                   ;LOW LIMIT
*
         END

B>
```

Figure 2.4 The contents of the edit buffer when the program, COMP, was first entered. It contains a number of obvious syntax errors that need to be corrected

inevitable typing errors and omissions, shown in Figure 2.4, had to be corrected. It is this aspect of the work we shall now concentrate on.

Getting started

The editor was called by typing,

    ED B:COMP.ASM

followed by a carriage-return-line feed (RETURN <cr> key on the VDU keyboard). Our source code file was to be named COMP.ASM and it was to be stored on the user disk in drive B. The editor responded with the message NEW FILE and then displayed the edit prompt which is an asterisk or star (*). After that text was inserted into the edit buffer using the I (insert) command. A reproduction of the first part of the edit session dialogue as shown on our printer is given below:

```
A>ED B:COMP.ASM

NEW FILE
*I
***********************************************************
```

Q2.6

```
*    PROGRAM NAME : COMP
```

Following the I<cr>, everything typed at the keyboard is entered into the edit buffer until a CTRL-Z is typed. (The control key is held down and a Z is typed.) CTRL-Z is the delimiting character which marks the end of any character string. On receiving a CTRL-Z, the edit prompt reappears so that new commands can be entered.

Having entered all the text, an obvious requirement is to go back to the beginning of the edit buffer so that the text can be checked. This means moving the character pointer (CP) so that it is in front of the first character in the buffer. The command to do this is +B or just B. Had we wanted to go to the end of the buffer (after the last character) the command would have been –B<cr>.

Other commands which explicitly move CP are:

±nC – move CP *n* characters towards the end of the text if +, or towards the start of the text if –. A + is assumed if no sign is specified.

±nL – move CP *n* lines forward (+) or backwards (–) from its current position. CP is moved to the beginning of the line (if it is not already there) before the command is executed. Consequently if $n = 0$, CP is moved to the beginning of the current line. If *n* is too large, movement stops at the beginning or end of the buffer.

Having positioned CP, portions of the text can be viewed using the T (for type) command. The format of this command is ±nT, where *n* is the number of lines to be typed, the + sign indicates typing the *n* lines after CP and the – sign indicates the *n* lines in front of CP.

Some of the mistakes in Figure 2.4 are only cosmetic in the sense that if they were not corrected they would not cause assembler errors. For instance, all mistakes in the program heading are unimportant. If a line begins with a star (*), the CP/M assembler treats it as a comment line and ignores it. Similarly any text following a semi-colon is ignored so mistakes here could be left uncorrected. We shall attempt to correct all obvious mistakes however, because comments and documentation are an integral part of any assembly language program and should be accurate.

Use of the RUBOUT key

Note that if typing errors had been spotted when they were made they could have been corrected using the RUBOUT key. Pressing RUBOUT deletes the last character entered and the deleted character is echoed (displayed) on the display but erased from the edit buffer. Repeatedly striking the RUBOUT key causes the succession of previously entered characters to be erased. For example, if we had just entered NVI instead of MVI, we could either leave the mistake and correct it later or use the RUBOUT key to delete I, V and N and then enter MVI. The display would then appear as:

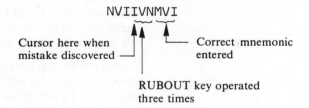

Although the display looks peculiar, the edit buffer at that point will contain only the characters MVI.

The ED/user dialogue

Returning to Figure 2.4, we shall identify the first few errors in the program and then decide how to correct them. The ED/user dialogue recorded during the session is shown in Figure 2.5.

In the first line of text there are three stars missing. The obvious way to correct this omission is just to insert (I) three stars. If CP is at the start of the buffer (following the B command) we need only type I***CTRL-Z. The character string *** will be inserted at the beginning of the line and the existing stars will all move along three

```
*B
*I***^Z0L1T
*******************************************************
*6L37C1DIE^Z0L1T
*   PROGRAM TO COMPARE A MEASURED TEMPERATURE STORED IN  *
*4L1T
* DEBUGGER, DDT, AND THE NUMBER IN REGISTRE B CHECKED
*1CI ^Z
*STRE^ZTER
*FED^ZI *^Z0L1T
*   DEBUGGER, DDT, AND THE NUMBER IN REGISTER B CHECKED  *
*2L1T
*                                                        *
*1CI     ^Z0L1T
*                                                        *
*FSTRUCTURE^ZI.                           *^Z0L1T
*               STRUCTURE.                                *
*4L1T
*       HLMT := AOH;                           *
*1CI ^ZF;^ZI     ^Z0L1T
*         HLMT := AOH;                                    *
*3L1CI     ^Z0L1T
*               CONTINUE    (* TO THE END WITH FLAG = 2*)  *
*8L1T
*       ENDIF                          *
*1CI ^ZFF^ZI               ^Z0L1T
*       ENDIF                                             *
*FSA^Z-1CI ^Z0L1T
*   NOTE, REGISTERS A, B, H AND L CORRUPTED.             *
*SEU^ZUE^Z0L1T
          LXI       H,VALUE          ;POINT (H,L) AT VALUE
*FM1^Z-1C1D0L1T
          MOV       A,M              ;GET VALUE
*FP^Z-1CI;^Z0L1T
          INR       H                ;POINT AT HLMT
*4L1T
          DEC       B          ;FLAG := FLAG -1
*FB^ZI ^Z0L1T
          DEC       B                ;FLAG := FLAG -1
*STIR^ZTUR^Z0L1T
BACK:     RET                        ;RETURN TO MAIN
*1L1K
*3L1T
VALUE:    DEFB      40               ;INITIAL TRIAL VALUE
*F0^ZIH^Z1LF0^ZIH^Z1LF0^ZIH^Z-2L3T
VALUE:    DEFB      40H              ;INITIAL TRIAL VALUE
HLMT:     DEFB      AOH              ;HIGH LIMIT
LLMT:     DEFB      10H              ;LOW LIMIT
*
```

Figure 2.5 The ED/user dialogue. Although this looks quite complicated, it simply records all the commands entered and the editor's response to each. At the end of the session the text in Figure 2.4 had been changed to the text shown in Figure 2.3

positions. To check that the insertion has been correctly made we could move CP back to the beginning of the line (0L) and then type the line (T). These commands can be entered as a string of command characters as shown in Figure 2.5, or, if preferred, each on a new line. Whenever a string of commands is entered the editor will wait until it receives a <cr> and then obey the commands one by one in the order they were entered. Notice that the string delimiting character CTRL-Z appears as ^Z on this printer. On the VDU screen it appears as ↑ Z.

The next error is in the seventh line. The word TEMPERATURE has been spelt wrongly. To correct this we could move CP so that it is between the P and the A, delete the A and insert an E. To position CP at the correct line the command 6L would be issued, followed by an nC command to move CP next to the incorrect A. The command to delete a character is ±nD which deletes *n* characters after CP if a plus sign is used or *n* characters in front of CP if *n* is negative. A plus sign is assumed if the sign is omitted.

The complete command line to correct this single error is therefore:

    6L37C1DIE^Z0LT<cr>

Q2.7

With practice you will be able to read and interpret these command lines quite easily. For example, our intention here is to:

1   Move CP on six lines (6L) from its present position.
2   Now move it on 37 characters (between P and A).
3   Delete the next character (1D).
4   Insert the character string E at that point. (Notice that the string, however long it is, is ended in a CTRL-Z.)
5   Go back to the beginning of the current line.
6   And type out the line.

If you have any difficulty interpreting the whole command line remember that each command can be entered separately and executed by typing the command character(s) followed by a <cr>. If you lost track of the character pointer or want reassurance that it is at the correct position then just enter T and the characters between CP and the end of the line will be displayed.

The 4L1T which is the next entry in Figure 2.5 was made for just this reason – we wanted to check that CP was at the beginning of the next line which contained errors. This line actually contains three errors. First of all we need to insert a space before the D of DEBUGGER, then correct the spelling of the word REGISTRE and finally insert a star at the end of the line.

With CP at the beginning of the line, the space is inserted in the correct place by moving CP to the right of the first star (1C) and then inserting a character string made up of one blank character. In this case a <cr> could have been used to mark the end of the string since no other commands were entered on this line.

We could change the string TRE, at the end of the word REGISTRE, to TER in much the same way as we previously corrected the word TEMPERATURE. The disadvantage of this technique is that we have to count the number of characters between CP and the point where the correction has to be made. A much neater method is to use the S (substitute string) command. This command substitutes one character string for another and has the form:

```
nSstring1^Zstring2^Z (or <cr>)
```

When it is executed ED searches forward through the edit buffer looking for string 1. When it finds it, string 1 is deleted and string 2 inserted and then the search continues until the substitution has been made *n* times or the end of the buffer is reached. The search always begins at the current position of CP and if *n* is omitted a 1 is assumed. The only note of caution to be added here is that string 1 should be unique.

For example, if the word TREAT was between the current position of CP and the TRE at the end of the word REGISTRE, when the command,

```
STRE^ZTER^Z (or <cr>)
```

Q2.4 was executed, the word TREAT would become TERAT and REGISTRE would be unchanged.

The final omission in this line is the star at the end. The easy way of aligning these stars is to use the tabulation (TAB) key. For tabulation purposes a line on the display is divided into fields of 8 character positions. Striking the TAB key moves the display cursor, or the carriage if your console is a teletypewriter, to the next preset TAB position. Therefore to insert a star at the correct position, CP is moved to the end of the word CHECKED and the character string 'TAB*' is inserted. Note that TAB is not a printable character, it just moves the cursor.

To locate the D in CHECKED we could, as before, move CP *n* characters from its current position. Alternatively we could ask the editor to find the string CHECKED, or just ED since this shorter string is not duplicated in the line. The format of the find (F) command is:

```
nFstringCTRL-Z (or <cr>)
```

When the command is executed, the editor searches for the *n*th occurrence of the string and, if it is located, CP is moved to the end of the string. The search is always made from the current position of CP towards the end of the buffer but if the string is not found, CP remains where it is and a query is displayed on the screen. As before the default value of *n* is 1.

It is clear then, that the command line needed here is:

```
FED^ZITAB*^ZOL1T<cr>
```

When the line is typed all the corrections should be evident.

The only other new command character used in Figure 2.5 is the K (kill lines) command which appears towards the end of the figure. This is used to erase lines from the buffer starting at the current setting of CP. The proper format of the command is:

±nK

where *n* is the number of lines to erase and the ± sign has the usual significance. Note that if CP is not at the beginning of a line when the command is issued, only a proportion of the line will be erased.

Q2.8, 2.9

2.5   Other ED commands

Of the remaining ED commands, only two are worth mentioning at this point. These are the R and Q commands. We can leave the others until you are thoroughly familiar with the basics.

The read library file command, R

It is common practice among software development engineers to build libraries of general-purpose subroutines which may be needed in many different programs. The library files are stored on the user disk and often have the .LIB extension. For example, a subroutine package stored on disk under the name CONIO.LIB (for console I/O library) may contain subroutines to get a character from the console (GETC), to print a character (PUTC), to print a message (MESP) and so on. When any, or all, of these subroutines are required in the program under development it is convenient to read CONIO.LIB into the edit buffer rather than type the individual subroutines. The R command provides this facility. Its format is:

Rfilename^Z (or <cr>)

The contents of filename are read from the disk into the edit buffer at the current position of CP, and automatically become part of the program being edited.

The quit command, Q

The normal exit from ED is made with the E command. This updates and closes the input and output files. As previously explained, the old input file, if it existed, is renamed filename.BAK and the output file is renamed filename.ASM. If exit is required without changing the original source code file, the Q command is used. To safeguard against typing errors, ED responds to the Q with

*Q-(Y/N)?

and the user can either confirm the Q command by typing Y, or cancel it by typing N.

Table 2.1 *Summary of some of the CP/M ED commands*

Class	Command character	Action
Enter text	I	Enter (Insert) text from the keyboard.
	A	Read (Append) n lines from the input file to the edit buffer.
	Rfilename	Read contents of filename and append to existing source code in the edit buffer. New source will be added at position of CP.
Move CP	B	Move CP to the beginning (+) or end (−) of the edit buffer.
	nC	Move CP n characters
	nL	Move CP n lines.
	nFstring	Move CP to the end of the nth occurrence of string. CP does not move if string does not occur n times.
Edit	nD	Delete n characters from the buffer.
	nK	Delete (Kill) n lines from the buffer.
	nSstring1^Z string2	Substitute string 1 for string 2, n times.
Write text	nW	Transfer n lines of edited text from the buffer to the output file and update the file pointers.
End editing	E	Exit, update and close input and output files.
	Q	Quit without changing the input file, delete the temporary output file.

A summary of these and all the other commands used in the example is given in Table 2.1.

2.6 Differences between ED and other editors

All but one of the command characters and associated actions listed in Table 2.1 have exactly the same significance when using the Intel text editor. However, this need not have been the case. Any command character could have been used to correspond with any action and, so long as the user is aware of the relationship between the two, the editor would be perfectly acceptable.

Specific differences between ED and some other editors amount to an alternative choice of command characters and differences in format. For example, a quite common choice of string delimiting character is ESC which is echoed on the console either as a $ (dollar sign) or a £ (pound sign). Very often commands can be strung together only if they are separated by an ESC and the command line is executed only if terminated in ESC ESC not <cr>.

This and other alternatives are listed in Table 2.2. The editors called EDIT and YALOE both run on North Star Horizon microcomputers and can be used to prepare 8080 source code programs for assembly. The relevance of Table 2.2 is that all four editors do the same job but are different in detail. An important step towards making efficient use of microprocessor development systems is 'learning the editor' so that its commands can be entered with speed and confidence.

Table 2.2   *A comparison between the CP/M editor, ED, and other string-orientated editors*

Action	CP/M ED	Intel	EDIT	YALOE
Edit Prompt	*	*	@	*
Command Separator	None	None	ESC	ESC/None
String Separator	CTRL-Z	ESC	ESC	ESC
Command Line Terminator	<cr>	ESC ESC	ESC ESC	ESC ESC
Insert text from keyboard	I	I	I	I
Append text from input file	A	A	A	None
Move CP *n* characters	nC	nC	nM	nJ
Move CP *n* lines	nL	nL	nL	nA
CP to top of buffer	+B	B	B	B
CP to end of buffer	−B	Z	Z	None
Find String	F	F	S	F
Delete *n* characters	nD	nD	nD	nD
Delete *n* lines	nK	nK	nK	nK
Substitute strings	S	S	C	C
Type *n* lines	nT	nT	nT	nL
End editing	E	E	E	QU

Questions

2.1 Review the method of developing assembly language programs using the CP/M utilities ED, ASM, LOAD and DDT.

2.2 Summarise the functions of an editor.

2.3 Distinguish between line-orientated editors, character- or string-orientated editors and cursor-orientated editors.

2.4 Given that a character-orientated editor has an S, substitute string, command, how would you edit the following line of source code

```
MVI A, MVIL
```

assuming that the line should read

```
MVI A, MVAL
```

and the character pointer is at the beginning of the line?

2.5 The CP/M and Intel editors both produce .BAK files at the end of editing an .ASM file. Why is this a useful facility?

2.6 Which two commands are used to put unedited source code into the edit buffer assuming first that there is an existing source code file and second that a new source code file is to be created? What is the format of each command?

2.7 Using the CP/M editor, what is the difference between typing,

```
*ITHIS IS A MESSAGE <cr>
```

and

```
*I <cr>
THIS IS A MESSAGE <cr>
```

2.8 The user/editor dialogue of Figure 2.5 could be summarised in the form shown in Table 2.3. Complete this table for every other command line shown in Figure 2.5.

Table 2.3

Command line	Action
B<cr>	CP to start of the buffer
I***^Z0LIT	Insert three stars at that point and move CP to the beginning of line. Type the line
6L37C1DIE^Z0L1T	Move CP forward 6 lines, then 37 characters into the line. Delete one character and then insert an E. Move CP to the beginning of the line and type the line.

```
        STRT:   LXI     H,LIST          ;GET LIST STRT ADD.
                MOV     B,M             ;FIRST ITEM TO B
                MVI     C,09H           ;INITIALISE ITEM COUNT
                INX     H               ;BUMP POINTER
        LOOP:   MOV     A,M             ;GET ITEM FROM LIST
                MVI     D,00H           ;CLEAR D
                XRA     B
                RLC                     ;CHECK FOR SAME SIGN
                JNC     GOON            ;JUMP IF SAME
                INR     D               ;OTHERWISE INC D
        GOON:   MOV     A,M             ;GET ITEM BACK
                CMP     B               ;AFFECTS ALL FLAGS
                DCR     D               ;DOESNT AFFECT CARRY
                JNC     L1              ;IS CARRY SET
                JM      CON+1
                JMP     CON
        L1:     JP      CON+1
        CON:    MOV     B,A             ;LARGEST TO B
                DCR     C               ;DECREMENT ITEM COUNT
                INX     H               ;BUMP POINTER
                JNZ     LOOP            ;LOOP IF NOT FINISHED
                MOV     M,B
        *
        LIST:   DS      0AH             ;ITEM LIST HERE
        *
                END

        B>
```

Figure 2.6

```
        STRT:   LXI     H,LIST          ;GET LIST STRT ADD.
                MOV     B,M             ;FIRST ITEM TO B
                MVI     C,09H           ;INITIALISE ITEM COUNT
                INX     H               ;BUMP POINTER
        LOOP:   MOV     A,M             ;GET ITEM FROM LIST
                MVI     D,00H           ;CLEAR D
                XRA     B
                RLC                     ;CHECK FOR SAME SIGN
                JNC     GOON            ;JUMP IF SAME
                INR     D               ;OTHERWISE INC D
                DCR     D               ;DOESNT AFFECT CARRY
                JNC     L1              IS CARRY SET
                JXYM    CON+1
                JMP     CON
        L1:     JP      CON+1
        CON:    MOV     B+A             ;LARGEST TO B
                DCR     C               ;DECREMENT ITEM COUNT
                INX     H               ;BUMP POINTER
                JNZ     LOP             ;LOOP IF NOT FINISHED
                MOV     M,B
        *
        LIST:   DS      0AH             ;ITEM LIST HERE
        *
        B>
```

Figure 2.7

2.9 Figure 2.6 shows a program which assembles without error and Figure 2.7 the same program with a number of omissions and syntax errors. Not all these errors will produce assembler error messages but they must all be corrected. Prepare a table, similar to Table 2.3, which identifies the error, the command line needed to correct it, and explains the intended action.

Chapter 3 The assembler

Objectives of this chapter *When you have completed studying this chapter you should be able to:*

1 *Understand how an assembler converts a source code program into hexadecimal object code.*
2 *Know how the symbol table is constructed and appreciate the advantages of symbolic addressing and labelled constants.*
3 *Know how to prepare a line of source code which the assembler will accept and be aware of the essential and optional fields in the line.*
4 *Know, and appreciate the use of, arithmetic, shift and logical operators in source code expressions.*
5 *Understand how each of the standard assembler directives, and the conditional assembly directives, are used in programs.*
6 *Know how to call and use the CP/M assembler to generate .HEX and .PRN files, and also know how to interpret any assembly error messages.*

3.1 Introduction

Having successfully used the editor to create a source code file, the next step is to translate the program text into a form that is much closer to the machine language of the microprocessor. The utility program which does this is the assembler and the process is called assembly.

Essentially, what an assembler does is to take each line of source code and translate it into one or more bytes of object code. Each byte is assigned to an address which, in the simplest case, is the address it will occupy when the program is loaded into memory and executed. Before returning control to the operating system the assembler saves the object code, usually as a sequence of hexadecimal numbers, in a disk file with the .OBJ or .HEX extension.

3.2 Symbolic addressing

From the foregoing description it is clear that an assembler must be able to interpret opcode mnemonics and translate them into the proper hexadecimal equivalents. It should also be able to interpret symbolic addresses used by a programmer. Symbolic addressing is the technique of attaching labels, or symbolic names, to instructions or items of data. The instruction or data item can then be referred to by name rather than by its absolute, numerical address. If we program a JMP instruction for example, and the destination of the jump has been labelled, we can write JMP LABEL rather than JMP 5C3BH or whatever. LABEL is a symbol we have attached to the address 5C3BH – it is a symbolic address.

The particular merit of this facility can best be understood by considering the identical instructions JMP START and JMP 1BC5H. It happens that START is a label attached to the instruction which begins at address 1BC5H, and, as you may have suspected, 1BC5H is the start address of a program. From the reader's point of view, JMP START is considerably more informative than JMP 1BC5H.

Apart from making programs more readable, labels can also reduce the amount of work we have to do in the editor. Imagine for instance that, while editing, we have to change the source code file by adding or deleting instructions. When the program is reassembled, instructions after the additions or deletions will obviously have different address. If the destination of a JMP was originally written as an absolute address and now, because of the previous edit activity, this address has changed, it will be necessary to go through the source code file changing all references to it. Had we used a label the assembler would have changed all referencing instructions for us.

Q3.3

3.3   Defining constants in programs

Labels need not always apply to addresses. Another very useful technique is to identify program constants by a label, or name. Instructions that initialise loop counters (MVI B,08H), read data from input ports (IN 0FEH) and send other data to output ports (OUT 0FFH) for example, could all be made more descriptive by labelling the count value or port number. How much more readable are the instructions IN ADC or OUT STEPPER?

As we shall see later, labelled constants are *defined* whereas symbolic addresses arise as a consequence of attaching labels to instructions or data items. The assembler treats all labels in much the same way however.

Q3.1 a

3.4   Assembler operations

The implications of symbolic addressing and labelled constants provide some clue as to how the assembler sets about the job of translating a source code program into hexadecimal object code. How, for example, does it interpret LXI H,VALUE when the data item labelled VALUE does not appear until several lines later? If it tried to assemble the complete program in one go, one pass as it is called, it would not know what to make of the word VALUE. What happens in practice, of course, is that most assemblers read through the source code twice – they are two-pass assemblers.

On the first pass the assembler identifies all the labels and the absolute addresses or values to which they refer. From this information it constructs a symbol table in which it enters the labels and their hexadecimal equivalents (addresses or values). For the COMP program, this symbol table might appear as,

COMP	0100H
BACK	0112H
VALUE	0113H
HLMT	0114H
LLMT	0115H

On the second pass, it takes each instruction in order and converts it to object code. The first byte is determined by looking up a table containing every opcode mnemonic and its hexadecimal equivalent. If a label is part of the operand, the assembler looks in the symbol table and extracts the second, or second and third bytes, of the instruction. Having assigned each of these bytes to an address, it continues with the next instruction until the end of the source code file is reached.

There is an apparent problem which exists when attempting to program an instruction such as MVI B,COUNT. The second byte of this two-byte instruction is a number which is to be moved into the 8-stage B register. The problem is that this number is stored in the symbol table as 16 bits. The complete symbol table entry may be,

COUNT	0008H

Q3.2, 3.4

Normally it is not possible to store 16 bits in an 8-stage register but, so long as the most significant 8 bits of the number are zero, the assembler will properly assemble the instruction. It is only when COUNT is defined as 0100H or some larger number that the assembler becomes confused and issues an error message.

3.5 Other assemblers

Since assemblers are programs and programs are the product of programmers, no two assemblers need work in precisely the same way. There are, for example, one-pass assemblers which do not allow forward references to labels, and three-pass assemblers which either do extra processing of the source code or translate it into object code by subdividing the task into a larger number of steps. Whatever the internal workings of the assembler, however, the outcome is always a program which is functionally identical with the source code but different in form.

The discussion of assemblers which follows is largely centred around the Intel and CP/M assemblers since, of all the 8080 assemblers, these are the most widely used and imitated.

3.6   The source code format

All assemblers impose rules about how lines of source code should be presented. If the rules are not obeyed the program may be assembled incorrectly or, more likely, the assembler will issue error messages. The basic rule is that lines of source code may contain up to four fields and must be set out in the following way:

Label: Operation   Operand   ;Comment
              or
            Opcode

A perfectly acceptable line of source code would be,

```
COMP: MVI B,02 ;initialise flag
```

The four fields are called the label field, the operation or opcode field, the operand field and the comment field and each must be separated from an adjacent field by some separating, or delimiting, character. The delimiting character can be one or more spaces or, more usually, a TAB (CTRL-I).

The label and comment fields are optional so that not all fields need be occupied. Equally, not every instruction needs an operand. Typically, instructions must be contained within a single line terminated in a carriage return – line feed. The CP/M assembler, ASM, is unusual in this respect in that it allows several instructions to be entered on a single line, provided that they are separated from one another by an exclamation mark. Thus ASM would accept a line of source code like,

```
SAVE: PUSH H! PUSH D! PUSH B! PUSH PSW ;save
                                    registers
```

whereas other assemblers would probably reject it.

The optional label must begin with a letter but the other characters can be letters, numbers or some special symbols like ?. The maximum number of characters in a label varies from assembler to assembler but there is always some limit. In the case of ASM for example, it is a generous 16 characters. The Intel assembler on the other hand will only accept labels if they contain no more than 6 characters and other assemblers place the limit at 4 characters.

Some assemblers, like the Intel assembler, insist that the label field be terminated in a colon while others allow colons but do not insist on them. Experience has shown that it is a good idea to include the colon because this is less likely to result in an error message.

The opcode field contains a valid 8080 opcode mnemonic or assembler directive. Assembler directives are discussed in Section 3.10. To make any sense, many opcode mnemonics require an entry in the operand field. It is here, in the operand field, that expressions containing constants, addresses of CPU register identifiers are entered. Where an opcode is qualified by two operands, such as

```
MOV  A,B
```

the first operand identifies the destination and the second the source.

The optional comment field is preceded by a semicolon and contains any explanatory text that is thought to make the program more understandable. The assembler ignores all comments and, although they are optional, programs are always improved by the addition of meaningful and accurate comments. You should guard against stating the obvious however. A comn.ent such as

```
MOV  A,B  ;move contents of B to A
```

adds nothing and will probably irritate the reader. Be even more careful about making comments accurate. A misleading comment is even worse than no comment at all.

One final point about comments. ASM, and several other assemblers, allow lines which consist only of comments to be preceded by a star. Like the comments in the comment field, these are ignored by the assembler but provide a very useful way of documenting programs. If your assembler rejects the star, begin comment lines with a semi-colon in the normal way.

Q3.5

3.7 Numeric constants in assembly language programs

Numeric constants are 8- or 16-bit numbers which do not change during the execution of a program. They may be declared as binary, octal, decimal or hexadecimal number by appending the letters B, O (or Q), D or H to the number. If the letter is omitted the assembler automatically assumes that the number is decimal. Two letters, O or Q, are allowed when declaring octal numbers because of the possible confusion which could result if a reader interprets an O as a 0.

In most cases numbers defined in assembly language programs are either decimal or hexadecimal. You will find yourselves using binary and, more particularly, octal numbers much less frequently. The reason for this is that decimal numbers are quite convenient when initialising loop counters – a very common requirement – and hexadecimal numbers are ideal for defining address constants. The only note of caution to add here is that hexadecimal numbers must always start with a digit. A number such as FFFFH for example, must be entered as 0FFFFH otherwise the assembler will interpret it as a label beginning with the letter F. As a result it will probably issue an error message, either because the label is undefined or is inappropriate in the context used.

3.8   String constants

Apart from numeric constants the assembler also allows the programmer to define string constants – sequences of ASCII characters which are enclosed within single quotation marks (apostrophes). Examples of string constants are:

```
'ENTER A BINARY NUMBER'
'A'
'ERROR - DO IT AGAIN'
```

We shall see later how these string constants are declared when, for example, messages are to be displayed on the console. The inevitable complication comes when the string being defined contains an apostrophe. In that case you must use two apostrophes at the point where the single apostrophe should occur. If you fail to do this, the assembler takes the single apostrophe as marking the end of the string and you are left with only part of a string defined. The remainder is still there in the source code file and is almost guaranteed to produce an assembler error message.

Q3.6

3.9   Arithmetic, shift and logical operators

The operand field in a line of source code can contain arithmetic and logical expressions which are evaluated by the assembler to reveal the effective operand. These expressions are formed using arithmetic, shift and logical operators.

Arithmetic operators

The five arithmetic operators are:

Operator	Meaning
+	Binary addition
–	Binary subtraction
*	Multiplication
/	Integer division – any remainder is discarded so that 10/3 = 3
MOD	Modulo. Expression evaluates to the remainder after integer division, e.g. 10 MOD 3 = 1

```
        *   PROGRAM TO ILLUSTRATE THE USE OF ARITHMETIC OPERATORS
        *
        *   1. THE + AND - OPERATORS
        *
        BGN1:   LDA     LIST+6          ;7TH ITEM IN LIST TO A
                MOV     B,A             ;SWOP TO B
                LDA     LEND-3          ;3TH FROM LAST TO A
        *
        LIST:   DB      01,02,03,04,05,06,07,08
        LEND:   DB      09
        *
        *   WHEN THIS PART OF THE PROGRAM RUNS, A WILL CONTAIN 06 AND B 07.
        *
        *   2. THE MULTIPLICATION OPERATOR, *
        *
        BGN2:   MVI     C,5+30*2        ;EVALUATES TO ASCII A
                RET
        *
        *   THE INSTRUCTION AT BGN2 LOADS REGISTER C WITH ASCII 'A'.
        *
        *   3. THE / AND MOD OPERATORS
        *
        BGN3:   MVI     D,NUMBR / 3     ;INTEGER DIVISION
                MVI     E,NUMBR MOD 3   ;INTEGER REMAINDER
                RET
        *
        NUMBR:  EQU     10
        *
        *   WITH NUMBR=10, D WILL BE LOADED WITH 3 AND E WITH 1
        *
                END

        B>
```

Figure 3.1   The arithmetic operators, +, -, *, / and MOD can be used in expressions in the operand field of source code statements

These can be used in a variety of ways as illustrated in the snippets of program shown in Figure 3.1. When these instructions are assembled (Figure 3.2) the expressions are evaluated and the proper hexadecimal object code is generated.

Notice how the DB and EQU mnemonics are used. EQU stands for 'equals' and the EQU statement means 'NUMBR equals decimal 10'. We are defining NUMBR as a constant and giving it the value 10.

The DB mnemonic stands for 'define a byte'. The numbers which follow DB are stored, one after another, in consecutive memory locations, with the address of the first number labelled LIST. We can pick out particular numbers in the list by referring to the contents of addresses beyond the LIST. For example, LIST is the symbolic address 0007H. The expression LIST + 6 evaluates to 0007H + 6 = 000DH, so the instruction

```
LDA LIST+6
```

picks out the number 07 and stores in register A.

```
              *  PROGRAM TO ILLUSTRATE THE USE OF ARITHMETIC OPERATORS
              *
              *  1. THE + AND - OPERATORS
              *
0000 3A0D00   BGN1:    LDA     LIST+6           ;7TH ITEM IN LIST TO A
0003 47                MOV     B,A              ;SWOP TO B
0004 3A0C00            LDA     LEND-3           ;3TH FROM LAST TO A
              *
0007 0102030405LIST:   DB      01,02,03,04,05,06,07,08
000F 09       LEND:    DB      09
              *
              *  WHEN THIS PART OF THE PROGRAM RUNS, A WILL CONTAIN 06 AND B 07.
              *
              *  2. THE MULTIPLICATION OPERATOR, *
              *
0010 0E41     BGN2:    MVI     C,5+30*2         ;EVALUATES TO ASCII A
0012 C9                RET
              *
              *  THE INSTRUCTION AT BGN2 LOADS REGISTER C WITH ASCII 'A'.
              *
              *  3. THE / AND MOD OPERATORS
              *
0013 1603     BGN3:    MVI     D,NUMBR / 3      ;INTEGER DIVISION
0015 1E01              MVI     E,NUMBR MOD 3    ;INTEGER REMAINDER
0017 C9                RET
              *
000A =        NUMBR:   EQU     10
              *
              *  WITH NUMBR=10, D WILL BE LOADED WITH 3 AND E WITH 1
              *
0018                   END
0018
000H USE FACTOR
END OF ASSEMBLY

A>
```

Figure 3.2　The assembler evaluates the expressions and assigns the value of each expression to an address

Incidentally, you may have noticed that the list of numbers to the left of the source code statement in Figure 3.2 is incomplete. Only the first five numbers have been printed although all of them have been assigned to addresses. This restricted display is characteristic of the CP/M assembler – other assemblers would show the complete list.

The shift operators

The permissible shift operators are:

```
    A   SHR   B
    A   SHL   B
```

In the first expression, operand A is shifted B bit positions to the right, and in the second, the same operand is shifted B positions to the left. In both cases zeros are shifted into the vacated bit positions. Thus if a binary constant, BYTE, is defined as 00001000, then BYTE SHR 3 evaluates to 00000001 and BYTE SHL 4 to 10000000.

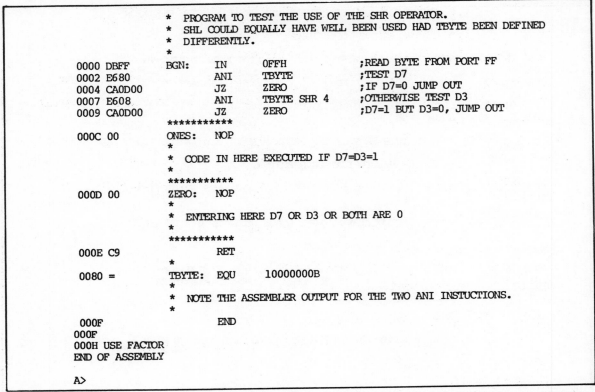

```
                      *   PROGRAM TO TEST THE USE OF THE SHR OPERATOR.
                      *   SHL COULD EQUALLY HAVE WELL BEEN USED HAD TBYTE BEEN DEFINED
                      *   DIFFERENTLY.
                      *
    0000 DBFF      BGN:    IN      0FFH          ;READ BYTE FROM PORT FF
    0002 E680              ANI     TBYTE         ;TEST D7
    0004 CA0D00            JZ      ZERO          ;IF D7=0 JUMP OUT
    0007 E608              ANI     TBYTE SHR 4   ;OTHERWISE TEST D3
    0009 CA0D00            JZ      ZERO          ;D7=1 BUT D3=0, JUMP OUT
                   **********
    000C 00        ONES:   NOP
                      *
                      *   CODE IN HERE EXECUTED IF D7=D3=1
                      *
                   **********
    000D 00        ZERO:   NOP
                      *
                      *   ENTERING HERE D7 OR D3 OR BOTH ARE 0
                      *
                   **********
    000E C9                RET
                      *
    0080 =         TBYTE:  EQU     10000000B
                      *
                      *   NOTE THE ASSEMBLER OUTPUT FOR THE TWO ANI INSTUCTIONS.
                      *
    000F                   END
    000F
    000H USE FACTOR
    END OF ASSEMBLY

    A>
```

Figure 3.3   With TBYTE defined as 80H, TBYTE SHR 4 evaluates to 08H as shown by the contents of 0008H

An application of the SHR operator is shown in Figure 3.3. The aim here is to check bits 7 and 3 of a byte without defining two separate constants. The shift operator provides a quite neat way of doing this.

The logical operators

The logical operators recognised by the Intel and CP/M assemblers are listed below and their application is illustrated in Figures 3.4, 3.5 and 3.6.

Operator	Meaning
NOT	Logical one's complement
AND	Logical AND of two binary numbers
OR	Logical OR of two binary numbers
XOR	Logical exclusive-OR of two binary numbers

Notice that Figure 3.4, which was mainly intended to demonstrate how the NOT operator might be used, also includes an AND. If the second ANI instruction is written as

```
ANI  NOT TBYTE
```

```
        *  PROGRAM TO TEST THE USE OF LOGICAL OPERATORS IN THE OPERAND
        *  FIELD OF ASSEMBLY LANGUAGE INSTRUCTIONS.
        *
        *  1. THE NOT AND LOGICAL AND OPERATORS.
        *
        *     PROGRAM TESTS FOR A 1 IN D7 OF A BYTE READ FROM AN INPUT PORT.
        *     (IS TWOS COMPLEMENT NUMBER NEGATIVE?).
        *     IF D7 IS A 1 A TEST IS MADE FOR A 1 IN ANY REMAINING BIT POSITION.
        *
0000 DBFF  BGN1:   IN      0FFH            ;READ BYTE
0002 47            MOV     B,A             ;SAVE IT IN B
0003 E680          ANI     TBYTE           ;TEST D7
0005 CA1000        JZ      POSTVE          ;IF D7=0, POSITIVE NUMBER
0008 78            MOV     A,B             ;GET BYTE BACK TO A
0009 E67F          ANI     NOT TBYTE AND 0FFH    ;TEST REMAINING BITS
000B CA0F00        JZ      NMAX            ;TO NMAX IF NUMBER=80H
           *
000E 00    NEG:    NOP
           *  HANDLE NEGATIVE NUMBER >-128 HERE
           *
000F 00    NMAX:   NOP
           *  HANDLE MAXIMUM NEGATIVE NUMBER HERE
           *
0010 00    POSTVE: NOP
           *  HANDLE POSITIVE NUMBERS HERE
           *
0080 =     TBYTE:  EQU     10000000B
           *
           *  AGAIN NOTE THE OBJECT CODE FOR THE TWO ANI INSTRUCTIONS
           *
0011               END
0011
000H USE FACTOR
END OF ASSEMBLY

A>
```

Figure 3.4 The important expression in this listing is (NOT TBYTE AND 0FFH) which, with TBYTE = 80H, evaluates to 07FH

the assembler flags an error. The purpose of this instruction is to form the one's complement of TBYTE (0111 1111) and then logically AND it with the byte stored in register A. The error results because, as you will hopefully recall, TBYTE is stored in the symbol table as a 16-bit number. Consequently the expression NOT TBYTE evaluates to 1111 1111 0111 1111 and not 01111111. Having evaluated the operand the assembler looks at the complete instruction and, rightly, concludes that you cannot sensibly AND two numbers of differing length. To remove (zero) the most significant 8 bits of the operand, a logical AND between it and the number 0FFH is necessary. The complete instruction is then

```
ANI  NOT TBYTE AND 0FFH
```

which assembles without error.

```
            *   LOGICAL OPERATOR TEST PROGRAM
            *   2. THE OR OPERATOR.
            *
            *      IN THIS FRAGMENT WE ARE TESTING A BYTE AS FOLLOWS:-
            *             IF D7 OF BYTE=1 EXECUTE 'D7' CODE.
            *             IF D3 OF BYTE=1 EXECUTE 'D3' CODE
            *             IF BOTH BITS ARE 1 EXECUTE 'BOTH' CODE
            *             IF NEITHER BIT IS A 1 EXECUTE 'ZEROS' CODE
            *
0000 DBFF   BGN2:   IN     0FFH              ;GET THE BYTE TO TEST
0002 E688           ANI    TBYTE OR (TBYTE SHR 4) AND 0FFH
            *
            *   TESTING BITS 7 AND 3 WITH A LOGICAL 'AND' INSTRUCTION
            *
0004 CA1200         JZ     ZEROS             ;BOTH ZEROS
0007 FE80           CPI    TBYTE             ;LOGICAL 'AND' RESULT=80H?
0009 CA1000         JZ     D7                ;YES, ONLY D7=1
000C DA1100         JC     D3                ;LESS THAN 80H, THEN D3=1, D7=0
            *
000F 00     BOTH:   NOP
            *
            *   FALLING THROUGH TO HERE MEANS LOGICAL 'AND' RESULT > 80H. D7=D3=1
            *
0010 00     D7:     NOP
            *
            *   D7 CODE WOULD GO IN HERE
            *
0011 00     D3:     NOP
            *
            *   D3 CODE WOULD GO IN HERE
            *
0012 00     ZEROS:  NOP
            *
            *   ZEROS CODE IN HERE
            *
0080 =      TBYTE:  EQU    10000000B
            *
0013                END
0013
000H USE FACTOR
END OF ASSEMBLY

A>
```

Figure 3.5   In this program TBYTE = 80H and the expression, (TBYTE OR (TBYTE SHR 4) AND 0FFH), evaluates to 88H

Operator precedence

When arithmetic and logical expressions contain more than one operator the assembler evaluates the effective operand by working from left to right through the expression. However, not all operators have the same precedence, and so, when expressions include operators of different precedence, the higher precedence operators are always acted upon first. The order of precedence is:

Highest: *, /, MOD, SHR, SHL
Next: +, –

```
        *  LOGICAL OPERATOR TEST PROGRAM
        *  3. THE XOR OPERATOR
        *
        *     IN THIS PROGRAM TWO CONSTANTS, CONS1 AND CON2, ARE DEFINED.
        *     THESE ARE USED ELSEWHERE IN THE PROGRAM. IN THIS PROGRAM
        *     FRAGMENT OUR AIM IS TO DISCOVER WHETHER D3 AND D7 OF THE
        *     BYTE STORED IN A ARE THE SAME, WITHOUT DEFINING FURTHUR
        *     CONSTANTS. WE MIGHT PROCEED AS FOLLOWS :-
        *
0000 47       BGN3:   MOV     B,A             ;SAVE THE BYTE IN B
0001 E680             ANI     CONS1           ;TEST D7
0003 78               MOV     A,B             ;RESTORE THE BYTE TO A
0004 CA1000           JZ      TSTD31          ;IF D7=0 TEST D3 FOR A 1
                                              ;OTHERWISE TEST D3 FOR A 0
0007 E608     TSTD30: ANI     CONS1 XOR CONS2
0009 CA1500           JZ      DIFF            ;D7=1 AND D3=0, DIFFERENT
000C 00       SAME:   NOP
        *
        *  THE CODE IN HERE IS EXECUTED IF THE BITS ARE THE SAME
        *
000D C31600           JMP     CONT
        *
0010 E608     TSTD31: ANI     CONS1 XOR CONS2
0012 CA0C00           JZ      SAME            ;D7=0 AND D3=0, SAME
0015 00       DIFF:   NOP
        *
        *  ARRIVE HERE IF THE BITS ARE DIFFERENT. IE. 10 OR 01
        *
              CONT:
        *
        *  CARRY ON WITH THE PROGRAM
        *
0080 =        CONS1:  EQU     10000000B
0088 =        CONS2:  EQU     10001000B
        *
        *  THE IMPORTANT THING HERE IS THE EVALUATION OF THE ANI OPERANDS.
        *
0016                  END
0016
000H USE FACTOR
END OF ASSEMBLY

A>
```

Figure 3.6 In this program CONS1 and CONS2 are defined as 80H and 88H, respectively. The expression (CONS1 XOR CONS2) therefore evaluates to 08H as shown by the contents of 0008H

Next:	NOT
Next:	AND
Lowest:	OR, XOR

This means that $5 + 4 * 3 + 7$ will be evaluated as $5 + 12 + 7 = 24$, because multiplication has a higher precedence than addition.

The natural order of precedence can be altered by enclosing parts of an expression within brackets (parentheses). Bracketed parts of an expression have the highest precedence of all. If one pair of brackets is enclosed within another the innermost bracket is expanded before anything else. Quite apart from assigning precedence however, the use of brackets adds significantly to the clarity of an expression and is generally a good idea.

Q3.7–3.9

3.10   Assembler directives

Assembler directives are instructions to the assembler to perform certain operations at assembly time. Since they are not instructions to the microprocessor, they do not generate object code. There are three main types of directive:

1   Those associated with macros.
2   Those associated with the various options in conditional assembly.
3   Those which can be described as standard directives.

Since the version of ASM we are using does not support macros we shall ignore this type of directive. (Assemblers which do support macros are usually called macro assemblers.) The conditional assembly directives will be explained in due course, so we shall begin this discussion by considering the standard directives.

Standard directives are commonly used to:

1   Define constants.
2   Define data areas.
3   Reserve blocks of memory.
4   Indicate the address at which source code, or segments of it, should be assembled.

Q3.10

Each directive is indicated by a pseudo-operation code mnemonic, or pseudo-op, which is entered in the opcode field of a line of source code. A pseudo-op may be preceded by a label (in some instances the label is mandatory), it will usually be followed by an operand and an optional comment can always be appended. In other words, lines which include pseudo-ops are little different from lines which include real opcodes. The difference comes at assembly time when real opcodes generate a byte of object code but pseudo-opcodes never do.

The EQU directive

We have already seen how this directive is used to define a constant. The format of the EQU statement is:

```
LABEL:   EQU   expression
```

At assembly time the expression is evaluated and assigned to LABEL and an entry to that effect is made in the symbol table. The EQU statement is the programmer's way of saying to the assembler: 'Every time you see LABEL substitute the value of expression because the two are equal'. Once LABEL has been defined in this way it cannot be redefined in another EQU statement later in the same program. No storage space is occupied by the value of expression except in the symbol table during assembly.

The SET directive

This works in almost exactly the same way as the EQU directive. The only difference between the two is that constants defined by SET can subsequently be redefined by another SET later in the same program. When a constant defined by SET is encountered during assembly, the assembler substitutes the latest value of the expression. This re-definition property of SET labels is illustrated in Figure 3.7. Notice again that the value of an expression assigned to a label using SET or EQU pseudo-ops is a 16-bit number. Notice also that values assigned by EQU are printed in the program listing, whereas values assigned by SET are not.

Q3.12

The ORG directive

During assembly, individual bytes of object are assigned to consecutive memory locations. In the absence of any directive to the contrary, the first byte is assigned to 0000H, the next byte to address is 0001H and so on. When the assembled program is eventually loaded into memory for execution each byte will go into its assigned address and the program will run from the start address which is 0000H. If we want our program to be assembled and loaded at an address other than 0000H, we must tell the assembler. The way to do this is to use the ORG, or origin, pseudo-op.

In ORG statements the entry in the operand field is, or must evaluate to, a 16-bit number which will be taken as the address to which the next byte of object code will be assigned. For example, if we insert at the head of our program

```
ORG   0100H
```

the first byte of object code will be assigned to 0100H and all succeeding bytes will be assigned to successively higher addresses until another ORG statement is encountered.

Most programs which run under CP/M will be assembled at 0100H because CP/M sets aside an area of memory, called the transient program area (TPA), which begins at 0100H and is specifically for user programs. If we assembled and loaded our program at 0000H it would not run because CP/M uses the address space from 0000H to 0100H for its own purposes.

```
                    *    PROGRAM TO DEMONSTRATE THE USE OF THE EQU AND SET PSEUDO-OPS.
                    *
                    *    1. THE EQU PSEUDO-OP.
                    *
  000A =           CNT:    EQU     0AH
  0002 =           NUM:    EQU     02H
                    *
                    *    THIS PROGRAM FRAGMENT COMPUTES CNT*NUM BY ADDING NUM TO ITSELF
                    *    CNT-1 TIMES.
                    *
  0000 3E02        BGN1:   MVI     A,NUM
  0002 0E0A                MVI     C,CNT
  0004 0D                  DCR     C             ;CNT-1 NOW IN C
  0005 C602        LOOP1:  ADI     NUM           ;ADD NUM TO RUNNING TOTAL
  0007 0D                  DCR     C             ;ONE LESS ADDITION TO DO
  0008 C20500              JNZ     LOOP1         ;LOOP IF NOT FINISHED
  000B C9                  RET
                    *
                    *    NOTE THAT CNT AND NUM ARE ENTERED IN THE SYMBOL TABLE AS 16-
                    *    BIT NUMBERS. WE CAN LOAD 8-STAGE REGISTERS WITH CNT AND NUM
                    *    ONLY BECAUSE THEIR MOST SIGNIFICANT BYTES ARE ZERO. TO
                    *    ILLUSTRATE THIS CONSIDER THE FOLLOWING :-
                    *
  FFFF =           TOP:    EQU     0FFFFH
  000C 210A00               LXI     H,CNT
  000F 11FFFF              LXI     D,TOP
                    *
                    *    BOTH THE ABOVE STATEMENTS ASSEMBLE CORRECTLY BUT IF WE TRY TO
                    *    LOAD A SINGLE-LENGTH REGISTER WITH 'TOP' THE ASSEMBLER WILL
                    *    ISSUE AN ERROR MESSAGE. FOR EXAMPLE :-
                    *
  V0012 06FF                MVI     B,TOP
                    *
                    *    THE ASSEMBLER HAS PRINTED A 'V' AGAINST THE INSTRUCTION
                    *    SIGNIFYING A VALUE ERROR. WE ARE TRYING TO STORE A 16-BIT NUMBER
                    *    IN AN 8-STAGE REGISTER.
                    *
                    *    2. THE SET PSEUDO-OP
                    *
                    *    THIS IS THE SAME PROGRAM AS ABOVE EXCEPT THAT WE CAN REDEFINE
                    *    THE LABEL
                    *
                   DATA:   SET     0AH
  0014 3E0A        BGN2:   MVI     A,DATA
                    *
                    *    NOW REDEFINE DATA AND CONTINUE
                    *
                   DATA:   SET     02H
  0016 0E02                MVI     C,DATA
  0018 0D                  DCR     C
  0019 C602        LOOP2:  ADI     DATA          ;ADD DATA TO RUNNING TOTAL
  001B 0D                  DCR     C             ;ONE LESS ADDITION TO DO
  001C C21900              JNZ     LOOP2         ;LOOP IF NOT FINISHED
  001F C9                  RET
                    *
  0020                     END
  0020
  000H USE FACTOR
  END OF ASSEMBLY

  A>
```

Figure 3.7

Programs may contain any number of ORG statements which need not specify addresses in any particular order. In other words, one ORG statement could set an origin at 1000H and the next at 0500H. The only thing to be aware of is that when multiple ORG statements are used, the assembler could effectively overwrite previously assembled code with new code. This could happen, for example, if we assembled one block of code at 0200H and the next at 0250H and then found it necessary to add to the first block. If this addition caused the block to expand beyond 50H bytes, the block starting at 0250H would reassign addresses previously assigned to the last part of the previous block, with obvious consequences.

Many modern assemblers remove this problem of choosing suitable assembly addresses by generating relocatable object code. What this means is that programs can be assembled at any address and subsequently relocated (moved) so that they execute at an entirely different address. We shall discuss relocation and other allied topics in Chapter 6.

The END directive

When the assembler reads this directive from the source code file it terminates the current pass thereby ignoring anything else which may have been entered after the END. Most assemblers insist that an END directive is used, although the CP/M assembler regards it as optional. If a CP/M source code file has no END, the assembler reads the end-of-file (EOF) character, which is always included, and terminates the current pass as before.

The define byte directive, DB

The DB directive is used to set aside and initialise a block of consecutive memory locations. Eight-bit values to be stored in the block are entered in the operand file of the DB statement and assigned to addresses in the same order as they are listed in the source code. For example, a DB statement might appear as

Q3.11   `BLOCK:  DB  24H,37H,0F4H,21H  ;test data`

When the assembler reaches this line during pass 2 it assigns 24H to the next unassigned address, 37H to the next, F4H to the next and so on. If entries in the operand field are expressions they should evaluate to 8-bit numbers, and their values are assigned to addresses as before.

The DB directive is also used when string constants are defined. These are entered in the operand field and enclosed within apostrophes as already explained. For example:

`MESSAGE:  DB 'THIS IS A MESSAGE'`

is a valid string definition.

```
                    *   PROGRAM TO DEMONSTRATE THE USE OF ORG AND DB DIRECTIVES.
                    *
0200 =          DATA:   EQU     0200H           ;START OF DATA AREA
0250 =          TEXT:   EQU     0250H           ;START OF TEXT AREA
0100 =          PROG1:  EQU     0100H           ;START OF FIRST PROGRAM
0150 =          PROG2:  EQU     0150H           ;START OF SECOND PROGRAM
                    *
                    *   THE FIRST PROGRAM JUST ADDS TWO NUMBERS STORED IN A LIST
                    *
0100                    ORG     PROG1           ;SET PROGRAM 1 ORIGIN
                    *
0100 210002     STRT:   LXI     H,LIST          ;POINT HL REGISTERS AT LIST
0103 7E                 MOV     A,M             ;GET FIRST ITEM FROM LIST
0104 23                 INX     H               ;BUMP LIST POINTER
0105 86                 ADD     M               ;ADD IN NEXT NUMBER
0106 C9                 RET
                    *
                    *   THE SECOND PROGRAM PRINTS A MESSAGE ON THE SYSTEM CONSOLE
                    *   THE MESSAGE MUST TERMINATE IN A NULL (00) CHARACTER
                    *
0150                    ORG     PROG2           ;PROGRAM 2 ORIGIN
                    *
0150 115002     MESP:   LXI     D,MESSGE        ;MESSAGE STRT ADD TO DE
0153 1A                 LDAX    D               ;GET CHARACTER FROM MESSAGE
0154 FE00               CPI     00H             ;IS IT A NULL ?
0156 C8                 RZ                      ;IF YES, RETURN
0157 47                 MOV     B,A             ;ELSE PUT CHARACTER INTO B
0158 CD3E29             CALL    PUTC            ;AND PRINT IT
015B 13                 INX     D               ;BUMP MESSAGE POINTER
015C C35301             JMP     MESP+3          ;AND GET NEXT CHARACTER
                    *
                    *   DATA AREA STARTS HERE
                    *
0200                    ORG     DATA
                    *
0200 0102       LIST:   DB      01,02
                    *
0250                    ORG     TEXT
                    *
0250 5448495320 MESSGE: DB      'THIS IS A MESSAGE'
0261 00                 NOP                     ;MESSAGE TERMINATOR
                    *
                    *   PUTC IS A SUBROUTINE WHICH PRINTS A CHARACTER ON THE CONSOLE.
                    *   WHEN IT IS WRITTEN IT WILL START AT 293EH.
                    *
293E =          PUTC:   EQU     293EH           ;DEFINED THIS WAY FOR TESTING
                    *
0262                    END
0262
000H USE FACTOR
END OF ASSEMBLY

A>
```

Figure 3.8

The assembler handles string constants by taking the ASCII equivalent of every character in the string, including spaces, and assigns them to memory in the usual way. The maximum length of the string is, typically, 64 characters but longer strings can be continued on the next line in another DB statement. Figure 3.8 illustrates the use of DB and ORG directives in greater detail.

The define word directive, DW

This directive is similar to DB except that entries in the operand field are interpreted as, or, if expressions, evaluated to, 16-bit (2-byte) words. These are stored with the least significant byte occupying the lower address of the pair. Since this is precisely the way in which addresses are stored, it is not surprising that the DW directive is typically used to store address constants. Figure 3.9 shows some examples of how DW may be used.

Q3.1b, 3.14, 3.15

```
            *   PROGRAM FRAGMENT TO DEMONSTRATE THE USE OF THE DW DIRECTIVE
            *
0000 0500   FIVE:   DW      05              ;NOTE, SINGLE BYTE 05 AND ASCII A
0002 41004142 ASCII: DW     'A','AB'        ;STORED AS REVERSED 16-BIT NUMBERS
0006 5634   CONS:   DW      3456H
0008 4523   BGN:    DW      STRT
            *
            *   ASSUME NEXT PROGRAM BLOCK SHOULD START AT 2345H
            *
2345                ORG     2345H
            *
2345 00     STRT:   NOP
            *
            *   INSTRUCTIONS IN HERE
            *
2346                END
2346
000H USE FACTOR
END OF ASSEMBLY

A>
```

Figure 3.9

The define storage directive, DS

When a DS directive is encountered in a source code program, the assembler evaluates the expression in the operand field and then reserves the number of bytes of memory given by the value of the expression. Nothing is stored in this block of memory, the assembler just skips over it before continuing with the assignment of object code to specific addresses.

Typically, a DS directive would be used to reserve memory designated as a data storage area. In the program of Figure 3.10, one

```
          *   PROGRAM TO ILLUSTRATE THE DS DIRECTIVE
          *
          *   THIS PROGRAM READS DATA FROM AN INPUT PORT (GETD SUBROUTINE)
          *   AND STORES IT IN A BUFFER. A MAXIMUM OF 255 ITEMS CAN BE READ
          *   AND READING WILL BE TERMINATED WHEN READ-COUNT REACHES 255 OR
          *   A NULL BYTE (00) IS READ. THE READ-COUNT IS STORED IN THE
          *   ADDRESS IMMEDIATELY BEFORE THE START OF THE BUFFER.
          *
          *   WE WILL ASSUME THAT GETD WILL START AT 1000H.
          *
1000 =       GETD:   EQU     1000H
          *
0100                 ORG     0100H
0100 AF      STORE:  XRA     A               ;CLEAR OUT A REGISTER
0101 322101          STA     NUMBR           ;INITIALIZE FINAL COUNTER AND
0104 4F              MOV     C,A             ;RUNNING COUNTER TO 0
0105 212201          LXI     H,BUFFER        ;POINT HL AT DATA BUFFER
          *
0108 CD0010  STRT:   CALL    GETD            ;READ A BYTE FROM INPUT PORT
010B FE00            CPI     00              ;IS IT A NULL ?
010D CA1C01          JZ      FINISH          ;IF YES, FINISH UP
0110 77              MOV     M,A             ;OTHERWISE STORE BYTE IN BUFFER
0111 0C              INR     C               ;INCREMENT RUNNING COUNTER
0112 79              MOV     A,C             ;PUT COUNT VALUE IN A AND
0113 FEFF            CPI     0FFH            ;TEST FOR 255 BYTES READ
0115 CA1C01          JZ      FINISH          ;IF 255 BYTES, FINISH
0118 23              INX     H               ;ELSE BUMP BUFFER POINTER
0119 C30801          JMP     STRT            ;AND READ NEXT BYTE
          *
011C 79      FINISH: MOV     A,C             ;RUNNING COUNTER INTO A
011D 322101          STA     NUMBR           ;STORE IN NUMBR
0120 C9              RET
          *
          *   BUFFER AREA
          *
0121         NUMBR:  DS      1               ;ONE BYTE FOR THE FINAL COUNT
0122         BUFFER: DS      255             ;255 BYTES FOR THE DATA
          *
0221 00              NOP                     ;NOTE THIS INSTRUCTION ADDRESS
          *
0222                 END
0222
000H USE FACTOR
END OF ASSEMBLY

A>
```

Figure 3.10

Q3.13 DS is used to define a counter location (NUMBR) and another to define a 255-byte data buffer. The counter location is initialised to zero because the DS directive does not assign values to reserved locations.

Conditional assembly directives

Conditional assembly directives provide a way of telling the assembler whether some part of a source code program is to be assembled or not. The code segment is enclosed between the words IF and ENDIF with a qualifying condition attached to the IF. The format of the statement is:

```
IF   expression
statement 1
statement 2
.
.
statement n
ENDIF
```

The assembler evaluates the expression and, if it evaluates to logical true (non-zero, usually –1), assembles the *n* instructions between IF and ENDIF. If the expression evaluates to logical false (zero) the *n*-instructions are ignored and therefore generate no object code.

We can demonstrate this technique with the example program of Figure 3.11. Imagine that there is some doubt in our minds as to whether a program executes a loop the correct number of times. To check, we have enclosed one instruction, INR C, between IF and ENDIF with the qualifying symbol, TRY, set to TRUE. On entry to the loop register C contains 0 and on exit it should contain the value of COUNT. Once we are satisfied that all is well the INR C instruction can effectively be removed by changing TRY from TRUE to FALSE. When the program is reassembled, the INR C instruction is missed out.

An application of conditional assembly Conditional assembly directives have a much wider application than simple debugging aids. Consider for example the case of a manufacturer who produces a microprocessor control data acquisition system. The complete system has many optional features each of which a prospective purchaser can include or omit depending on his application. Every hardware option has some supporting software and when a system is sold the commissioning engineer must tailor the software to the hardware. If each optional software block is enclosed between IF and ENDIF directives this usually amounts to changing a few SET statements.

A segment of the complete software package may be written as:

```
* OPTION 1 CODE
INCLUDE: SET   TRUE (or FALSE)
         IF    INCLUDE          ;is true
         Include this optional software
         ENDIF
```

(Continued on page 69)

```
 1:
 2:
 3:                       *    PROGRAM TO ILLUSTRATE SIMPLE CONDITIONAL ASSEMBLY STATEMENTS
 4:                       *
 5:                       *    FIRST DEFINE TRUE AND FALSE
 6:                       *
 7: FFFF =                TRUE:   EQU     -1
 8: 0000 =                FALSE:  EQU     0
 9:                       *
10:                       *    OUR TEST INSTRUCTION WILL BE ASSEMBLED ONLY IF 'TRY' IS TRUE
11:                       *
12:                       TRY:    SET     TRUE            ;SO WE WILL ASSEMBLE
13:                       *
14: 000A =                COUNT:  EQU     10              ;SUPPOSED TIMES THROUGH THE LOOP
15: 0000 060A             BGN:    MVI     B,COUNT         ;LOOP COUNTER INITIALISED
16: 0002 0E00                     MVI     C,00            ;AND SO IS TRIAL COUNTER
17:                       *
18:                       *    NOW START THE LOOP
19:                       *
20: 0004 1A               LOOP:   LDAX    D               ;DUMMY INSTRUCTIONS HERE
21:                       *
22:                               IF      TRY             ;********************
23: 0005 0C                       INR     C               ;* TEST INSTRUCTION *
24: 0006 00                       NOP
25:                               ENDIF                   ;********************
26:                       *
27: 0007 05                       DCR     B
28: 0008 C20400                   JNZ     LOOP
29:                       *
30:                       *    HAVING LEFT THE LOOP WE CAN CHECK THAT C CONTAINS 10 AS IT SHOULD
31:                       *
32: 000B                          END
```

```
 1:
 2:
 3:                       *
 4:                       *    SAME PROGRAM BUT NOW SET 'TRY' TO FALSE
 5:                       *
 6:                       *    FIRST RE-DEFINE SOME LABELS
 7:                       *
 8: 0000 =                FALSE:  EQU     0
 9: 000A =                COUNT:  EQU     10
10:                       *
11:                       TRY:    SET     FALSE
12:                       *
13: 0000 060A             STRT:   MVI     B,COUNT
14: 0002 0E00                     MVI     C,00
15: 0004 1A               HERE:   LDAX    D
16:                               IF      TRY
17:                               INR     C               ;NOTE NO OBJECT CODE THIS TIME
18:                               NOP
19:                               NOP
20:                               ENDIF
21: 0005 05                       DCR     B
22: 0006 C20400                   JNZ     HERE
23:                       *
24: 0009                          END
```

Figure 3.11

```
* OPTION 2 CODE
INCLUDE: SET   TRUE (or FALSE)
         IF    INCLUDE
         Include this block
         ENDIF
etc.
```

The commissioning engineer would simply edit the source code file so that INCLUDE is TRUE for all those options which must be included and FALSE for every other option. When the source code is assembled and eventually committed to (EP)ROM the software supports all the selected hardware options.

This example also illustrates the value of being able to redefine labels with the SET directive. The apparent multiple definitions of INCLUDE would have been rejected had any other directive been used.

Q3.16, 3.17

The Intel conditional assembly directives As well as the simple IF-ENDIF directive, the Intel assembler allows one block of code to be assembled if the tested condition is true, and another if the condition is false. The format of this statement is:

```
IF  expression          ;is true
Assemble instructions in here
ELSE                    ;if condition is false
Assemble these instructions
ENDIF
```

Only one ELSE can be paired with an IF, but blocks can be nested to eight levels, allowing a large number of separate conditions to determine which blocks of code are assembled. As in the CP/M assembler, the expression which qualifies an IF commonly contains logical operators because it must evaluate to TRUE or FALSE. One additional feature of the Intel assembler is the comparison operators which are also used in logical expressions. These are listed below but we shall not discuss them further. For the most part their action is obvious anyway.

Operator	Meaning
EQ	Equal
NE	Not equal
LT	Less than
LE	Less than or equal to
GT	Greater than
GE	Greater than or equal to

3.11   Using the assembler

So far we have concentrated exclusively on how the assembler works and the facilities it provides. It is now time to think about how we use it to assemble a short program like COMP. Since the CP/M editor was used to prepare the source code it is only logical that we should use the CP/M assembler to assemble it. Recall that our program is in a file called COMP.ASM on disk B. When we ask CP/M to assemble that program we must supply four pieces of information:

1   The name of the file. (Assumed to have the .ASM extension.)
2   The disk (A or B) on which it is stored.
3   Where the hexadecimal object code should be stored.
4   Whether a listing file should be created and where, if anywhere, it should be stored.

The process of assembly is illustrated in Figure 3.12.

A listing file is the programmer's record of the assembly. It contains the original source code together with the object code for every instruction and the address to which the first byte of every instruction has been assigned. All the figures in this chapter apart from Figures 3.1 and 3.12 are examples of program listings.

Information is passed to the CP/M assembler by entering the command

```
ASM  FILENAME.abc
```

when the CP/M prompt is displayed. The extension abc is interpreted as shown in Table 3.1.

Consequently if we enter the command

```
A>ASM  COMP.BBX
```

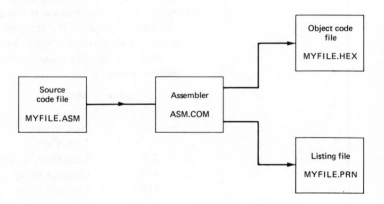

Q3.18   *Figure 3.12*   Assembling a program under CP/M

Table 3.1

Letter	Possibilities	Meaning
a	A or B	Indicates which disk drive contains the source code to be assembled
b	A or B	Indicates which disk drive should receive the hexadecimal object code
	Z	Means that an object code file should not be generated. Assembly will go ahead however, with any error messages displayed on the console
c	A or B	Indicates which disk drive will receive the listing file. (FILENAME.PRN)
	X	Sends the listing file to the console instead of storing it on disk
	Z	Suppresses the generation of a listing

CP/M will respond by loading the assembler from drive A and COMP.ASM from disk B. ASM will then assemble the source code in COMP.ASM, the object code will be written to COMP.HEX on disk B and the listing file will be printed on the console.

Not surprisingly the COMP. listing file shown in Figure 3.13 includes a number of error messages which appear as letters immediately to the left of the address column. We have, for instance, one U, two instructions which have not been assembled at all and have been tagged with an S, and another four lines which have an L in front of them. These letters are reasonably well chosen to give some idea about the nature of the error. An L, for example, indicates a label error – there is something wrong with the label.

In actual fact there is nothing wrong with any of the labels. The problem is that three of them have been defined incorrectly and there is some confusion about the fourth, BACK, because there is an error in the preceding line. This brings out a very significant point about error messages – they are seldom explicit and sometimes misleading. When a listing file contains error messages you may conclude that there is something wrong with the source code at about the point where the messages occurred, but do not conclude anything else. The action which follows the discovery of an error message is a detailed examination of the source code to uncover the mistakes.

If we look back at the COMP listing for instance, the error message against the LXI H,VALUE instruction stems from the fact that VALUE,HLMT and LLMT have all been defined using the Z80

```
       **********************************************************
       *  PROGRAM NAME : COMP                                   *
       *                                                        *
       *  PROGRAMMER : M.J.MORSE                                *
       *  DATE : 3 2 81                                         *
       *                                                        *
       *  PROGRAM TO COMPARE A MEASURED TEMPERATURE STORED IN   *
       *  ADDRESS 'VALUE' WITH UPPER AND LOWER LIMITS STORED    *
       *  IN ADDRESSES 'HLMT' AND 'LLMT'. WHEN TESTING, THE     *
       *  CONTENTS OF 'VALUE' SHOULD BE CHANGED IN THE          *
       *  DEBUGGER, DDT, AND THE NUMBER IN REGISTER B CHECKED   *
       *  AT THE END OF THE PROGRAM.                            *
       *                                                        *
       *  IF THE (VALUE) > (HLMT) THEN (B) SHOULD BE 02         *
       *  IF THE (VALUE) < (LLMT) THEN (B) SHOULD BE 01         *
       *  OTHERWISE (B) SHOULD BE 00.                           *
       *                                                        *
       *                  STRUCTURE.                            *
       *                  ''''''''                              *
       *  BEGIN                                                 *
       *      FLAG := 2;                                        *
       *      HLMT := A0H;                                      *
       *      LLMT := 10H;                                      *
       *      IF (VALUE) > (HLMT) THEN                          *
       *          CONTINUE    (* TO THE END WITH FLAG = 2*)     *
       *      ELSE                                              *
       *          FLAG := FLAG -1;                              *
       *          IF (VALUE) < (LLMT) THEN                      *
       *              CONTINUE (* TO THE END WITH FLAG = 1*)    *
       *          ELSE                                          *
       *              FLAG := FLAG - 1;                         *
       *          ENDIF                                         *
       *      ENDIF                                             *
       *  END.                                                  *
       *                                                        *
       *  NOTE, REGISTERS A, B, H AND L CORRUPTED.              *
       **********************************************************
       *
  0100                    ORG      0100H
  0100 0602      COMP:     MVI      B,02H        ;FLAG CONTAINED IN B
U0102 210000               LXI      H,VALUE      ;POINT (H,L) AT VALUE
  0105 7E                  MOV      A,M          ;GET VALUE
  0106 24                  INR      H            ;POINT AT HLMT
  0107 BE                  CMP      M            ;(VALUE) > (HLMT)
  0108 DA1001              JC       BACK         ;CY SET MEANS VALUE HIGH
  010B 24                  INR      H            ;POINT AT LLMT
S                          DEC      B            ;FLAG := FLAG -1
  010C BE                  CMP      M            ;(VALUE) < (LLMT)
  010D D21001              JNC      BACK         ;CY = 0 MEANS VALUE LOW
S                          DEC      B            ;FLAG NOW ZERO
L0110 C9        BACK:      RET                   ;RETURN TO MAIN
       *
       *  DATA AREA
       *
L               VALUE:     DEFB     40H          ;INITIAL TRIAL VALUE
L               HLMT:      DEFB     A0H          ;HIGH LIMIT
L               LLMT:      DEFB     10H          ;LOW LIMIT
       *
  0111                     END
  0111
  000H USE FACTOR
  END OF ASSEMBLY

A>
```

Figure 3.13 The error messages are single letters to the left of the address column

```
**********************************************************
*    PROGRAM NAME : COMP                                 *
*                                                        *
*    PROGRAMMER : M.J.MORSE                              *
*    DATE : 3 2 81                                       *
*                                                        *
*    PROGRAM TO COMPARE A MEASURED TEMPERATURE STORED IN *
*    ADDRESS 'VALUE' WITH UPPER AND LOWER LIMITS STORED  *
*    IN ADDRESSES 'HLMT' AND 'LLMT'. WHEN TESTING, THE   *
*    CONTENTS OF 'VALUE' SHOULD BE CHANGED IN THE        *
*    DEBUGGER, DDT, AND THE NUMBER IN REGISTER B CHECKED *
*    AT THE END OF THE PROGRAM.                          *
*                                                        *
*    IF THE (VALUE) > (HLMT) THEN (B) SHOULD BE 02       *
*    IF THE (VALUE) < (LLMT) THEN (B) SHOULD BE 01       *
*    OTHERWISE (B) SHOULD BE 00.                         *
*                                                        *
*                  STRUCTURE.                            *
*                  '''''''''                             *
*    BEGIN                                               *
*        FLAG := 2;                                      *
*        HLMT := A0H;                                    *
*        LLMT := 10H;                                    *
*        IF (VALUE) > (HLMT) THEN                        *
*            CONTINUE    (* TO THE END WITH FLAG = 2*)    *
*        ELSE                                            *
*            FLAG := FLAG -1;                            *
*            IF (VALUE) < (LLMT) THEN                    *
*                CONTINUE (* TO THE END WITH FLAG = 1*)* *
*            ELSE                                        *
*                FLAG := FLAG - 1;                       *
*            ENDIF                                       *
*        ENDIF                                           *
*    END.                                                *
*                                                        *
*    NOTE, REGISTERS A, B, H AND L CORRUPTED.            *
**********************************************************
*
0100                  ORG     0100H
0100 0602   COMP:      MVI     B,02H           ;FLAG CONTAINED IN B
0102 211301            LXI     H,VALUE         ;POINT (H,L) AT VALUE
0105 7E                MOV     A,M             ;GET VALUE
0106 24                INR     H               ;POINT AT HLMT
0107 BE                CMP     M               ;(VALUE) > (HLMT)
0108 DA1201            JC      BACK            ;CY SET MEANS VALUE HIGH
010B 24                INR     H               ;POINT AT LLMT
010C 05                DCR     B               ;FLAG := FLAG -1
010D BE                CMP     M               ;(VALUE) < (LLMT)
010E D21201            JNC     BACK            ;CY = 0 MEANS VALUE LOW
0111 05                DCR     B               ;FLAG NOW ZERO
0112 C9     BACK:      RET                     ;RETURN TO MAIN
            *
            *  DATA AREA
            *
0113 40     VALUE:     DB      40H             ;INITIAL TRIAL VALUE
0114 A0     HLMT:      DB      0A0H            ;HIGH LIMIT
0115 10     LLMT:      DB      10H             ;LOW LIMIT
            *
0116                   END
0116
000H USE FACTOR
END OF ASSEMBLY

A>
```

Figure 3.14   After editing, the program assembles without error

pseudo-op DEFB instead of the 8080 pseudo-op DB. If we correct these mistakes, the LXI H,VALUE will assemble correctly.

There is, however, another error in the data definition area which has not been flagged at all. The intended value of HLMT is A0H, but all hexadecimal numbers must begin with a digit. In other words A0H should be 0A0H. This mistake was masked by the error in defining HLMT, but it will need to be corrected when we re-edit COMP.ASM.

The other two error messages are against DEC B instructions. If you have studied the Z80 instruction set you will know that DEC B is the Z80 equivalent of DCR B. Although the microprocessor in the North Star system is a Z80, the assembler is written for the 8080 and it will not accept Z80 mnemonics. If we correct these mistakes as well, the program assembles without error as shown in Figure 3.14. Of course, the fact that COMP.ASM now assembles without error is no guarantee that it will work as we expect it to. The next step of program development is to check the program logic in the debugger.

Q3.19

Questions

3.1 *(a)* Define the term symbolic addressing.

(b) Which of the following are symbolic addresses and which are label declarations?

```
TABLE:   DS    10
LOOP :   MVI   A,03
TWO  :   EQU   02
STRT :   DW    BGN
```

3.2 Explain how the assembler deals with symbolic addresses and other labels.

3.3 State the two main advantages of symbolic addressing in assembly language programs.

3.4 Construct a symbol table for the program listed in Figure 3.2.

3.5 Explain the format of a line of source code of an assembly language program.

3.6 Define a numeric constant and a string constant. How is the radix of the number system indicated when numeric constants are defined?

3.7 *(a)* Write down the five arithmetic operators in their order of precedence.

(b) Evaluate the following arithmetic expressions:
   (i)   10 MOD 3 * 3
   (ii) 10 + 4 * 3 − 2
   (iii) (10 + 4) * 3 − 2

        (iv)   (10 + 4) * (3 – 2)

        (v)   13/2 + 13 MOD 2

3.8   *(a)*   Define the shift operators recognised by the Intel and CP/M assemblers.

      (b)   If a byte labelled MASK is defined as 44H evaluate the following expressions:

        (i)   MASK SHR 2

        (ii)   MASK SHL 2

        (iii)   MASK SHR 2 + 4

        (iv)   MASK SHL 1 – 40H

3.9   *(a)*   Write logical operators in their order of precedence.

      (b)   Given the previous definition of MASK evaluate the following logical expressions and state whether they evaluate to logical TRUE or FALSE.

        (i)   MASK AND MASK SHR 2

        (ii)   MASK AND NOT MASK

        (iii)   MASK OR MASK SHR 2

        (iv)   MASK XOR MASK SHR 2

        (v)   MASK XOR MASK SHR 2 AND MASK SHL 2

3.10   State the common uses of the standard assembler directives.

3.11   How does a pseudo-op differ from a real opcode? Give two examples of each type of opcode which would be accepted by the Intel assembler.

3.12   Explain how the SET and EQU pseudo-ops differ.

3.13   A program requires that a block of 127 memory locations starting at address 3F47H and identified by the name BUFFER, be defined. Explain how this facility would be provided.

3.14   A program contains two definitions:

```
MESSGE:   DB    'AB'
 ASCII:   DW    'AB'
```

Write down the hexadecimal object code for these two definitions.

3.15   Given that MESSGE is defined as in the previous, write a subroutine which prints the message, assuming that the string terminating character is a $ (dollar sign). Each character in the string is sent to the console using a routine called PCHAR which starts at address 530FH.

3.16   Describe the format and two applications of conditional assembly.

3.17   Three parameters, COND1, COND2 and COND3, are defined in a program. A particular block of code is to be assembled if COND1 and COND2 are TRUE and COND3 is FALSE. FALSE is defined as 0 and TRUE is defined as a 1 in least significant bit position. Write

down the structure of a conditional assembly statement, or statements, which ensure that the block is assembled only if the stated
conditions are satisfied.

3.18   The CP/M assembler produces a .HEX file which includes some
error-checking data and the hexadecimal object code. Ignoring this
error-checking information, what would be the effect of using the
CP/M TYPE command to display the contents of this file?
Remember that the TYPE command only works properly if the typed
file contains ASCII characters. Is it possible to transfer the contents
of the .HEX file to memory as it is, and execute it directly?

3.19   How should the programmer interpret error messages when signalled
by the assembler?

Chapter 4 The debugger

Objectives of this chapter *When you have completed studying this chapter you should be able to:*

1 Appreciate the need for a debugger when developing assembly language programs.
2 Understand the important differences between monitor programs and debuggers.
3 Understand all the DDT monitor and debugging commands.
4 Appreciate how the debug commands can be used to isolate user program errors.

4.1 The need for a debugger

Having safely stored our .HEX file on the disk, the easy part of program development is over. All we have done to this point is use the editor to enter a list of instructions that the assembler will accept. We hope that the program is logically correct, but the expectation is not high.

People new to programming are always surprised at how difficult it is to write a program of any consequence and get it to work first time. This difficulty is particularly true of assembly language programs in which instructions are a lot less descriptive and lot less powerful than high-level language program statements. Programmers know what the program should do, but on reading through the source code, there is always that lingering suspicion that, maybe, the mnemonics, or the order in which they have been entered, are not precisely what is required for every conceivable set of data.

The fact is, of course, that most programs are created with mistakes (bugs) in them. Help is needed to correct these mistakes (debug) and the utility program which provides that help is the debugger.

4.2 Debug facilities

The debugger works by allowing us to execute our program while it retains overall control. The term often used to describe this situation is 'running under debug'. When our program and the debugger are loaded from the disk into memory the debugger starts working by displaying some prompt character. In reply to this prompt we may enter a command which, for example, instructs the debugger to transfer control to our program for a given number of program steps. After that we may wish to examine the CPU registers or a part of memory to check that our program has executed correctly to that point. If it hasn't we may want to make some changes to our program and re-try, but this time in trace mode with the debugger reporting what has happened as each instruction is executed. There are commands which invoke these and other debug facilities and, as we go through this chapter, we shall be looking at each of them in detail.

Of course, there is no universally accepted set of debug commands just as there is no universally accepted set of edit commands or assembler facilities. A debugger described, impartially, as 'powerful' will probably have a greater range of commands than one that is not, but powerful is a very imprecise word.

In keeping with our idea of concentrating on system utilities which are used in many different 8080 systems, the debugger we shall describe is the CP/M utility, DDT. DDT stands for 'dynamic debugging tool'. Together with ED and ASM it forms a comprehensive set of system utilities for developing assembly language programs.

4.3   Monitors and debuggers

One way of regarding a debugger is as a monitor program with extensions. Typically, a monitor provides the ability to examine and modify the contents of memory, to fill a block of memory with a byte value and to copy from one block of memory into another. The extra facilities that a debugger provides include commands to disassemble object code into assembly language mnemonics, to trace program execution one step at a time, to insert breakpoints into user programs and to examine and modify CPU registers.

Admittedly some monitor programs, particularly those supplied with microprocessor evaluation systems, have some or all of these extra features, but they are not designed to work with disk-based systems. The various BUG programs, such as JBUG which runs in the M6800 evaluation system, are monitors of this kind.

If the discussion is restricted to monitors supplied with a disk operating system, the usual range of monitor commands is:

1   Compare two blocks of memory and print out any differences in contents. (Very useful for comparing an original block of code with a copy just committed to EPROM.)
2   Fill a block of memory with a byte.
3   Move the contents of one block of memory to another block.
4   Search a block of memory for a specific byte or a specific byte sequence.

5 Test a block of memory – write and then read back.
6 Display the contents of a block of memory as a sequence of hexadecimal numbers.
7 Display a block of memory in hexadecimal and ASCII.
8 Display the contents of one location for possible alteration.
9 Jump to an address – usually the start address of a program.

Of course, a particular monitor may have more, or different, commands, but this list is fairly typical. What a monitor will not have is any commands that control execution of a user program or permit examination of the CPU registers.

Q4.1 A debugger such as DDT will provide most of the monitor commands listed above and certainly all that would be useful for debugging programs.

4.4 Starting a debug session

A debug session is started by loading the debugger and the program to be debugged from the disk into memory. When using DDT there are two ways of doing this. The first is to type:

```
DDT FILENAME.HEX (or .COM) <cr>
```

DDT is loaded first and then our file, FILENAME.HEX. Since the .HEX file contains a list of hexadecimal numbers (ASCII characters 0 to F), DDT actually converts these numbers to binary as it reads them off the disk. Alternatively the .HEX file could have been converted to a binary, .COM, file by using the CP/M utility, LOAD, before DDT was called. Had that been done, no conversion would have been necessary and the command line would have been:

```
DDT FILENAME.COM
```

Q4.2 The LOAD utility is considered in Chapter 6.

The addresses occupied by the binary equivalent of FILENAME.HEX are those allocated during assembly which, since our program is designed to run under CP/M, will be from 0100H upwards. When DDT is loaded it overwrites a part of CP/M so that when it is eventually dismissed, a 'warm boot' has to be performed. This involves reloading the overwritten part of CP/M and is achieved by typing CTRL-C or G0 when the DDT prompt is displayed.

The second way of calling the debugger is to simply type,

```
DDT
```

After signing on, DDT issues its prompt. At this point two commands, one after the other, are issued. The first is the I (input) command and has the form,

```
IFILENAME.HEX
```

```
A>DDT B:COMP.HEX
DDT VERS 1.4
NEXT   PC
0116 0000
-
```

Figure 4.1 The DDT sign-on message when DDT and the program COMP.HEX are loaded into memory. The dash character is the DDT prompt

What this does is to declare FILENAME.HEX as the source of all subsequent input. After that a single R is typed to read the nominated input file.

There is one restriction on this second way of loading DDT and a user program – both files must reside on the same disk. In Figure 4.1 we have used the first method because our program, COMP.HEX, is on disk B and DDT is on disk A.

When DDT signs on it shows the next free location in the user program area (0116H) and the current setting of the program counter (0000H). The dash character is the DDT prompt which we interpret as a request for a command.

4.5   DDT monitor commands

These are typical of many different monitors although, of course, the command format will probably vary from monitor to monitor. To illustrate the sort of commands that exist we shall consider each of the DDT monitor commands in turn.

The display command, D

This is possibly the first command we may wish to try after loading our program. The format of the command is:

```
D<start address>,<finish address>
```

Since our program was loaded into addresses 0100H to 0115H we might enter:

```
D100,115
```

The display (Figure 4.2) shows the hexadecimal contents of each address in the block and its ASCII equivalent. Any non-printable ASCII character is displayed as a full stop.

Every complete line of the display contains 16 (10H) byte values with their ASCII equivalents to the right. If we were to type D without a start and finish address the contents (hex and ASCII) of the 12×16 addresses from 0100H onwards are displayed. Any further D, on its own, displays the next 12×16 block. Having already displayed addresses 0100H to 0115H, however, the second D in Figure 4.2 displays the remainder of the 12×16 block previously started.

The advantage of having the ASCII as well as the hex display is that string constants stored with program text can be easily located and checked.

One final point about the D command. When large blocks of memory are to be examined the display can scroll off the screen before it can be

```
      D100,115
      0100 06 02 21 13 01 7E 24 BE DA 12 01 24 05 BE D2 12 ..!..~$....$....
      0110 01 05 C9 40 A0 10 ...@..
      -D
      0116 37 38 2C 20 44 49 47 49 54 41 78, DIGITA
      0120 4C 20 52 45 53 45 41 52 43 48 20 20 20 20 20 20 L RESEARCH
      0130 44 44 54 20 56 45 52 53 20 31 2E 34 24 31 00 02 DDT VERS 1.4$1..
      0140 C5 C5 11 30 01 0E 09 CD 05 00 C1 21 07 00 7E 3D ...0.......!..~=
      0150 90 57 1E 00 D5 21 00 02 78 B1 CA 65 01 0B 7E 12 .W...!..x..e..~.
      0160 13 23 C3 58 01 D1 C1 E5 62 78 B1 CA 87 01 0B 7B .#.X....bx.....{
      0170 E6 07 C2 7A 01 E3 7E 23 E3 6F 7D 17 6F D2 83 01 ...z..~#.o}.o...
      0180 1A 84 12 13 C3 69 01 D1 2E 00 E9 2A 7C 1D EB 0E .....i.....*|...
      0190 1A CD 67 1B C9 3E 0C D3 01 3E 08 D3 01 DB 01 07 ..g..>...>......
      01A0 07 07 1F DA A9 08 C3 9D 08 DB 03 E6 7F C9 21 83 ..............!.
      01B0 1D 70 2B 71 2A 82 1D 44 4D CD A1 07 0E 3A CD 86 .p+q*..DM....:..
      01C0 07 0E 20 CD 86 07 3A 5F 1D 32 84 1D 3A 60 1D 21 .. ...:_.2..:`.!
      -
```

Figure 4.2 The display memory command, D. D100,115 displays our program code and data, and a further D displays the remainder of the 12 × 16 memory block which begins at 0100H

checked. If this is likely to happen a CTRL-S entered at the console stops the display until another CTRL-S is entered. In this way segments of the block can be viewed in comfort.

The set command, S

With this command we can display the contents of a single address with the option of changing it, leaving it unaltered and examining the next location, or return to the debug command level. At the debug command level the debug prompt is displayed so that a further command can be entered. The format of the S command is

    S<address>

The hexadecimal contents of the address are displayed and then DDT waits for some operator input. If that input is a carriage-return-line feed (RETURN key) the contents of the address remain unaltered and the next address and its contents are displayed on the next line.

A new value is written into the address by typing the value and following it with a RETURN. As before, the hexadecimal contents of the next address are then displayed on a new line. If the operator input is a full stop the set command is terminated and the DDT prompt reappears. Figure 4.3 shows each of these three operator responses when using the set command.

```
-S200
0200 C3 10
0201 83
0202 06 11
0203 00 12
0204 00 13
0205 00 14
0206 C3 .
-D200,205
0200 10 83 11 12 13 14 ......
-
```

Figure 4.3 The set command, S. The contents of an address can be changed by typing a new hexadecimal value. Entering a full stop returns control to DDT

The fill-memory command, F

The format of this command is:

    F<start address>,<finish address>,<byte value>

```
     -F200,21F,FF
     -D200,21F
     0200 FF FF FF FF FF FF FF FF FF FF FF FF FF FF FF FF ................
     0210 FF FF FF FF FF FF FF FF FF FF FF FF FF FF FF FF ................
     -
```

Figure 4.4   The fill memory command, F. The 32 addresses from 0200H to 021FH are filled with the number 0FFH

The function of the command is to fill a block of memory from start to finish, inclusively, with the byte value. In Figure 4.4 the block of memory from 0200H to 021FH is filled with byte FFH.

The move command, M

This command copies from one block of memory into another of equal length. The format of the command is:

```
M<start of source>,<finish of source>,
                    <start of destination>
```

To illustrate the use of this command (Figure 4.5) we have copied from the block between 0200H and 021FH which was previously filled with FFH, into a block of equal length beginning at 0300H.

```
      D300,31F
     0300 C2 18 05 0D 79 C1 C9 CD F1 00 FE 04 CA 18 05 C9 ....y...........
     0310 CD F1 00 FE 03 CA 18 05 FE 04 C0 3D C9 21 7A 06 ...........=.!z.
     -M200,21F,300
     -D300,31F
     0300 FF FF FF FF FF FF FF FF FF FF FF FF FF FF FF FF ................
     0310 FF FF FF FF FF FF FF FF FF FF FF FF FF FF FF FF ................
     -
```

Figure 4.5   The move command, M. Data contained in addresses 0200H to 021FH are copied to a block starting at 0300H. The D commands, before and after the M, show that the move has worked properly

DDT monitor commands – conclusion

This completes the list of identifiable monitor commands. Together with the jump-to-address command (covered in the next section), the list accounts for six of the nine commands which were said to be typical of disk-based monitor programs. All of them are useful but do not provide much assistance when debugging programs. What we need are the extra debug commands.

4.6   DDT debug commands

The list (or disassemble) command

When the .HEX file was loaded into memory, DDT converted the

```
L100,112
   0100   MVI   B,02
   0102   LXI   H,0113
   0105   MOV   A,M
   0106   INR   H
   0107   CMP   M
   0108   JC    0112
   010B   INR   H
   010C   DCR   B
   010D   CMP   M
   010E   JNC   0112
   0111   DCR   B
   0112   RET
   0113
-
```

Figure 4.6 The list command L. This command disassembles the hexadecimal numbers in a block of addresses, displaying the address contents as equivalent 8080 mnemonics

```
A200
0200   MOV   A,B
0201   LXI   H,FFFF
0204   MVI   B,02
0206   .
-L200,204
   0200   MOV   A,B
   0201   LXI   H,FFFF
   0204   MVI   B,
-
```

Figure 4.7 The assemble command, A. This is similar to the S command, except that instructions are entered in mnemonic rather than hexadecimal form

hexadecimal contents of that file to binary, and stored each byte in its assigned address. The D command was then used to check that the loaded program was intact. The display would have been much more informative, however, had it included 8080 mnemonics instead of hexadecimal numbers.

The conversion of hexadecimal numbers to instruction mnemonics is the opposite of assembly – in other words, disassembly. The DDT disassembly command character is L, for list. The list command format is

    L<start address>,<finish address>

so to disassemble our COMP program we would enter

    L100,112

The DDT response is shown in Figure 4.6. Notice that all symbolic addresses have now been made absolute. Symbolic addresses only have significance while the symbol table is active. At the end of assembly the symbol table was discarded and so the .HEX file only contains references to absolute addresses.

If an L is entered without the start and finish addresses, the 12 instructions, beginning at the present setting of the program counter, are disassembled.

The assemble command, A

If, during debugging, it is found that an instruction is incorrect, there are two possible courses of action. Assuming that the correct instruction is known, you could look up the appropriate hexadecimal opcode and then use the S command to overwrite the incorrect value. Alternatively, you could use the A command to enter the correct instruction in assembler mnemonics. The format of the A command is

    A<address>

In response, DDT prints the address and then waits for an instruction to be entered. Labels and pseudo-ops are not allowed, only valid 8080 mnemonics and hexadecimal numbers.

When the instruction has been entered, DDT prints the start address of the next instruction and then waits for further input. When all the entries have been made, a full-stop terminates the A command and returns control to the DDT command level. Figure 4.7 shows how this command may be used.

The examine registers command, X

Another facility that a debugger must provide is the ability to examine and possibly change numbers in CPU registers. A display of all registers is obtained by typing X at the DDT command level. As shown in Figure 4.8, the individual status flags are displayed, together with each of the working registers, the stack pointer, S, the program counter, P, and the instruction pointed at by the program counter. The flags are labelled:

C – for carry
Z – for zero
M – for minus
E – for even parity
I – for interdigit carry

In the 8080 manuals, the E and I flags are identified by the letters P (parity) and AC (auxiliary carry). The letters E and I are used here to avoid confusion between the *P*arity flag and *P*rogram counter, and *A*uxiliary carry and the *A* register.

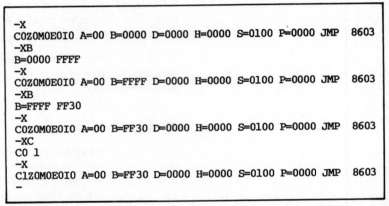

```
-X
C0Z0M0E0I0 A=00 B=0000 D=0000 H=0000 S=0100 P=0000 JMP   8603
-XB
B=0000 FFFF
-X
C0Z0M0E0I0 A=00 B=FFFF D=0000 H=0000 S=0100 P=0000 JMP   8603
-XB
B=FFFF FF30
-X
C0Z0M0E0I0 A=00 B=FF30 D=0000 H=0000 S=0100 P=0000 JMP   8603
-XC
C0 1
-X
C1Z0M0E0I0 A=00 B=FF30 D=0000 H=0000 S=0100 P=0000 JMP   8603
-
```

Figure 4.8   The examine registers command, X. An X on its own displays all the registers and the instruction that starts at the address contained in the program counter. Typing X and a single-letter register (or flag) idenrification letter, opens the register, enabling its contents to be changed

Individual registers or flag bits can be examined by typing X and then a single letter. For example, when XB is typed the current contents of the B,C register pair are displayed and then DDT waits for some operator input. If the input is a RETURN, the register contents are left unaltered and control returns to the DDT command level. A new value is loaded into the B,C register pair by typing a valid hexadecimal number and then RETURN.

Since the 8-bit registers, apart from register A, cannot be referenced separately, the only way of changing the contents of C, for example, without changing the contents of B, is to enter a four-character hexadecimal number in which the first two characters (destined for register B) are the same as the existing number in B. Figure 4.8 illustrates the procedure.

The go command, G

This is the first of three commands used to execute user programs under debug. The command 'go', is interpreted as 'go to an address and begin executing instructions from that address onwards'. Once this command is issued the DDT program ceases execution until an instruction in the executing program returns control to DDT. The instruction which returns control is RST 7.

You will know by now that an RST 7 instruction is a single byte CALL to address 0038H. At 0038H is a JMP instruction (put there when DDT was loaded) which returns control to DDT at the point where a prompt character is displayed. This means, of course, that user programs must end in an RST 7. Normally, standalone programs which run under CP/M, end in a RET or JMP 0000H instruction. During testing, however, this must be changed.

When a G is entered on its own, the contents of the program counter are taken as the address at which program execution is to begin. The several other forms of the G command are shown below. In this list <strt> is the execution start address and <bp> is a breakpoint address.

1	G<strt>	Go to start address.
2	G<strt>,<bp>	Insert breakpoint at bp, then go to start address.
3	G<strt>,<bp1>,<bp2>	Insert two breakpoints, at bp1 and bp2, and then go to start address.
4	G,<bp>	As 2 but the start address is now contained in the program counter.
5	G,<bp1>,<bp2>	As 3 but the start address is contained in the program counter.

DDT inserts breakpoints by temporarily replacing the byte at the breakpoint address with an RST 7 instruction. Assuming, naturally enough, that the breakpoint is inserted in the user program area, control returns to DDT when the breakpoint RST 7 is executed. The whole range of other DDT commands are then available to check program execution up to the breakpoint. If, after checking, a further G is entered, the user instruction is restored in the breakpoint address and program execution continues from the breakpoint until another RST 7 is encountered.

If a breakpoint is used when debugging programs you must make sure that it replaces the first byte of an instruction, otherwise it will have no effect. Instead, the RST 7 opcode (FF) will have replaced the second or third byte of an instruction, with unpredictable results. Another thing to be aware of is that, since the breakpoint instruction is RST 7, user programs may not include that instruction. Neither can DDT be used to debug interrupt service routines which start at 0038H. Usually, however, this is a small restriction to set against the advantages of a debugger like DDT.

Q4.3

Figure 4.9 illustrates several forms of the G command. With the program COMP.HEX in memory, it was first necessary to change the last instruction at 0112H to an RST 7 using the A command. After the program counter had been set to the start address of the program (0100H), a single G runs the program through to the end. DDT then prints the address at which the RST 7 instruction was located (0112H) and awaits a new command character.

```
-A112
0112   RST 7         Change last instruction to RST 7
0113   .      _ _ _ _ _ _ _ _ _ _
-XP
P=0000 0100          Put 0100 in program counter, then go from there – stops
-G                   at RST 7 in 0112
*0112
-G100   _ _ _ _ _ _ _ _ _ _ _
*0112                Combine above two commands
-G100,105   _ _ _ _ _ _ _ _
*0105                Breakpoint at 0105. Go from 0100 to breakpoint
-G      _ _ _ _ _ _ _ _ _ _
*0112                Continue from breakpoint
-G100,105,108   _ _ _ _ _ _
*0105                Breakpoints at 0105 and 0108. Go from 0100
-G      _ _ _ _ _ _ _ _ _ _
*0112                Continue from 0105 breakpoint; note 0108 breakpoint
        _ _ _ _ _ _ _ _ _ _          ignored
-G100,105
*0105                Go with just one breakpoint at 0105
-G,108   _ _ _ _ _ _ _ _ _ _
*0108                Continue from 0105 with breakpoint at 0108
-G      _ _ _ _ _ _ _ _ _
*0112                Continue from 0108 to the end
-
```

Figure 4.9   The various forms of the go command, G

Using the second form of the G command, the execution start address is supplied to the G. Once again the program runs to the end (0112) and stops. Finally the program was executed with breakpoints at 0105H, and then at 0105H and 0108H. This time the program runs as far as the breakpoint (0105H) and then stops. Entering a further G at this point continues execution from the breakpoint to the end of the program. Remember that at a breakpoint the program counter contains the breakpoint address – in this case 0105H.

With the two breakpoints inserted, the program runs from the start

address to the first breakpoint, just as before, and when another G is
entered it continues to the end of the program, again just as before.
Notice that it does not stop at the second breakpoint (0108H). This is
because *both* breakpoints are removed when *either* breakpoint
instruction is executed. Had we particularly wanted to continue from
0105H and stop at 0108H we should have entered G,108 at the first
breakpoint.

The trace command, T

Using some debuggers you occasionally reach a point where the
program still does not work properly and you cannot think what to
try next. The best course of action in a situation like that is either to
switch off and try again tomorrow, or find a debugger with a program
trace facility.

The format of the DDT trace command is

    Tn

where *n* is the number of program steps to trace, written as a hexadecimal number. If *n* is omitted a 1 is assumed. In trace mode, a
program executes normally, starting at the address contained in the
program counter, but at each step the contents of all the CPU
registers and the flags are displayed.

In Figure 4.10 we have entered the command T4. The first line of the
display shows the initialised state of the registers and the instruction
which has just been executed. The second line shows what happened
to the registers and flags as a result of executing the first instruction
and, again, the instruction which has just been executed. Thus the
display always shows the CPU state before and after execution of all
but the last step. After executing the fourth instruction the trace
command terminates showing the next instruction address (0107H),
but we do not see what happened when the INR H instruction was
executed. If we were particularly interested in what the INR H
instruction did, we could always examine the registers with an X
command.

```
-XP
P=0000 0100
-T4
C1Z0M0E0I0 A=00 B=0000 D=0000 H=0000 S=0100 P=0100 MVI   B,02
C1Z0M0E0I0 A=00 B=0200 D=0000 H=0000 S=0100 P=0102 LXI   H,0113
C1Z0M0E0I0 A=00 B=0200 D=0000 H=0113 S=0100 P=0105 MOV   A,M
C1Z0M0E0I0 A=40 B=0200 D=0000 H=0113 S=0100 P=0106 INR   H*0107
-
```

Figure 4.10 The trace command, T. The register display relates to the situation that existed *before* the attached
instruction was executed

The value of the trace command should now be evident – it enables the programmer to watch the program executing. Each step can be verified and as soon as something unexpected occurs, the probable cause of the error can be isolated to one particular instruction. To judge from Figure 4.10, our COMP program has behaved exactly as expected – so far!

Since trace reports the CPU state at each step, programs take much longer to execute under trace. This is often called the trace overhead. Consequently, timing (delay) loops and other time-critical program segments are rather more difficult to debug under trace than other segments which are independent of time. Nevertheless, the logic of all segments can be checked, whether they involve timing loops or not.

Q4.4

The untrace command, U

Untrace works in much the same way as trace except that the CPU state is not reported at each step. The format of the DDT command is

Un

where, as before, *n* is the (hexadecimal) number of program steps to untrace and has a default value of 1.

At first sight this command may seem little different to the G command which uses a breakpoint. Instead of specifying an absolute breakpoint address, we are specifying a number of program steps to execute. You may say that if the chosen number of steps bring us to what would have been a breakpoint address, there is no evident difference between the two commands. This is perfectly true providing that you can guarantee that we will eventually reach the breakpoint. Programs have been known to 'run away', by which we mean that, somehow or other, the program counter gets loaded with an address that is outside our program area. If that happens, the undefined contents of other memory locations are executed as though they were programmed instructions. It is quite possible then, that a program could run away before reaching the breakpoint. The usual result of this is that the system will not respond to any command and the only way to recover is to reboot, reload DDT and start again.

Untrace prevents this situation from occurring by suspending execution of the user program after the prescribed number of steps have been taken. Control then returns to DDT. If we have arrived at a point outside the program area, the program counter will show this, so we can go back and find out where the mistake occurred.

Q4.5

Figure 4.11 shows the effect of executing a U3 command with our COMP program in memory. Untrace begins in the same way as trace by displaying the initial state of the registers and the instruction just executed. Having gone through the three steps, it prints the next

```
       XP
       P=0000 0100
       -U3
       COZOMOEOIO A=00 B=0000 D=0000 H=0000 S=0100 P=0100 MVI  B,02*0106
       -X
       COZOMOEOIO A=40 B=0200 D=0000 H=0113 S=0100 P=0106 INR  H
       -
```

Figure 4.11   The untrace command, U. The last instruction executed was MOV A,M. The next instruction to execute is INR H

instruction address (0106H) and then returns control to DDT. When the registers are displayed with an X command, the instruction contained in the next instruction address and the current CPU state are printed as before.

Notice that the register display is the same as the last line of Figure 4.10. (The C-flag is different but that is not relevant at this point.) Had we issued a U4 command and then examined the registers, the effect of executing INR H would have been registered. For reasons which will become clear, we would like to defer executing this instruction for just a little while longer.

4.7   Debugging COMP.HEX

Ever optimistic, we begin this debugging session by loading our program, changing the last instruction to RST 7 and then executing it. Knowing the contents of VALUE (40H), HLMT (A0H) and LLMT (10H) we predict that, because the measured value is between the two limits, register B should contain 00H when we examine the registers. (If you have forgotten how the program works, refer back to Section 2.4.) When we do this (Figure 4.12) we see immediately that B contains the wrong number and debugging begins in earnest.

To help in uncovering program errors, Figure 4.12 also shows a part of the COMP listing. Since register B contains its initialised value of 02H when the last instruction is executed, it must mean that when the contents of VALUE are compared with HLMT, the jump BACK from 0108H was taken. Our first thought is that the conditional jump instruction is wrong and will have to be changed.

There is however another oddity in the register display. The H,L register pair are seen to contain the number 0213H, which is an address well away from our data area. H and L were loaded with the address of VALUE in the second instruction and, two lines later, its contents should have been incremented to point at HLMT (0114H). Instead of incrementing H and L as a pair, we have only incremented H, so that H,L now contains 0213H instead of 0114H. When the compare instruction was executed, we actually compared the contents of A with the undefined contents of 0213H and not HLMT.

```
A>DDT B:COMP.HEX
DDT VERS 1.4
NEXT  PC
0116 0000
-A0112
0112  RST 7
0113  .
-XP
P=0000 0100
-G
*0112
-X
C1Z0M1E0I1 A=40 B=0200 D=0000 H=0213 S=0100 P=0112 RST  07
-


0100                    ORG     0100H
0100 0602    COMP:      MVI     B,02H           ;FLAG CONTAINED IN B
0102 211301             LXI     H,VALUE         ;POINT (H,L) AT VALUE
0105 7E                 MOV     A,M             ;GET VALUE
0106 24                 INR     H               ;POINT AT HLMT
0107 BE                 CMP     M               ;(VALUE) > (HLMT)
0108 DA1201             JC      BACK            ;CY SET MEANS VALUE HIGH
010B 24                 INR     H               ;POINT AT LLMT
010C 05                 DCR     B               ;FLAG := FLAG -1
010D BE                 CMP     M               ;(VALUE) < (LLMT)
010E D21201             JNC     BACK            ;CY = 0 MEANS VALUE LOW
0111 05                 DCR     B               ;FLAG NOW ZERO
0112 C9      BACK:      RET                     ;RETURN TO MAIN
             *
             *   DATA AREA
             *
0113 40      VALUE:     DB      40H             ;INITIAL TRIAL VALUE
0114 A0      HLMT:      DB      0A0H            ;HIGH LIMIT
0115 10      LLMT:      DB      10H             ;LOW LIMIT
             *
0116                    END
0116
000H USE FACTOR
END OF ASSEMBLY

A>
```

Figure 4.12 Loading COMP.HEX and executing it for the first time

The conditional jump instruction may still be wrong, but, from the evidence gathered so far, we do not know whether it is or not!

To confirm our suspicion that the INR H instruction is wrong, we have traced the first program steps (Figure 4.13). It is clear that INR H should be INX H – a mistake which has occurred twice in the same program. We have then changed both instructions using the A command and retraced the program to check that all is now well.

Retaining our optimism for a little longer we have then executed the program again, in the hope that, maybe, these were the only two errors in the program. The last register display in Figure 4.13 again

```
-XP
P=0000 0100
-T5
C0Z0M0E0I0 A=00 B=0000 D=0000 H=0000 S=0100 P=0100 MVI   B,02
C0Z0M0E0I0 A=00 B=0200 D=0000 H=0000 S=0100 P=0102 LXI   H,0113
C0Z0M0E0I0 A=00 B=0200 D=0000 H=0113 S=0100 P=0105 MOV   A,M
C0Z0M0E0I0 A=40 B=0200 D=0000 H=0113 S=0100 P=0106 INR   H
C0Z0M0E0I0 A=40 B=0200 D=0000 H=0213 S=0100 P=0107 CMP   M*0108
-A0106
0106  INX H
0107  .
-A010B
010B  INX H
010C  .
-XP
P=0108 0100
-T5
C1Z0M1E0I1 A=40 B=0200 D=0000 H=0213 S=0100 P=0100 MVI   B,02
C1Z0M1E0I1 A=40 B=0200 D=0000 H=0213 S=0100 P=0102 LXI   H,0113
C1Z0M1E0I1 A=40 B=0200 D=0000 H=0113 S=0100 P=0105 MOV   A,M
C1Z0M1E0I1 A=40 B=0200 D=0000 H=0113 S=0100 P=0106 INX   H
C1Z0M1E0I1 A=40 B=0200 D=0000 H=0114 S=0100 P=0107 CMP   M*0108
-G100
*0112
-X
C1Z0M1E1I0 A=40 B=0200 D=0000 H=0114 S=0100 P=0112 RST   07
-
```

Figure 4.13 Listing the trace facility to verify that the INR H instruction should be INX H. Even when this change is made, however, the program still executes incorrectly

shows that register B contains the wrong number – it should be 00H. We suspect that the conditional jump instruction at 0108H is, indeed, wrong and, rather more cautiously, have executed the program to that point and then examined the registers (Figure 4.14).

```
-G100,108
*0108
-X
C1Z0M1E1I0 A=40 B=0200 D=0000 H=0114 S=0100 P=0108 JC    0112
-
```

Figure 4.14 Executing the program as far as the conditional jump instruction. Since the carry flag is set, the jump to 0112 takes place, which accounts for the error

After the CMP instruction, the carry flag is set so that, quite properly, the jump is taken, even though VALUE contains 40H and HLMT contains A0H. There is clearly some misunderstanding about how the flags are affected by a CMP instruction.

The CMP instruction and flags

The CMP instruction is similar to a subtraction except that neither of the operands, the number in A or the number being subtracted from it, are changed. The flags, however, may change. After a CMP they will be set or reset as though the subtraction had taken place. The question is: what state will they be in after comparing the contents of VALUE (now in register A) with the contents of HLMT, given that (VALUE) can be greater than, less than or equal to (HLMT)?

The way to think of the CMP (or subtract) instruction is,

1   If the number to take away is bigger than the number in A, we will have to borrow in order to do the subtraction. If we have to borrow, the carry flag is set. Addition instructions may generate a carry, subtraction instructions may generate a borrow. The same flag bit is used in both cases. Therefore, when comparing the contents of HLMT with the number in A, the carry flag is set if HLMT contains the larger (unsigned binary) number. We can confirm this by referring to Figure 4.14. (A) = (VALUE) = 40H <(HLMT) = A0H

2   If the numbers are equal, we can subtract without borrowing, so the C flag bit will be a 0. However, the Z flag will be set because a subtraction would have produced a zero result.

3   If the number in A is the larger there is no borrow and neither will the Z flag be set.

Relating all this to our program and remembering that, when the CMP instruction is executed, the contents of VALUE are in A, we can summarise the situation as follows,

Condition	C flag	Z flag	Action
(VALUE) > (HLMT)	0	0	High alarm
(VALUE) = (HLMT)	0	1	No alarm
(VALUE) < (HLMT)	1	0	No alarm

We need to test not one flag, but two, the C and Z flags. Our test could be phrased as:

1   If C = 1, go to 4 (continue checking, no alarm).
2   Else (C = 0), check Z flag.
3   If Z = 0, high alarm, return with 02 in B.
4   No high alarm here, continue.

Translating this into source code, we could write:

```
        CMP   M      ;original instruction
        JC    CONT
        JNZ   BACK
CONT:   INX   H      ;original instruction,
                     ;new label
```

```
 2:
 3:                    ************************************************************
 4:                    *    PROGRAM NAME : COMP                                  *
 5:                    *    REVISION 1.0                                         *
 6:                    *                                                         *
 7:                    *    PROGRAMMER : M.J.MORSE                               *
 8:                    *    DATE : 3 2 81                                        *
 9:                    *                                                         *
10:                    *    PROGRAM DESCRIPTION AS IN ORIGINAL                   *
11:                    *                                                         *
12:                    *                    STRUCTURE.                           *
13:                    *                    '''''''''                            *
14:                    *    BEGIN                                                *
15:                    *        FLAG := 2;                                       *
16:                    *        HLMT := A0H;                                     *
17:                    *        LLMT := 10H;                                     *
18:                    *        IF (VALUE) > (HLMT) THEN                          *
19:                    *            CONTINUE    (* TO THE END WITH FLAG = 2*)    *
20:                    *        ELSE                                             *
21:                    *            FLAG := FLAG -1;                             *
22:                    *            IF (VALUE) < (LLMT) THEN                      *
23:                    *                CONTINUE (* TO THE END WITH FLAG = 1*)*
24:                    *            ELSE                                         *
25:                    *                FLAG := FLAG - 1;                        *
26:                    *            ENDIF                                        *
27:                    *        ENDIF                                            *
28:                    *    END.                                                 *
29:                    *                                                         *
30:                    *    NOTE, REGISTERS A, B, H AND L CORRUPTED.             *
31:                    ************************************************************
32:                    *
33:   0100                      ORG     0100H
34:   0100 0602        COMP:    MVI     B,02H           ;FLAG CONTAINED IN B
35:   0102 211601               LXI     H,VALUE         ;POINT (H,L) AT VALUE
36:   0105 7E                   MOV     A,M             ;GET VALUE
37:   0106 23                   INX     H               ;POINT AT HLMT
38:   0107 BE                   CMP     M               ;(VALUE) > (HLMT)
39:   0108 DA0E01               JC      CONT            ;IF C=1 NO ERROR, CONTINUE
40:   010B C21501               JNZ     BACK            ;ELSE IF C=Z=0, ERROR, GO BACK
41:   010E 23          CONT:    INX     H               ;POINT AT LLMT
42:   010F 05                   DCR     B               ;FLAG := FLAG -1
43:   0110 BE                   CMP     M               ;(VALUE) < (LLMT)
44:   0111 D21501               JNC     BACK            ;CY = 0 MEANS VALUE LOW
45:   0114 05                   DCR     B               ;FLAG NOW ZERO
46:   0115 C9          BACK:    RET                     ;RETURN TO MAIN
47:                    *
48:                    *   DATA AREA
49:                    *
50:   0116 40          VALUE:   DB      40H             ;INITIAL TRIAL VALUE
51:   0117 A0          HLMT:    DB      0A0H            ;HIGH LIMIT
52:   0118 10          LLMT:    DB      10H             ;LOW LIMIT
53:                    *
54:   0119                      END
```

Figure 4.15 COMP program after the high limit test instruction had been changed in the editor and the program reassembled

Continuing the debug session

We have now added one instruction to our original program, and changed another. It is not difficult to change instructions in DDT so long as the change does not amount to extra bytes of object code. When we add to a program in DDT, everything after the change has to be re-entered, and so does everything before the change which references instructions or data after the change. In a situation like this it is usually easier to leave DDT (enter G0 or CTRL-C) and edit the source code file properly. We have chosen to do this and the new listing is now as given in Figure 4.15 on page 93.

Having created a new .HEX file we can reload DDT and test the alterations. To do this we have chosen to insert a breakpoint at CONT (010EH) and run the program with different numbers stored in VALUE. When (VALUE) are less than or equal to (HLMT), the program should stop at the breakpoint. If (VALUE) are greater than (HLMT) the breakpoint will be missed out. We can change the contents of VALUE using the S command, as shown in Figure 4.16. The text shows that, as far as the high limit is concerned, the program is correct.

The next step is to run the program through to the end and check that the B register now contains the correct number. However, Figure 4.17 shows that doing this with (VALUE) equal to 40H still does not produce the expected result. Register B now contains 01H indicating a low alarm condition. As before we must have the wrong conditional jump instruction.

```
S116
0116 40
0117 A0 .
-G100,10E
*010E
-X
C1Z0M1E1I0 A=40 B=0200 D=0000 H=0117 S=0100 P=010E INX  H
-S116
0116 40 A0
0117 A0 .
-G100,10E
*010E
-X
C0Z1M0E0I0 A=A0 B=0200 D=0000 H=0117 S=0100 P=010E INX  H
-S116
0116 A0 A1
0117 A0 .
-G100,10E
*0115
-
```

Figure 4.16 Testing revision 1 of the COMP program. With a breakpoint at 010EH and a different number in VALUE (0116H), execution halts at the breakpoint when no alarm exists, and at the end of the program otherwise

```
-S116
0116 40 .
-G100
*0115
-X
C0Z0M0E0I0 A=40 B=0100 D=0000 H=0118 S=0100 P=0115 RST   07
-A111
0111   JC 0115
0114   .
-L110,115
  0110  CMP   M
  0111  JC    0115
  0114  DCR   B
  0115  RST   07
  0116
-
```

Figure 4.17   Revision 1 of the program still does not produce the expected result when the registers are examined. The JNC instruction is incorrect and is changed to JC as shown

If we consider the CMP instruction and the CPU flags in relation to the low alarm condition, the following statements are true.

Condition	C flag	Z flag	Action
(VALUE) > (LLMT)	0	0	No alarm
(VALUE) = (LLMT)	0	1	No alarm
(VALUE) < (LLMT)	1	0	Low alarm

If the C (borrow) flag is set after the CMP instruction at 0110H, we have a low alarm condition. At 0111H then, we should have a JC 0115 instruction instead of the JNC instruction. Making this final change (Figure 4.17) we can now test the complete program as shown in Figure 4.18 (overleaf).

Having executed the program with the contents of VALUE between limits, equal to both limits, greater than the high limit and less than the low limit, we are, at last, sure that it is correct. Final verification is provided by tracing program execution.

One final job remains and that is to update the source and object code files with the latest change. The correct program is now listed in Figure 4.19 and we can turn our attention to the next program. In future though, we shall adopt some systematic approach when designing programs (Chapter 5) so that we do not have to exercise the debugger so much.

Questions

There is really only one way to learn about a debugger and that is to use one with a test program. If you do this, after studying the DDT commands described in the text and answering this limited set of self-

```
                    -S116
                    0116 40 .
                    -G100
                    *0115
                    -X
                    C0Z1M0E0I0 A=40 B=0000 D=0000 H=0118 S=0100 P=0115 RST  07
                    -S116
                    0116 40 A0
                    0117 A0 .
                    -G100
                    *0115
                    -X
                    C0Z1M0E0I0 A=A0 B=0000 D=0000 H=0118 S=0100 P=0115 RST  07
                    -S116
                    0116 A0 A1
                    0117 A0 .
                    -G100
                    *0115
                    -X
                    C0Z0M0E0I0 A=A1 B=0200 D=0000 H=0117 S=0100 P=0115 RST  07
                    -S116
                    0116 A1 10
                    0117 A0
                    0118 10 .
                    -G100
                    *0115
                    -X
                    C0Z1M0E0I0 A=10 B=0000 D=0000 H=0118 S=0100 P=0115 RST  07
                    -S116
                    0116 10 0F
                    0117 A0 .
                    -G100
                    *0115
                    -X
                    C1Z0M1E0I0 A=0F B=0100 D=0000 H=0118 S=0100 P=0115 RST  07
                    -S116
                    0116 0F 40
                    0117 A0 .
                    -XP
                    P=0115 100
                    -TOC
                    C1Z0M1E0I0 A=0F B=0100 D=0000 H=0118 S=0100 P=0100 MVI  B,02
                    C1Z0M1E0I0 A=0F B=0200 D=0000 H=0118 S=0100 P=0102 LXI  H,0116
                    C1Z0M1E0I0 A=0F B=0200 D=0000 H=0116 S=0100 P=0105 MOV  A,M
                    C1Z0M1E0I0 A=40 B=0200 D=0000 H=0116 S=0100 P=0106 INX  H
                    C1Z0M1E0I0 A=40 B=0200 D=0000 H=0117 S=0100 P=0107 CMP  M
                    C1Z0M1E1I0 A=40 B=0200 D=0000 H=0117 S=0100 P=0108 JC   010E
                    C1Z0M1E1I0 A=40 B=0200 D=0000 H=0117 S=0100 P=010E INX  H
                    C1Z0M1E1I0 A=40 B=0200 D=0000 H=0118 S=0100 P=010F DCR  B
                    C1Z0M0E0I0 A=40 B=0100 D=0000 H=0118 S=0100 P=0110 CMP  M
                    C0Z0M0E0I0 A=40 B=0100 D=0000 H=0118 S=0100 P=0111 JC   0115
                    C0Z0M0E0I0 A=40 B=0100 D=0000 H=0118 S=0100 P=0114 DCR  B
                    C0Z1M0E0I0 A=40 B=0000 D=0000 H=0118 S=0100 P=0115 RST  07*0115
                    -
```

Figure 4.18   Testing revision 2 of the COMP program

```
 1:
 2:
 3:              ************************************************************
 4:              *   PROGRAM NAME : COMP                                    *
 5:              *   REVISION 2.0                                           *
 6:              *                                                          *
 7:              *   PROGRAMMER : M.J.MORSE                                 *
 8:              *   DATE : 3 2 81                                          *
 9:              *                                                          *
10:              *   PROGRAM DESCRIPTION AS IN ORIGINAL                     *
11:              *                                                          *
12:              *                 STRUCTURE.                               *
13:              *                 '''''''''                                *
14:              *   BEGIN                                                  *
15:              *       FLAG := 2;                                         *
16:              *       HLMT := A0H;                                       *
17:              *       LLMT := 10H;                                       *
18:              *       IF (VALUE) > (HLMT) THEN                           *
19:              *           CONTINUE    (* TO THE END WITH FLAG = 2*)      *
20:              *       ELSE                                               *
21:              *           FLAG := FLAG -1;                               *
22:              *           IF (VALUE) < (LLMT) THEN                       *
23:              *               CONTINUE (* TO THE END WITH FLAG = 1*)     *
24:              *           ELSE                                           *
25:              *               FLAG := FLAG - 1;                          *
26:              *           ENDIF                                          *
27:              *       ENDIF                                              *
28:              *   END.                                                   *
29:              *                                                          *
30:              *   NOTE, REGISTERS A, B, H AND L CORRUPTED.               *
31:              ************************************************************
32:              *
33: 0100                   ORG     0100H
34: 0100 0602     COMP:    MVI     B,02H          ;FLAG CONTAINED IN B
35: 0102 211601            LXI     H,VALUE        ;POINT (H,L) AT VALUE
36: 0105 7E               MOV     A,M            ;GET VALUE
37: 0106 23               INX     H              ;POINT AT HLMT
38: 0107 BE               CMP     M              ;(VALUE) > (HLMT) ?
39: 0108 DA0E01           JC      CONT           ;IF C=1 NO ERROR, CONTINUE
40: 010B C21501           JNZ     BACK           ;ELSE IF C=Z=0, ERROR, GO BACK
41: 010E 23      CONT:    INX     H              ;POINT AT LLMT
42: 010F 05               DCR     B              ;FLAG := FLAG -1
43: 0110 BE               CMP     M              ;(VALUE) < (LLMT)
44: 0111 DA1501           JC      BACK           ;CY = 1 MEANS VALUE LOW
45: 0114 05               DCR     B              ;FLAG NOW ZERO
46: 0115 C9      BACK:    RET                    ;RETURN TO MAIN
47:              *
48:              *   DATA AREA
49:              *
50: 0116 40      VALUE:   DB      40H            ;INITIAL TRIAL VALUE
51: 0117 A0      HLMT:    DB      0A0H           ;HIGH LIMIT
52: 0118 10      LLMT:    DB      10H            ;LOW LIMIT
53:              *
54: 0119                  END
```

A>

Figure 4.19 The finally correct version of the COMP program

assessment questions, you should be well prepared for serious debugging.

4.1 Describe a typical set of monitor commands and then explain what extra facilities are provided in a debugger.

4.2 When a .HEX file is loaded into memory with DDT, what changes are made to the .HEX file?

4.3 All debuggers have some means of implementing a breakpoint facility. Explain how DDT handles breakpoints.

4.4 The trace command is one of the most useful of all debug facilities. Describe in terms of some of the other commands how the DDT trace command works.

4.5 Explain the difference between the DDT untrace command and the Go command with a breakpoint address attached, and why the difference is so significant.

Chapter 5 Programming methods

Objectives of this chapter *When you have completed studying this chapter you should be able to:*

1 Appreciate the need for a logical approach to program design.
2 Understand the terms and techniques known as modular programming and top-down design.
3 Know the basic program structures used for constructing assembly language programs.
4 Appreciate the disadvantages of flowcharts.
5 Be convinced of the need to exhaustively test all programs.

5.1 Introduction

In the early days of microprocessors, software production was very much a hit and miss affair. There were no rules about how programming problems should be tackled or how solutions should be presented. The 'good' programmers were those who could save the odd byte of object code or the odd microsecond of execution time, and still make the system work. At that time processors and memories were expensive and slow so, not unnaturally, there was much emphasis on keeping hardware costs down.

As the hardware became cheaper, faster and more powerful and the range of microprocessor applications expanded, attention was focused on software production. Microprocessors had long since ceased to be just programmable replacements for discrete logic systems, and, as more ambitious projects were attempted, it was found that more and more time, and therefore money, was being spent on adapting and debugging software. The attitude had always been that, so long as a program worked, it didn't much matter how it worked. Consequently, when a previously undetected bug was discovered after a job was finished, no one, including the author, could unravel the program logic, and so it was virtually impossible to formulate a sensible strategy for testing it. Software reliability was poor. If documentation existed it was probably out of date or incomplete.

The eventual solution to this problem was to set out program design rules which, first of all, dictated how the design stage should be approached and, after that, how the design should be implemented. The same sort of rules had been applied in electronic circuit/system design for many years previously so, with hindsight, it was surprising that it took so long for the software engineers to adopt the same code of practice.

5.2   Modular programming and top-down design

Faced with the problem of designing an electronic system, the electronic engineer will start by drawing a block diagram which identifies the major system functions needed to satisfy the system specification. Taking each block in turn, he will then sub-divide its function into a number of smaller tasks – perhaps stages of amplification or logical functions – until this simplification process reaches the point where individual components can be selected.

When the same technique is applied in software production it is called modular programming. Given the specification for a software package, the software engineer will isolate a number of separate tasks contained within the overall task. After that, the problem will be subdivided still further until separate specifications for the smaller, more manageable, modules can be written.

During this planning stage we, the software engineers, are more concerned with the function a module will perform rather than how it will perform it. Neither are we too concerned about the order in which these modules will be put together. What we are trying to do is to contain the complexity of the problem in a number of simple problems. We can decide how they all go together once we know what there is to be done.

This modular design technique is summarised in Figure 5.1. Notice that at each succeeding level the whole problem is defined in a larger

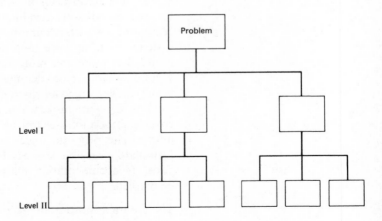

Figure 5.1 The modular design technique. A problem is divided into a number of smaller problems, each of which are solved separately

number of simpler program tasks. The simplification process ends when the lowest-level modules cannot easily be split up any further. At that point the planning stage is over.

With each of our modules defined we can now think about the order in which they will be connected together. In top-down program design we begin the coding stage at the top-most level by writing a simple main program, or executive, which may consist only of a series of CALL instructions. The subroutines called are the major problem subdivisions identified in the planning stage, and the order in which they are called is the order in which they will be executed. When the main program is tested, each subroutine can be written as a single RET instruction and the overall program logic checked.

At the next level down each of the subroutines is handled separately. Again, they may comprise no more than calls to other subroutines, but the testing procedure is exactly the same as before. If a lower-level subroutine passes data to the calling program, that data can be generated in the debugger so that the calling program can be properly tested. In this way the highest-level modules are completely tested before any lower-level module is written. When eventually the lowest-level modules have been written and tested, program development is complete.

The advantages of this design technique can be summarised as follows:

1   Since we start at the top, major errors in the program logic come to light early in the design because the most important modules are tested first.
2   Errors within modules are easier to locate because only small code segments are tested at one time.
3   Testing is altogether a more manageable task since it is spread over the whole design period. It is sometimes impossible to properly test programs which are written as one large block of code.
4   By adding tested modules to an expanding package of modules, data interfacing problems are solved as they arise. In other words, the way in which data is passed between modules can be defined to
Q5.1   suit the calling program.

5.3 Structured programming

Top-down design is a philosophy for constructing large programs. When attention is focused on the instruction sequences which make up the modules, the rules of structured programming come into effect. The aim of structured programming is to produce tightly knit, well defined and easily recognised blocks of codes, instead of

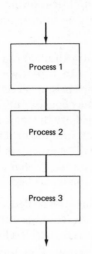

Figure 5.2 The sequence structure. Each process or group of instructions is executed in turn

rambling instruction sequences which are all but impossible to decipher.

Note that even at the top-most level, the program has a structure comprising modules which are executed one after another. In structured programming terminology this would be referred to as a sequence structure. The other two basic structures are:

1 The DO-WHILE (or WHILE-DO) structure.
2 The IF-THEN-ELSE structure.

The first of these is a way of building loops into programs and the second a way of providing conditional branching. The fundamental rule of structured programming states that every structure must have only one inlet and one outlet so that unconfined jumps (GOTOs) are not allowed.

The sequence structure

This is the simplest structure and consists of consecutive instructions or groups of instructions which are executed one after the other. In Figure 5.2 these are referred to as processes. If a structure includes subroutine calls the subroutines must act like a single instruction. There is no possibility of returning control to any other point but the normal return address.

The WHILE-DO structure

This is sometimes written as DO-WHILE, but the normal high-level language statement is WHILE-DO. The format of the structure is:

```
WHILE (condition is true) DO
        statement 1
        statement 2
            .
            .
        statement n
ENDDO
```

In the high-level language PASCAL, this program structure would be written as:

```
WHILE (condition is true) DO
BEGIN
        statement 1
        statement 2
            .
            .
        statement n
END
```

In both cases the intention is clear; if the condition is logically true the *n* statements are executed. The condition is then re-tested and if it is still true, the *n* statements are executed again. This looping continues until eventually the condition is not true. At this point the structure following is entered.

Notice that the condition is tested before the loop is entered so that the *n* statements may not be executed at all if the condition is initially false. As an example of the WHILE-DO structure, consider a program which multiplies two numbers by repeatedly adding the multiplicand to itself. We will assume that the multiplicand and multiplier are parameters passed to this module from some earlier module, and that the numbers are now stored in two locations labelled MCAND and MPLIER, respectively. We shall further assume that both the multiplicand and multiplier are 8-bit unsigned binary numbers (maximum value 255) and, for the moment, that their magnitudes are such that the product is also an 8-bit number. Figure 5.3 shows how the structure may be written.

```
*    MULTIPLICATION BY REPEATED ADDITION
*
*        STRUCTURE
*        iiiiiiiii
*
*    BEGIN
*        PARTPROD := 0
*        WHILE MULTIPLIER > 0 DO
*        BEGIN
*            PARTPROD := PARTPROD + MULTIPLICAND
*            MULTIPLIER := MULTIPLIER - 1
*        END;
*        RESULT := PARTPROD;
*    END.
*
```

Figure 5.3 The WHILE-DO structure applied in a simple multiplication program

We need a WHILE-DO structure here to cater for the situation in which the multiplier starts at zero. If this were the case the product must retain its initial value of zero and the multiplication statements must be missed out.

Testing at this stage is usually best done by constructing a table with trial values representing multiplier and multiplicand. For instance we might proceed as follows:

Partprod	Multiplicand	Multiplier	Comment
0	4	3	;initial status
4		2	;after one loop
8		1	;second
12		0	;third

```
          *    PROGRAM TO DEMONSTRATE THE WHILE..DO STRUCTURE
          *
          *    MULTIPLICATION BY REPEATED ADDITION
          *    PROGRAM STRUCTURE LISTED IN THE PREVIOUS FIGURE
          *
          *    REGISTER USAGE :-
          *                       PARTIAL PRODUCT (PARTPROD) ACCUMULATED IN D
          *                       MULTIPLIER IN B
          *                       MULTIPLICAND IN C
          *                       REGISTER A USED FOR ARITHMETIC
          *
0100                   ORG     0100H
0100 AF       MULT:    XRA     A                ; CLEAR A
0101 57                MOV     D,A              ; (D) = PARTPROD  := 0
0102 3A1C01            LDA     MPLIER
0105 47                MOV     B,A              ; (B) = MULTIPLIER
0106 3A1D01            LDA     MCAND
0109 4F                MOV     C,A              ; (C) = MULTIPLICAND
              *
              ***TEST MULTIPLIER FOR ZERO*****
              *
010A 78       WHILE:   MOV     A,B              ; GET MULTIPLIER
010B FE00              CPI     0                ; IS IT ZERO ?
010D CA1701            JZ      ENDWHL           ; ENDWHILE IF YES
              *
              ***UPDATE PRODUCT***************
              *
0110 7A                MOV     A,D              ; GET PARTPROD
0111 81                ADD     C                ; PARTPROD := PARTPROD + MCAND
0112 57                MOV     D,A              ; RESTORE PARTPROD
              *
              ***DECREMENT MULTIPLIER*********
              *
0113 05                DCR     B                ; MPLIER := MPLIER - 1
0114 C30A01            JMP     WHILE            ; TEST AGAIN
              *
              ***RE-TEST MULTIPLIER**********
              *
0117 7A       ENDWHL:  MOV     A,D              ; GET PARTPROD
0118 321E01            STA     RESULT           ; STORE IT
011B C9                RET
              *
              *   DATA AREA
              *
011C 03       MPLIER:  DB      3                ; TEST DATA, CHANGE
011D 04       MCAND:   DB      4                ; UNDER DDT
011E          RESULT:  DS      1                ; RESULT INTO HERE
              *
011F                   END
011F
000H USE FACTOR
END OF ASSEMBLY

A>
```

Figure 5.4 The multiplication program written from the structure of Figure 5.3

When the multiplier is reduced to zero the test fails and we move on to the next module in the sequence. A program which conforms exactly with the structure is listed in Figure 5.4.

Incidentally, the use of rigid structures does not necessarily yield the most efficient program in terms of the number of instructions used. The listings of Figure 5.19 and 5.20 in the questions at the end of this chapter show alternative ways of programming the same problem. These use either 4 or 5 fewer instructions than our structured solution **Q5.3** but this is often the case. There is a price to be paid for conformity.

The DO-UNTIL or REPEAT-UNTIL structure

Mathematically it can be shown that all program requirements can be expressed in terms of the three basic structures referred to earlier. Although not essential, the DO-UNTIL structure arises so naturally in all sorts of programming that it is usually included with the other three. The format of this structure is:

```
DO UNTIL condition is true
    statement 1
    statement 2
        .
        .
    statement n
ENDDO
```

What happens here is that, on entry to the structure, the *n* statements between DO and ENDDO are executed. The condition is then tested and, if false, the *n* statements are executed again. This continues until the tested condition becomes true at which point execution of the loop ceases. Since the test is made at the end of the loop, rather than at the beginning as was the case in the WHILE-DO structure, the *n* statements are always executed at least once. This difference between DO-UNTIL and WHILE-DO structures is neatly summarised in the flowcharts of Figure 5.5 (overleaf).

The equivalent PASCAL control statement is:

```
REPEAT
    statement 1
    statement 2
        .
        .
    statement n
UNTIL condition is true
```

This is rather more descriptive than the pseudo-high-level language DO-UNTIL statement because it shows more clearly that the test is

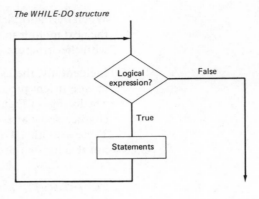

The WHILE-DO structure

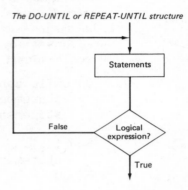

The DO-UNTIL or REPEAT-UNTIL structure

Figure 5.5 The difference between WHILE-DO and REPEAT-UNTIL structures

made at the end of the loop instead of at the beginning. It is for this reason that we shall use REPEAT-UNTIL instead of DO-UNTIL.

The multiplication program could be written with a REPEAT-UNTIL structure if the multiplier were always greater than zero. We have assumed this to be the case in Figure 5.6. We have also assumed, as before, that the product can be contained in an 8-bit number.

Perhaps a more common application of this structure is in delay routines – programs which waste time. The technique here is to load a register, or register pair, with a number which is proportional to the amount of time to be wasted. The register contents are then decremented until they become zero, at which point the delay time has elapsed. For example, we might write:

```
        LDA   DLYPARM   ;initialise for display
 REPT:  DCR   A         ;DLYPARM:=DLYPARM - 1
UNTIL:  JNZ   REPT      ;repeat until DLYPARM = 0
        RET
```

```
        *   PROGRAM TO ILLUSTRATE THE REPEAT-UNTIL STRUCTURE
        *
        *   MULTIPLICATION BY REPEATED ADDITION - AGAIN !
        *   IN THIS CASE THE MULTIPLIER MUST BE GREATER THAN ZERO ON ENTRY.
        *
        *               STRUCTURE.
        *               '''''''''
        *   BEGIN
        *      INITIALISE MULTIPLICAND
        *      INITIALISE MULTIPLIER
        *      PARTPROD := 0
        *      REPEAT
        *         PARTPROD := PARTPROD + MULTIPLICAND
        *         MULTIPLIER := MULTIPLIER - 1
        *      UNTIL MULTIPLIER = 0
        *      RESULT := PARTPROD
        *   END
        *
        *   REGISTER USAGE
        *               PRODUCT ACCUMULATED IN A
        *               MULTIPLICAND IN C
        *               MULTIPLIER IN B
        *
0100                    ORG     0100H
0100 3A1301    BGN:     LDA     MCAND
0103 4F                 MOV     C,A         ; (C) = MULTIPLICAND
0104 3A1201             LDA     MPLIER
0107 47                 MOV     B,A         ; (B) = MULTIPLIER
0108 AF                 XRA     A           ; (A) = INITIAL PARTPROD = 0
0109 81       REPT:     ADD     C           ; PARTPROD := PARTPROD + MULTIPLICAND
010A 05                 DCR     B           ; MULTIPLIER := MULTIPLIER - 1
010B C20901   UNTIL:    JNZ     REPT        ; REPEAT UNTIL ZERO
010E 321401             STA     RESULT      ; RESULT := FINAL PARTPROD
0111 C9                 RET
        *
        *   DATA AREA
        *
0112 03       MPLIER:   DB      3           ; TRIAL VALUES FOR MULTIPLIER
0113 04       MCAND:    DB      4           ; AND MULTIPLICAND
0114          RESULT:   DS      1           ; RESULT INTO HERE
        *
0115                    END
0115
000H USE FACTOR
END OF ASSEMBLY

A>
```

Figure 5.6   Multiplication using a REPEAT-UNTIL structure

If DLYPARM is zero on entry to the loop, the delay will be the equivalent of 256 loop execution times since DLYPARM is decremented before the test-for-zero is made. The minimum delay would result if DLYPARM was 01H. We shall discuss delay routines in more detail in Chapter 7.

Q5.4

The IF-THEN-ELSE structure

The previous two structures are used when loops have to be built into programs. The IF-THEN-ELSE structure is used when alternative instruction sequences are to be executed depending upon the outcome of some test. We have met this structure before when considering conditional assembly directives. Its format is:

```
IF condition is true THEN
       statement 1
           .
           .
       statement n
   ELSE
       statement 1
           .
           .
       statement n
   ENDIF
```

The equivalent PASCAL control statement is almost identical but the word ENDIF is not used. On entry the condition is tested and, if found to be true, the *n* statements between IF and ELSE are executed. If the condition is not true the *n* statements between ELSE and ENDIF are executed instead. When no alternative statement sequence is specified in the event that the condition is not true, the word ELSE, and the statements which follow it, can be omitted. This leads to the two forms of the structure shown in Figure 5.7.

IF structures in which no alternative action is specified are usually clearer if an empty sequence is included rather than no sequence at

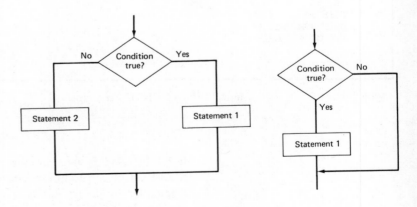

Figure 5.7　Two versions of the IF-THEN-ELSE structure

all. For instance, imagine that we want to execute a block of instructions if a number X is greater than 10, but miss out the instructions otherwise. We could write:

```
IF X>10 THEN
    Execute these instructions
ENDIF
```

Alternatively we could say:

```
IF X>10 THEN
    Execute these instructions
ELSE
    Do nothing
ENDIF
```

or even,

```
IF X<=10 THEN
    Do nothing
ELSE
    Execute these instructions
ENDIF
```

By explicitly stating that there is no alternative action, the intention is definitely clearer.

To illustrate the use of an IF-THEN-ELSE structure in assembly language programming, consider the problem of processing a list of numbers to see how many are odd and how many are even. You will probably realise that odd numbers have a 1 in the least significant bit position and even numbers have a 0. Therefore to test for odd or even we need only test the least significant bit of each number in the list. We shall assume that the list is of undefined length but terminates in a zero and that the number of odd or even numbers cannot be greater than 255.

The program and its structure are given in Figure 5.8. Notice that we have used a WHILE-DO structure first of all because the very first item in the list might be zero. The ODDS and EVENS counters are initialised to zero and should remain like that if we are processing an empty list.

The same program could be written in several different ways using different structures. For example, if we wanted to use an IF-THEN-ELSE structure with no alternative specified we could write,

```
BEGIN
        ODDS:=0
        COUNT:=0
        READ FIRST NUMBER
```

(continued on page 111)

```
                        *   PROGRAM TO COUNT THE NUMBER OF ODD AND EVEN NUMBERS IN A LIST
                        *   ILLUSTRATING THE USE OF THE IF-THEN-ELSE STRUCTURE
                        *
                        *                    STRUCTURE
                        *                    ''''''''''
                        *   BEGIN
                        *       ODDS := 0
                        *       EVENS := 0
                        *       READ THE FIRST NUMBER IN THE LIST
                        *       WHILE NUMBER <> 0 DO
                        *       BEGIN
                        *          IF NUMBER IS EVEN THEN
                        *              EVENS := EVENS + 1
                        *          ELSE
                        *              ODDS := ODDS + 1
                        *          ENDIF
                        *          READ NEXT NUMBER
                        *       END
                        *       ODDCNT := ODDS
                        *       EVNCNT := EVENS
                        *   END
                        *
                        *   REGISTER USAGE:
                        *              ODDS ACCUMULATED IN D
                        *              EVENS ACCUMULATED IN E
                        *              (HL) USED AS A LIST POINTER
                        *              REGISTER A IS CORRUPTED
                        *
     0100                       ORG    0100H
     0100 AF          BGN:      XRA    A              ; CLEAR A
     0101 57                    MOV    D,A            ; (D) = ODDS = 0
     0102 5F                    MOV    E,A            ; (E) = EVENS = 0
     0103 212501                LXI    H,LIST         ; SET LIST POINTER
     0106 7E                    MOV    A,M            ; GET FIRST NUMBER
     0107 B7          WHILE:    ORA    A              ; TEST FOR ZERO NUMBER
     0108 CA1A01                JZ     NDWHL          ; IF ZERO THEN NDWHL
     010B E601                  ANI    01H            ; NOT ZERO, TEST LS BIT
     010D CA1401                JZ     EVEN           ; IF LSBIT = 0, NUMBER EVEN
     0110 14          ODD:      INR    D              ; ELSE, ODDS := ODDS + 1
     0111 C31501                JMP    ENIF           ; EXIT IF STATEMENT
     0114 1C          EVEN:     INR    E              ; EVENS := EVENS + 1
     0115 23          ENIF:     INX    H              ; POINT AT NEXT NUMBER
     0116 7E                    MOV    A,M            ; READ IT
     0117 C30701                JMP    WHILE          ; AND RE-TEST
     011A 7A          NDWHL:    MOV    A,D
     011B 322301                STA    ODDCNT         ; ODDCNT := ODDS
     011E 7B                    MOV    A,E
     011F 322401                STA    EVNCNT         ; EVNCNT := EVENS
     0122 C9                    RET
                        *
                        *   DATA AREA
                        *
     0123              ODDCNT:   DS     1
     0124              EVNCNT:   DS     1
     0125              LIST:     DS     510      ; MAX. EXTENT OF LIST
       *
     0323                        END
     0323
     000H USE FACTOR
     END OF ASSEMBLY
```

Figure 5.8 The IF-THEN-ELSE structure used in a simple ODD/EVEN sort program

```
            WHILE NUMBER<>0 DO
            BEGIN
                    IF NUMBER = EVEN THEN
                            DO NOTHING
                    ELSE
                            ODDS:=ODDS+1
                    ENDIF
                    COUNT:=COUNT+1
                    GET NEXT NUMBER
            END (*OF LOOP*)
            ODDCNT:=ODDS
            EVNCNT:=COUNT-ODDS
    END
```

In this program we have to be sure that COUNT does not exceed 255 otherwise it will spread over into two locations (16 bits) and the subtraction at the end will be a 16-bit subtraction. These are not insurmountable problems, but we can do without them for the moment.

Q5.2, 5.5–5.9

5.4   Structure statements versus flowcharts

You will have noticed that each of the structures discussed have been related to equivalent flowchart symbols. Since flowcharts are familiar devices for describing program operation, it could be argued that, because the structures have a flowchart equivalent, structure statements are unnecessary. This would be an acceptable argument if every flowchart was constructed from the components presented here. Since this is patently not the case, the need for structures remains.

The main problem with flowcharts is that there are no rules which govern how they should be constructed and no obvious way of knowing when the flowchart is drawn whether the corresponding code will be sensible. A flowchart may look logical but when the code is written it is often necessary to include unconditional jumps in order to make the code match the flowchart. A properly structured program will have no unconditional jumps except those which jump over the ELSE part of an IF-THEN-ELSE structure, or take control back to the start of a WHILE-DO block. In both cases these jumps are part of the structure. There are none which transfer control from one part of a program to another part which, because it had to go somewhere, was inserted at that point.

The structured technique forces the programmer to think of each section of code as an entity, and then think of the way it connects with adjacent sections. Since each section is a standard construction, it can be readily understood and, if necessary, modified.

Admittedly there is, as we have said before, a price to be paid for this clarity. Programming 'tricks', so beloved of assembly language programmers over the years, are not allowed, even though they may result in shorter programs. If the meaning of a section of program is not clear, it is a bad section of program. It is only in exceptional circumstances that clever (which usually means obscure) code is worth the inconvenience of producing a program which few can easily understand. Most software experts now agree that flowcharts add nothing to a well structured and properly documented program. Some high level languages, like PASCAL, and unlike BASIC, force the programmer to adopt a logical and structured approach to program design. In assembly language programming there is no compulsion, but the added clarity and easy adaptability of structured

Q5.10 programs should be encouragement enough.

5.5 Programming example

To illustrate this top-down design procedure and the way in which structures are used, we will write and test a program which is part of the software for controlling a data acquisition system. We have deliberately attempted a fairly large program so that the benefits of modular programming can be properly appreciated.

A (simulated) transducer is connected to the input of an analogue-to-digital converter (ADC) which can handle input voltages in the range 0 to 5 V. The ADC converts these voltages to 8-bit numbers and our program is required to:

1 Generate a signal which starts the converter.
2 Wait for the converter to finish.
3 Read the ADC digital output.
4 Translate this to a number between 0.00 and 5.00.
5 Print the number on the console.

In a real situation this sequence of events may be initiated by some external timing signal – perhaps we need to make a measurement once every minute. For the moment we will simulate this timing signal by connecting a push-button to the system and only begin a conversion cycle when the push-button is pressed.

At the top-most level we can describe the program in three short statements:

1 Read a value.
2 Convert to an equivalent decimal number.
3 Print the number.

This is what we need to do and the order in which we need to do it. If each of the statements is written as a CALL to an appropriate sub-routine, our main program becomes as shown in Figure 5.9.

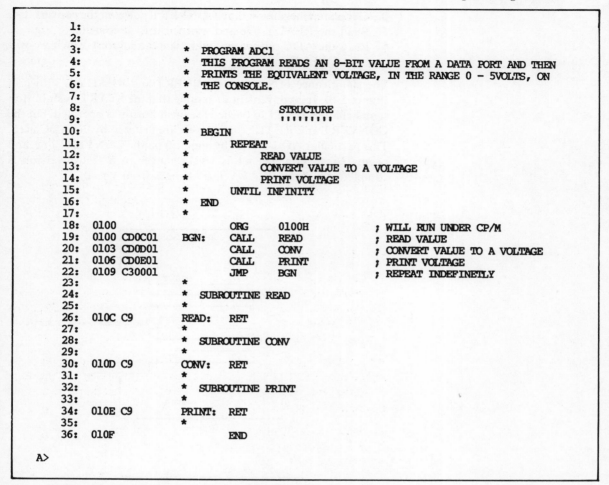

```
 1:
 2:
 3:                     *   PROGRAM ADC1
 4:                     *   THIS PROGRAM READS AN 8-BIT VALUE FROM A DATA PORT AND THEN
 5:                     *   PRINTS THE EQUIVALENT VOLTAGE, IN THE RANGE 0 - 5VOLTS, ON
 6:                     *   THE CONSOLE.
 7:                     *
 8:                     *              STRUCTURE
 9:                     *              '''''''''
10:                     *   BEGIN
11:                     *       REPEAT
12:                     *               READ VALUE
13:                     *               CONVERT VALUE TO A VOLTAGE
14:                     *               PRINT VOLTAGE
15:                     *       UNTIL INFINITY
16:                     *   END
17:                     *
18:   0100                      ORG     0100H           ; WILL RUN UNDER CP/M
19:   0100 CD0C01       BGN:    CALL    READ            ; READ VALUE
20:   0103 CD0D01               CALL    CONV            ; CONVERT VALUE TO A VOLTAGE
21:   0106 CD0E01               CALL    PRINT           ; PRINT VOLTAGE
22:   0109 C30001               JMP     BGN             ; REPEAT INDEFINETLY
23:                     *
24:                     *   SUBROUTINE READ
25:                     *
26:   010C C9           READ:   RET
27:                     *
28:                     *   SUBROUTINE CONV
29:                     *
30:   010D C9           CONV:   RET
31:                     *
32:                     *   SUBROUTINE PRINT
33:                     *
34:   010E C9           PRINT:  RET
35:                     *
36:   010F                      END

A>
```

Figure 5.9   The main ADC program at the top-most level

It is fairly certain that this program will work; assuming, of course, that the as-yet unwritten subroutines work properly. What we have done so far is to establish an overall structure for the program – it is just an endless REPEAT-UNTIL. The next stage is to descend one level and begin work on the individual subroutines.

The READ subroutine

The single function of this subroutine is to return an 8-bit number which represents the measured transducer output voltage. In achieving this it will have to:

1   Read the START push-button signal and wait for it to become 0 (the simulated timing signal).

2   Generate a negative-going CONVERT pulse on the convert line.
3   Read the READY line and wait for it to become 0.
4   Read the ADC output and store it in an address which we will label VALUE.

The significance of START, CONVERT and READY is shown in Figure 5.10. It is convenient to assume that the START push-button signal changes from 1 to 0 when the push-button is operated, but the CONVERT and READY logic levels are dictated by the ADC used. This particular ADC is reset by a logic 0 on the CONVERT line, and begins conversion when this level changes to a 1. Conversion is complete when the READY line changes from 1 to 0.

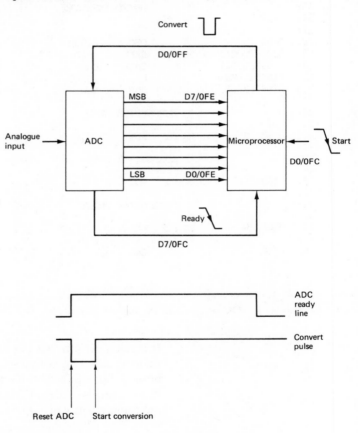

Figure 5.10   The ADC connection diagram and its handshake signals

These signals, and the ADC output itself, are connected to port registers which are simple 8-bit latches. When data or control signals are sent to an output port, the decoded port address enables one particular register for the duration of the OUT instruction. At the end of this instruction the data bus contents are latched into the register and remain there until new data or control information is sent to the same port by another OUT instruction.

The input port registers have tri-state outputs which are connected to the data bus. When an IN instruction is executed, one of the input registers is enabled and input data are connected through the registers to the data bus and subsequently read by the processor.

It is tempting to write each of the four READ functions as a separate subroutine, but common sense dictates that, if a subroutine is just one or two instructions, there is no particular merit in that. Consequently we shall take each function in turn and examine it separately.

A conversion begins when the START push-button is operated. This changes the logic level at the START input from 1 to 0 and it is this change, rather than the zero level itself, which starts the read-convert-print cycle. Defining START in this way prevents the main program loop from repeating continuously when an operator keeps the push-button pressed down. If this happened and the start condition was defined as START = 0, the display screen would very rapidly fill up with near-identical numbers.

Therefore a controlled start-up sequence must be:

```
REPEAT          (*Until push-button is released*)
    READ START
UNTIL START = 1
REPEAT          (*Until push-button is pressed*)
    READ START
UNTIL START = 0
```

The PASCAL style of adding comments between the character combinations (* and *), is adopted here just to make the meaning clearer.

This is a nice, neat, self-contained program function which can quite conveniently be written and tested as a separate subroutine. We shall call it START.

The next function of READ was to generate a negative-going pulse on the CONVERT line. When the system is first switched on, CONVERT could be at either logic level. However, this is not important so long as we always reset the ADC by sending a 0 and then start conversion by sending a 1, before making a measurement. After the first measurement CONVERT will always start off at a 1 and an identifiable pulse will be generated. Again a subroutine called PULSE could conveniently contain these instructions.

The remaining functions of READ are best included within the subroutine itself. The detection of a READY signal is a simple read-test-conditional jump sequence and reading the value is one IN instruction followed by an STA (store) instruction.

Figure 5.11

```
 1:
 2:
 3:              *   SUBROUTINE READ
 4:              *   THIS SUBROUTINE READS AN 8-BIT NUMBER FROM AN ADC OUTPUT
 5:              *   AND STORES IT IN ADDRESS 'VALUE'.
 6:              *
 7:              *   THE SYSTEM INPUTS ARE:
 8:              *       START   - FROM PUSHBUTTON - 1 TO 0 CHANGE STARTS CYCLE
 9:              *       READY   - FROM ADC - CHANGES FROM 1 TO 0 WHEN ADC FINISHED
10:              *       VALUE   - FROM ADC - READ WHEN ADC FINISHED CONVERSION
11:              *   THE ONLY SYSTEM OUTPUT IS:
12:              *       CONVERT - A 1 TO 0 CHANGE ON THIS LINE STARTS THE ADC
13:              *
14:              *                   STRUCTURE
15:              *                   '''''''''
16:              *   BEGIN
17:              *       WAIT FOR A START SIGNAL
18:              *       PULSE THE ADC CONVERT COMMAND LINE
19:              *       REPEAT
20:              *           READ THE READY LINE
21:              *       UNTIL READY LINE = 0
22:              *       READ AND STORE VALUE READ
23:              *   END
24:              *
25:              *   REGISTER USAGE:
26:              *       ONLY REGISTER A IS USED
27:              *
28:   0150                   ORG     0150H          ; ORIGIN FOR READ
29:   0150 CD6401    READ:   CALL    START          ; WAIT FOR START SIGNAL
30:   0153 CD7301            CALL    PULSE          ; PULSE CONVERT LINE
31:              *
32:   0156 DBFC     WAIT:    IN      CTRPRT         ; READ FROM CONTROL PORT
33:   0158 E601              ANI     01H            ; TEST ADC READY LINE
34:   015A C25601            JNZ     WAIT           ; WAIT UNTIL READY = 0
35:              *
36:   015D DBFE     STORE:   IN      DATAPT         ; READ VALUE FROM DATA PORT
37:   015F 326301            STA     VALUE          ; STORE IN VALUE
38:   0162 C9                RET
39:              *
40:              *   DATA AND PORT ASSIGNMENTS
41:              *
42:   00FC =      CTRPRT:  EQU     0FCH           ; CONTROL PORT ADDRESS
43:   00FE =      DATAPT:  EQU     0FEH           ; DATA PORT ADDRESS
44:   0163        VALUE:   DS      1              ; BINARY VALUE STORED HERE
45:              *
46:              *
47:              *   SUBROUTINE START
48:              *   THIS SUBROUTINE READS THE START INPUT AND RETURNS CONTROL TO
49:              *   THE CALLING PROGRAM WHEN START CHANGES FROM 1 TO 0.
50:              *   IT IS ONLY CALLED FROM READ.
51:              *
52:              *                   STRUCTURE
53:              *                   '''''''''
54:              *   BEGIN
55:              *       REPEAT (* UNTIL PUSHBUTTON RELEASED *)
56:              *           READ START INPUT
57:              *       UNTIL START = 1
```

(Continued)

Figure 5.11 continued

```
58:                    *         REPEAT (* UNTIL PUSHBUTTON PRESSED *)
59:                    *            READ START INPUT
60:                    *         UNTIL START = 0
61:                    *  END
62:                    *
63:  0164 DBFC  START:  IN    CTRPRT       ; READ FROM CONTROL PORT
64:  0166 E680          ANI   80H          ; CHECK START INPUT
65:  0168 CA6401 UNTIL2: JZ    START        ; REPEAT UNTIL START = 1
66:  016B DBFC  REPT3:  IN    CTRPRT       ; READ FROM CONTROL PORT AGAIN
67:  016D E680          ANI   80H          ; RE-CHECK START
68:  016F C26B01 UNTIL3: JNZ   REPT3        ; REPEAT UNTIL START = 0
69:  0172 C9            RET
70:                    *
71:                    *  SUBROUTINE PULSE
72:                    *  GENERATES A NEGATIVE GOING PULSE ON THE ADC CONVERT LINE
73:                    *
74:                    *                STRUCTURE
75:                    *                IIIIIIIII
76:                    *  BEGIN
77:                    *      SEND A LOGIC 0 TO CONVERT LINE
78:                    *      NOW SEND A 1
79:                    *  END
80:                    *
81:                    *  PORT ASSIGNMENT
82:  00FF =     OUTPRT: EQU   0FFH
83:                    *
84:  0173 AF    PULSE:  XRA   A            ; CLEAR A
85:  0174 D3FF          OUT   OUTPRT       ; CONVERT LINE = 0
86:  0176 C601          ADI   01H          ; MAKE DO = 1
87:  0178 D3FF          OUT   OUTPRT       ; CONVERT LINE (DO OF FF) = 1
88:  017A C9            RET
A>
```

Figure 5.11 Subroutine READ and its supporting subroutines

READ and its subsidiary subroutines are listed in Figure 5.11; the complete program at this stage of development is shown in Figure 5.12. When READ was first written, subroutines START and PULSE only contained a RET instruction. The ADC output was replaced by an array of 8 switches and the READY line was connected to the single-shot output of a pulse generator. It was assumed that START and PULSE could be made to work properly, and so testing effort was concentrated on the remaining parts of READ. After that, START and its push-button were added and a breakpoint was inserted at the START return address. In this way it was verified that PULSE would only be entered if the push-button was first released and then operated. The PULSE subroutine was then checked on its own by including it in an endless loop. An oscilloscope connected to the PULSE line verified that the subroutine was working properly and then it was added to READ. Finally, the eight switches and the pulse generator were removed and the ADC connected in their place. The whole subroutine was then tested with

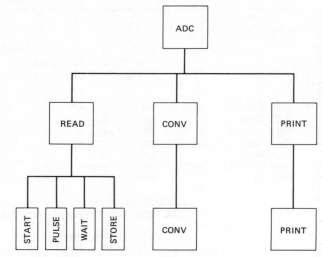

Figure 5.2 Subroutine READ has now been divided into four separate modules

the main program, and attention was turned on the CONV subroutine.

The CONV subroutine

Data passed to this subroutine are a single 8-bit number stored in an address labelled VALUE. Since this value is eventually printed as a decimal number, CONV is a subroutine which converts a binary number into binary-coded decimal. With a maximum ADC input of 5 V, the most significant binary digit must represent an equivalent analogue voltage of 2.5 V. Similarly, the next most significant bit is equivalent to 1.25 V, and so on. (If this idea is unfamiliar to you, take it on trust for the moment, or refer to the first sections of Chapter 7.)

By continuing in this fashion a table which lists each binary digit and its analogue equivalent can be compiled – see Table 5.1.

Table 5.1

Bit number		Equivalent voltage
8	(D7)	2.5
7	(D6)	1.25
6	(D5)	0.625
5	(D4)	0.3125
4	(D3)	0.15625
3	(D2)	0.078125
2	(D1)	0.0390625
1	(D0)	0.01953125

The resolution of the ADC is 1 in 256 (2^8) so the resolution of our CONV subroutine need be no better than that. In other words, there is no point in expressing the analogue equivalent of the least significant bit to 8 decimal places. A resolution of 1 in 256 is approximately 2 in 500 or 0.02 V in 5 V. Consequently if we round-off the decimal equivalent of each bit to two decimal places, we shall be claiming less for the ADC than it can produce, but it will not be gross under-estimation. The conversion table not reduces to that shown in Table 5.2.

Table 5.2

Bit number	Equivalent voltage
8	2.50
7	1.25
6	0.63
5	0.31
4	0.16
3	0.08
2	0.04
1	0.02

Looking at this table, an obvious conversion technique is to store the analogue equivalent of each bit with the program, and then examine the contents of VALUE bit-by-bit. If a particular bit is a 1, its analogue equivalent is added to a running total; if the bit is a 0, nothing is added. The running total will start off at zero, so, at the end of CONV, we will have accumulated the analogue equivalent of the binary number. This conversion technique leads to the following program structure:

```
BEGIN
    TOTAL:=0
    BITCOUNT:=8
    READ CONTENTS OF VALUE
    IDENTIFY THE FIRST (NEXT) TABLE ENTRY
    REPEAT (*Until all bits of VALUE checked*)
            ISOLATE BIT NUMBER, BITCOUNT, OF VALUE
            IF BIT = 0 THEN
                    DO NOTHING
            ELSE
                    TOTAL:=TOTAL + NEXT TABLE ENTRY
            ENDIF
            IDENTIFY NEXT TABLE ENTRY
            BITCOUNT:=BITCOUNT-1
    UNTIL BITCOUNT=0
END
```

With this program the most significant bit of VALUE (bit number 8) is examined first. If this is a 1 the first table entry is added to the total, and then the next bit is examined. When eventually BITCOUNT is reduced to zero, TOTAL contains the decimal (BCD) number. The table entries are exactly as shown above.

Several decisions, or in some cases, observations, need to be made before any code can be written from this structure:

1   Each of the table entries will be 3 BCD numbers, or 12 bits, and must therefore occupy two memory locations, or 16 bits. The last four bits of each entry will be 0000.
2   Since each table entry is 16 bits, TOTAL will also be 16 bits and occupy two memory locations. The least significant byte of the running total will be stored in the address TOTAL, and the most significant byte in address TOTAL + 1.
3   When a table entry is added to the running total, the least significant byte will be added first and then the most significant byte. After each addition a decimal adjust (DAA) instruction will be executed to convert the new running total to BCD.
4   Register pair H and L will contain the address of the next table entry (a table pointer) and register B will be used as a bit counter containing an initial value of 8.

Having got this far we can now decide whether there are any obvious subsections of CONV. The only thing which is immediately apparent is that the conditional BCD addition statement is a subroutine in itself. If we partition this off and call it ADDBCD, the program should be easier to test and understand.

The full listing for CONV is given in Figure 5.13. Notice that VALUE is redefined here so that CONV can be tested on its own. Once satisfied that CONV was working correctly, the reference to VALUE was removed and the new subroutine added to the main program. Further testing showed that the complete package, now summarised in Figure 5.14, worked correctly.

The PRINT subroutine

The purpose of this subroutine is to print the BCD numbers stored in TOTAL and TOTAL + 1. The required format is, for example:

3.75

with each value printed on a new line. On entry to the subroutine the two most significant characters are stored left-to-right in TOTAL + 1 with the two least significant characters (5 and 0) stored in TOTAL. We can summarise the functions of PRINT as follows,

1   Read contents of TOTAL and TOTAL + 1.

Figure 5.13

```
  1:
  2:
  3:                      *    SUBROUTINE CONV
  4:                      *    THIS CONVERTS AN 8-BIT NUMBER IN ADDRESS VALUE TO 4 BCD
  5:                      *    CHARACTERS STORED IN TOTAL AND TOTAL + 1. THE LEAST SIGNIFICANT
  6:                      *    BYTE IS STORED IN TOTAL.
  7:                      *
  8:                      *                 STRUCTURE
  9:                      *                 ''''''''''
 10:                      *    BEGIN
 11:                      *        TOTAL := 0
 12:                      *        BITCOUNT := 8
 13:                      *        READ CONTENTS OF VALUE
 14:                      *        IDENTIFY NEXT (FIRST) TABLE ENTRY
 15:                      *        REPEAT   (* UNTIL ALL BITS OF VALUE CHECKED *)
 16:                      *              ISOLATE A BIT OF VALUE
 17:                      *              IF BIT = 0 THEN
 18:                      *                    DO NOTHING
 19:                      *              ELSE
 20:                      *                    TOTAL := TOTAL + NEXT TABLE ENTRY
 21:                      *              ENDIF
 22:                      *              IDENTIFY NEXT TABLE ENTRY
 23:                      *              BITCOUNT := BITCOUNT -1
 24:                      *        UNTIL BITCOUNT = 0
 25:                      *    END
 26:                      *
 27:                      *    REGISTER USAGE:
 28:                      *                 A IS USED FOR ALL ARITHMETIC OPERATIONS
 29:                      *                 H AND L HOLD THE TABLE POINTER
 30:                      *                 B IS USED AS THE BIT COUNTER
 31:                      *                 D AND E HOLD THE NEXT TABLE ENTRY
 32:                      *                 C IS USED TO HOLD A SHIFTED REPLICA OF VALUE
 33:                      *
 34: 0200                          ORG     0200H              ; CONV ORIGIN
 35: 0200 AF              CONV:    XRA     A                  ; CLEAR A
 36: 0201 321D02                   STA     TOTAL
 37: 0204 321E02                   STA     TOTAL+1            ; TOTAL := 0
 38: 0207 0608                     MVI     B,08H              ; (B) = BITCOUNT = 8
 39: 0209 3A4602                   LDA     VALUE              ; GET BINARY VALUE
 40: 020C 211F02                   LXI     H,TABLE            ; INITIALISE TABLE POINTER
 41: 020F 07              REPT4:   RLC                        ; ISOLATE ONE BIT IN CY
 42: 0210 D21602          IF1:     JNC     ENIF               ; IF BIT = 0, DO NOTHING
 43: 0213 CD2F02          ELSE1:   CALL    ADDBCD             ; ELSE ADD TO RUNNING TOTAL
 44: 0216 23              ENIF:    INX     H
 45: 0217 23                       INX     H                  ; POINT AT NEXT TABLE ENTRY
 46: 0218 05                       DCR     B                  ; BITCOUNT := BITCOUNT - 1
 47: 0219 C20F02          UNTIL4:  JNZ     REPT4              ; REPEAT UNTIL BITCOUNT = 0
 48: 021C C9                       RET
 49:                      *
 50:                      *    DATA AREA
 51:                      *
 52: 021D                 TOTAL:   DS      2                  ; TWO LOCATIONS FOR TOTAL
 53: 021F 25001250        TABLE:   DB      25H,00H,12H,50H
 54: 0223 06300310                 DB      06H,30H,03H,10H
 55: 0227 01600080                 DB      01H,60H,00H,80H       ; TABLE ENTRIES
 56: 022B 00400020                 DB      00H,40H,00H,20H
 57:                      *
```

(Continued)

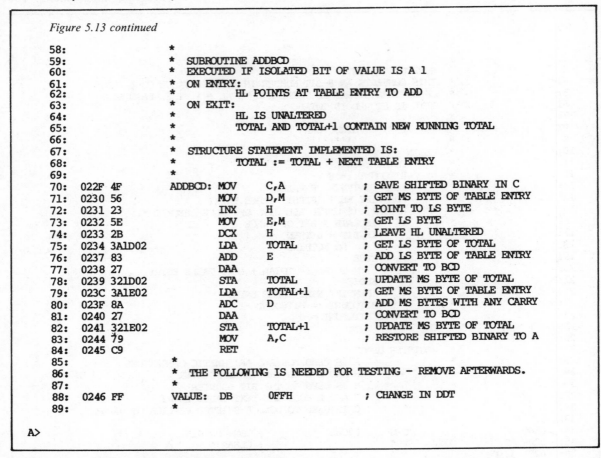

Figure 5.13 continued

```
58:                     *
59:                     *  SUBROUTINE ADDBCD
60:                     *  EXECUTED IF ISOLATED BIT OF VALUE IS A 1
61:                     *  ON ENTRY:
62:                     *        HL POINTS AT TABLE ENTRY TO ADD
63:                     *  ON EXIT:
64:                     *        HL IS UNALTERED
65:                     *        TOTAL AND TOTAL+1 CONTAIN NEW RUNNING TOTAL
66:                     *
67:                     *  STRUCTURE STATEMENT IMPLEMENTED IS:
68:                     *        TOTAL := TOTAL + NEXT TABLE ENTRY
69:                     *
70:  022F 4F      ADDBCD: MOV   C,A          ; SAVE SHIFTED BINARY IN C
71:  0230 56            MOV   D,M          ; GET MS BYTE OF TABLE ENTRY
72:  0231 23            INX   H            ; POINT TO LS BYTE
73:  0232 5E            MOV   E,M          ; GET LS BYTE
74:  0233 2B            DCX   H            ; LEAVE HL UNALTERED
75:  0234 3A1D02        LDA   TOTAL        ; GET LS BYTE OF TOTAL
76:  0237 83            ADD   E            ; ADD LS BYTE OF TABLE ENTRY
77:  0238 27            DAA                ; CONVERT TO BCD
78:  0239 321D02        STA   TOTAL        ; UPDATE MS BYTE OF TOTAL
79:  023C 3A1E02        LDA   TOTAL+1      ; GET MS BYTE OF TABLE ENTRY
80:  023F 8A            ADC   D            ; ADD MS BYTES WITH ANY CARRY
81:  0240 27            DAA                ; CONVERT TO BCD
82:  0241 321E02        STA   TOTAL+1      ; UPDATE MS BYTE OF TOTAL
83:  0244 79            MOV   A,C          ; RESTORE SHIFTED BINARY TO A
84:  0245 C9            RET
85:                     *
86:                     *  THE FOLLOWING IS NEEDED FOR TESTING - REMOVE AFTERWARDS.
87:                     *
88:  0246 FF      VALUE:  DB    0FFH         ; CHANGE IN DDT
89:                     *

A>
```

Figure 5.13   The CONV and ADDBCD subroutines

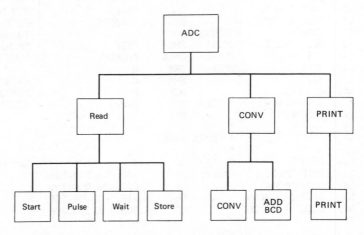

Figure 5.14   The program structure after CONV has been developed

2 Print left-hand character of TOTAL + 1.
3 Print decimal point.
4 Print right-hand character of TOTAL + 1.
5 Print left-hand character of TOTAL.
6 Print carriage return-line feed.

Printing of the left and right-hand characters can be handled in two subroutines called PRNLFT and PRNRGT, respectively. Similarly, printing a carriage-return-line-feed can be written as a separate subroutine called NEWL.

A common link between these three subroutines is the need for another subroutine which sends a character to the console. Subroutines of this sort are standard facilities with the console attached to one port and its control/status handshake signals attached to another. The relevant status signal in this case is labelled 'ready to receive' (RTR), or something similar, and when the console is ready

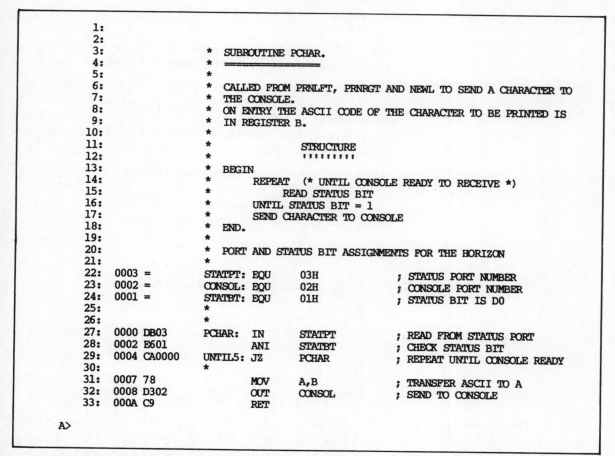

```
 1:
 2:
 3:              *   SUBROUTINE PCHAR.
 4:              *   ================
 5:              *
 6:              *   CALLED FROM PRNLFT, PRNRGT AND NEWL TO SEND A CHARACTER TO
 7:              *   THE CONSOLE.
 8:              *   ON ENTRY THE ASCII CODE OF THE CHARACTER TO BE PRINTED IS
 9:              *   IN REGISTER B.
10:              *
11:              *               STRUCTURE
12:              *               '''''''''
13:              *   BEGIN
14:              *       REPEAT  (* UNTIL CONSOLE READY TO RECEIVE *)
15:              *            READ STATUS BIT
16:              *       UNTIL STATUS BIT = 1
17:              *       SEND CHARACTER TO CONSOLE
18:              *   END.
19:              *
20:              *   PORT AND STATUS BIT ASSIGNMENTS FOR THE HORIZON
21:              *
22:  0003 =      STATPT: EQU     03H              ; STATUS PORT NUMBER
23:  0002 =      CONSOL: EQU     02H              ; CONSOLE PORT NUMBER
24:  0001 =      STATBT: EQU     01H              ; STATUS BIT IS D0
25:              *
26:              *
27:  0000 DB03   PCHAR:  IN      STATPT           ; READ FROM STATUS PORT
28:  0002 E601           ANI     STATBT           ; CHECK STATUS BIT
29:  0004 CA0000 UNTIL5: JZ      PCHAR            ; REPEAT UNTIL CONSOLE READY
30:              *
31:  0007 78             MOV     A,B              ; TRANSFER ASCII TO A
32:  0008 D302           OUT     CONSOL           ; SEND TO CONSOLE
33:  000A C9             RET

A>
```

Figure 5.15 The PCHAR (print character) routine

to accept a new character, RTR becomes a 1. We shall call this subroutine PCHAR and list it (Figure 5.15) without further comment, except to say that the ASCII code of the character to be printed must be in register B on entry.

This brings out another point of course. When characters have to be printed it is necessary to form their ASCII equivalent code and then send that to the printing device. In the case of numbers, this involves adding 30H to the BCD number (00H to 09H), and for the decimal point it means looking up the appropriate ASCII code. There are also unique codes for control characters like carriage return and line feed.

The PRINT subroutine is now completely defined, but it is difficult to properly test it without its subsidiary subroutines, particularly PRNLFT and PRNRGT. The first of these, PRNLFT, will operate as follows:
1 Mask off (zero) the right-hand four bits.
2 Shift the left-hand BCD character four places right.
3 Convert to ASCII by adding 30H.
4 Call the PCHAR routine. (Print it.)

PRNRGT will operate in much the same way, except that the left-hand four bits will be masked off and shifting will not be necessary.

When all of these subroutines are put together, the PRINT listing of Figure 5.16 results. Again for testing, extra statements, in this case definitions of TOTAL and TOTAL + 1, are included. When testing was complete, these were removed and then PRINT was added to our expanding main program.

The overall structure of the program is now shown in Figure 5.17.

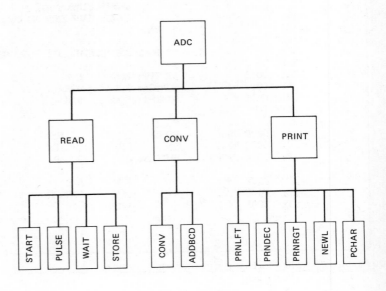

Figure 5.17 The complete ADC program is now described in terms of separate subroutines or instruction sequences

Figure 5.16

```
 1:
 2:
 3:                       *   SUBROUTINE PRINT
 4:                       *   THIS SUBROUTINE PRINTS THE BCD CHARACTERS STORED IN TOTAL AND
 5:                       *   TOTAL+1.
 6:                       *
 7:                       *              STRUCTURE
 8:                       *              '''''''''
 9:                       *   BEGIN
10:                       *       READ CONTENTS OF TOTAL AND TOTAL+1
11:                       *       PRINT LEFT-HAND CHARACTER OF TOTAL+1
12:                       *       PRINT A DECIMAL POINT
13:                       *       PRINT RIGHT-HAND CHARACTER IN TOTAL+1
14:                       *       PRINT LEFT-HAND CHARACTER OF TOTAL
15:                       *       PRINT A CARRAIGE RETURN-LINE FEED
16:                       *   END
17:                       *
18:                       *   REGISTER USAGE:
19:                       *              H AND L WILL BE LOADED WITH THE BCD NUMBER
20:                       *              ( MOST SIGNIFICANT IN H, LEAST SIGNIFICANT IN L)
21:                       *              A AND B ARE USED IN THE PCHAR ROUTINE
22:                       *
23:  0250                     ORG    0250H              ; PRINT ORIGIN
24:  0250 2A9402     PRINT:  LHLD   TOTAL              ; (L) = (TOTAL), (H) = (TOTAL+1)
25:  0253 7C                 MOV    A,H                ; GET FIRST TWO CHARACTERS
26:  0254 CD6802             CALL   PRNLFT             ; PRINT THE LEFT ONE
27:                       *
28:  0257 062E       PRNDEC: MVI    B,'.'              ; GET ASCII DECIMAL POINT
29:  0259 CD8902             CALL   PCHAR              ; PRINT IT
30:                       *
31:  025C 7C                 MOV    A,H                ; GET FIRST TWO CHARACTERS BACK
32:  025D CD7502             CALL   PRNRGT             ; PRINT THE RIGHT ONE
33:  0260 7D                 MOV    A,L                ; GET LS TWO CHARACTERS
34:  0261 CD6802             CALL   PRNLFT             ; PRINT THE LEFT ONE
35:  0264 CD7E02             CALL   NEWL               ; PREPARE NEW LINE FOR OUTPUT
36:  0267 C9                 RET
37:                       *
38:                       *   SUBROUTINE PRNLFT
39:                       *   CALLED FROM 'PRINT' TO PRINT THE BCD CHARACTER WHICH,
40:                       *   ON ENTRY, IS IN THE LEFT-HAND HALF OF REGISTER A.
41:                       *
42:                       *              STRUCTURE
43:                       *              '''''''''
44:                       *   BEGIN
45:                       *       ZERO RIGHT-HAND FOUR BITS
46:                       *       SHIFT REMAINING BITS FOUR PLACES RIGHT
47:                       *       CONVERT TO ASCII BY ADDING 30H
48:                       *       PRINT THE ASCII CHARACTER
49:                       *   END
50:                       *
51:  0268 E6F0       PRNLFT: ANI    0F0H               ; ZERO MS FOUR BITS
52:  026A 0F                 RRC
53:  026B 0F                 RRC                       ; SHIFT RIGHT FOUR PLACES
54:  026C 0F                 RRC
55:  026D 0F                 RRC
56:  026E C630               ADI    30H                ; CONVERT TO ASCII
57:  0270 47                 MOV    B,A                ; STORE IN B
58:  0271 CD8902             CALL   PCHAR              ; PRINT ASCII CHARACTER
59:  0274 C9                 RET
60:                       *
```

(Continued)

Figure 5.16 continued

```
61:                     *  SUBROUTINE PRNRGT
62:                     *  CALLED FROM 'PRINT' TO PRINT THE BCD CHARACTER WHICH,
63:                     *  ON ENTRY, IS IN THE RIGHT-HAND HALF OF REGISTER A.
64:                     *
65:                     *               STRUCTURE
66:                     *               '''''''''
67:                     *  BEGIN
68:                     *      ZERO LEFT-HAND FOUR BITS
69:                     *      CONVERT TO ASCII BY ADDING 30H
70:                     *      PRINT ASCII CHARACTER
71:                     *  END
72:                     *
73:  0275 E60F          PRNRGT: ANI   0FH            ; ZERO LEFT-HAND FOUR BITS
74:  0277 C630                  ADI   30H            ; CONVERT TO ASCII
75:  0279 47                    MOV   B,A            ; STORE IN B
76:  027A CD8902                CALL  PCHAR          ; PRINT ASCII CHARACTER
77:  027D C9                    RET
78:                     *
79:                     *  SUBROUTINE NEWL
80:                     *  CALLED FROM 'PRINT' TO PREPARE A NEW LINE FOR SUBSEQUENT OUTPUT
81:                     *
82:                     *               STRUCTURE
83:                     *               '''''''''
84:                     *  BEGIN
85:                     *      FETCH CARRAIGE RETURN ASCII CODE
86:                     *      PRINT IT
87:                     *      FETCH LINE-FEED ASCII CODE
88:                     *      PRINT IT
89:                     *  END
90:                     *
91:  027E 060D          NEWL:   MVI   B,0DH          ; ASCII FOR CARRAIGE-RETURN
92:  0280 CD8902                CALL  PCHAR          ; PRINT IT
93:  0283 060A                  MVI   B,0AH          ; ASCII FOR LINE-FEED
94:  0285 CD8902                CALL  PCHAR          ; PRINT IT
95:  0288 C9                    RET
96:                     *
97:                     *  SUBROUTINE PCHAR
98:                     *  CALLED FROM THE ABOVE ROUTINES TO SEND A CHARACTER TO THE CONSOLE
99:                     *  WHICH, ON ENTRY, MUST BE IN THE B REGISTER.
100:                    *
101:                    *               STRUCTURE
102:                    *               '''''''''
103:                    *  BEGIN
104:                    *      REPEAT  (* UNTIL CONSOLE READY TO RECEIVE *)
105:                    *          READ STATUS BIT
106:                    *      UNTIL STATUS BIT = 1
107:                    *      SEND CHARACTER TO CONSOLE
108:                    *  END
109:                    *
110:                    *  PORT AND STATUS BIT ASSIGNMENTS FOR NORTH STAR
111:  0003 =            STATPT: EQU   03H            ; STATUS PORT NUMBER
112:  0002 =            CONSOL: EQU   02H            ; CONSOLE PORT NUMBER
113:  0001 =            STATBT: EQU   01H            ; STATUS BIT IS D0
114:                    *
115:  0289 DB03         PCHAR:  IN    STATPT         ; READ FROM STATUS PORT
116:  028B E601                 ANI   STATBT         ; CHECK STATUS BIT
117:  028D CA8902       UNTIL5: JZ    PCHAR          ; REPEAT UNTIL CONSOLE READY
118:  0290 78                   MOV   A,B            ; TRANSFER ASCII TO A
119:  0291 D302                 OUT   CONSOL         ; SEND TO CONSOLE
120:  0293 C9                   RET
121:                    *
122:                    *  TOTAL AND TOTAL+1 REDEFINED HERE FOR TESTING
123:                    *
124:  0294 4750         TOTAL:  DB    47H,50H        ; CHANGE IN DDT
125:                    *
```

A>

Figure 5.16   The complete PRINT subroutine

Each of the boxes represents a tested, structured sequence of statements and when they are integrated in a single program (Figure 5.18) the text is easily understandable. At several times during program development, there were opportunities for introducing programming short cuts – more compact instruction sequences – which produced the same result. The temptation was resisted, however, because although shorter, these sequences are more difficult to understand and, in practically every case, would have meant a change in the program structure. Once a program structure has been written and tested it is fixed; the code should fit the structure, not the other way around.

Q5.11, 5.12

Questions

5.1 State the main advantages of top-down program design of assembly language programs.

5.2 Describe the four basic structures from which all assembly language programs should be constructed.

5.3 Write a WHILE-DO structure for a program fragment which counts the number of numbers in a list. The list is terminated in 00H and could be empty, i.e. the first entry could be 00H. The maximum number of list entries is 255.

5.4 Write a REPEAT-UNTIL structure for the same program fragment defined in Question 5.3 assuming that the list comprises at least one non-zero entry.

5.5 Now combine the REPEAT-UNTIL structure with an IF-THEN-ELSE to cater for the fact that the list may be empty.

5.6 Figure 5.3 shows a program which multiplies two numbers by repeated addition of the multiplicand to itself. Figures 5.19 and 5.20 show three versions of the same program. Even though it is always bad practice to write program structures after the code has been written, make an exception in this case and write a structure for each program.

5.7 In the multiplication program, it is now required to test the multiplicand before the main program is entered. If the multiplicand is zero the repeated addition part of the program is not executed. Write a structure for this program and, from that, the program itself.

5.8 Modify the structure and program of Question 5.7 to cater for a 16-bit product. In what order will the two bytes of the product be stored in RESULT and RESULT + 1?

5.9 Write a program which agrees with the alternative structure of the ODDS/EVEN program.

Figure 5.18

```
 1:
 2:
 3:                        *  PROGRAM ADC2
 4:                        *  THIS PROGRAM READS AN 8-BIT VALUE FROM A DATA PORT AND THEN
 5:                        *  PRINTS THE EQUIVALENT VOLTAGE, IN THE RANGE 0 - 5VOLTS, ON
 6:                        *  THE CONSOLE.
 7:                        *
 8:                        *                STRUCTURE
 9:                        *                '''''''''
10:                        *  BEGIN
11:                        *      REPEAT
12:                        *            READ VALUE
13:                        *            CONVERT VALUE TO A VOLTAGE
14:                        *            PRINT VOLTAGE
15:                        *      UNTIL INFINITY
16:                        *  END
17:                        *
18:  0100                        ORG      0100H           ; WILL RUN UNDER CP/M
19:  0100 CD5001    BGN:    CALL     READ            ; READ VALUE
20:  0103 CD0002            CALL     CONV            ; CONVERT VALUE TO A VOLTAGE
21:  0106 CD5002            CALL     PRINT           ; PRINT VOLTAGE
22:  0109 C30001            JMP      BGN             ; REPEAT INDEFINETLY
23:                        *
24:                        *  SUBROUTINE READ
25:                        *  ===============
26:                        *  THIS SUBROUTINE READS AN 8-BIT NUMBER FROM AN ADC OUTPUT
27:                        *  AND STORES IT IN ADDRESS 'VALUE'.
28:                        *
29:                        *  THE SYSTEM INPUTS ARE:
30:                        *      START   - FROM PUSHBUTION - 1 TO 0 CHANGE STARTS CYCLE
31:                        *      READY   - FROM ADC - CHANGES FROM 1 TO 0 WHEN ADC FINISHED
32:                        *      VALUE   - FROM ADC - READ WHEN ADC FINISHED CONVERSION
33:                        *  THE ONLY SYSTEM OUTPUT IS:
34:                        *      CONVERT - A 1 TO 0 CHANGE ON THIS LINE STARTS THE ADC
35:                        *
36:                        *                STRUCTURE
37:                        *                '''''''''
38:                        *  BEGIN
39:                        *      WAIT FOR A START SIGNAL
40:                        *      PULSE THE ADC CONVERT COMMAND LINE
41:                        *      REPEAT
42:                        *            READ THE READY LINE
43:                        *      UNTIL READY LINE = 0
44:                        *      READ AND STORE VALUE READ
45:                        *  END
46:                        *
47:                        *  REGISTER USAGE:
48:                        *      ONLY REGISTER A IS USED
49:                        *
50:  0150                        ORG      0150H           ; ORIGIN FOR READ
51:  0150 CD6401    READ:   CALL     START           ; WAIT FOR START SIGNAL
52:  0153 CD7301            CALL     PULSE           ; PULSE CONVERT LINE
53:                        *
54:  0156 DBFC      WAIT:   IN       CTRPRT          ; READ FROM CONTROL PORT
55:  0158 E601              ANI      01H             ; TEST ADC READY LINE
56:  015A C25601            JNZ      WAIT            ; WAIT UNTIL READY = 0
57:                        *
58:  015D DBFE      STORE:  IN       DATAPT          ; READ VALUE FROM DATA PORT
59:  015F 326301            STA      VALUE           ; STORE IN VALUE
60:  0162 C9                RET
61:                        *
62:                        *  DATA AND PORT ASSIGNMENTS
63:                        *
64:  00FC =         CTRPRT: EQU      0FCH            ; CONTROL PORT ADDRESS
```

(Continued)

Figure 5.18 continued

```
65:  00FE =              DATAPT: EQU     0FEH            ; DATA PORT ADDRESS
66:  0163               VALUE:  DS      1               ; BINARY VALUE STORED HERE
67:                     *
68:                     *
69:                     *   SUBROUTINE START
70:                     *   THIS SUBROUTINE READS THE START INPUT AND RETURNS CONTROL TO
71:                     *   THE CALLING PROGRAM WHEN START CHANGES FROM 1 TO 0.
72:                     *   IT IS ONLY CALLED FROM READ.
73:                     *
74:                     *               STRUCTURE
75:                     *               '''''''''
76:                     *   BEGIN
77:                     *       REPEAT (* UNTIL PUSHBUTTON RELEASED *)
78:                     *           READ START INPUT
79:                     *       UNTIL START = 1
80:                     *       REPEAT (* UNTIL PUSHBUTTON PRESSED *)
81:                     *           READ START INPUT
82:                     *       UNTIL START = 0
83:                     *   END
84:                     *
85:  0164 DBFC          START:  IN      CTRPRT          ; READ FROM CONTROL PORT
86:  0166 E680                  ANI     80H             ; CHECK START INPUT
87:  0168 CA6401        UNTIL2: JZ      START           ; REPEAT UNTIL START = 1
88:  016B DBFC          REPT3:  IN      CTRPRT          ; READ FROM CONTROL PORT AGAIN
89:  016D E680                  ANI     80H             ; RE-CHECK START
90:  016F C26B01        UNTIL3: JNZ     REPT3           ; REPEAT UNTIL START = 0
91:  0172 C9                    RET
92:                     *
93:                     *   SUBROUTINE PULSE
94:                     *   GENERATES A NEGATIVE GOING PULSE ON THE ADC CONVERT LINE
95:                     *
96:                     *               STRUCTURE
97:                     *               '''''''''
98:                     *   BEGIN
99:                     *       SEND A LOGIC 0 TO CONVERT LINE
100:                    *       NOW SEND A 1
101:                    *   END
102:                    *
103:                    *   PORT ASSIGNMENT
104: 00FF =             OUTPRT: EQU     0FFH
105:                    *
106: 0173 AF            PULSE:  XRA     A               ; CLEAR A
107: 0174 D3FF                  OUT     OUTPRT          ; CONVERT LINE = 0
108: 0176 C601                  ADI     01H             ; MAKE D0 = 1
109: 0178 D3FF                  OUT     OUTPRT          ; CONVERT LINE (D0 OF FF) = 1
110: 017A C9                    RET
111:                    *
112:                    *   SUBROUTINE CONV
113:                    *   ===============
114:                    *   THIS CONVERTS AN 8-BIT NUMBER IN ADDRESS VALUE TO 4 BCD
115:                    *   CHARACTERS STORED IN TOTAL AND TOTAL + 1. THE LEAST SIGNIFICANT
116:                    *   BYTE IS STORED IN TOTAL.
117:                    *
118:                    *               STRUCTURE
119:                    *               '''''''''
120:                    *   BEGIN
121:                    *       TOTAL := 0
122:                    *       BITCOUNT := 8
123:                    *       READ CONTENTS OF VALUE
124:                    *       IDENTIFY NEXT (FIRST) TABLE ENTRY
125:                    *       REPEAT  (* UNTIL ALL BITS OF VALUE CHECKED *)
126:                    *           ISOLATE A BIT OF VALUE
127:                    *           IF BIT = 0 THEN
128:                    *               DO NOTHING
```

(Continued)

Figure 5.18 continued

```
129:                    *              ELSE
130:                    *                  TOTAL := TOTAL + NEXT TABLE ENTRY
131:                    *              ENDIF
132:                    *              IDENTIFY NEXT TABLE ENTRY
133:                    *              BITCOUNT := BITCOUNT -1
134:                    *          UNTIL BITCOUNT = 0
135:                    * END
136:                    *
137:                    * REGISTER USAGE:
138:                    *              A IS USED FOR ALL ARITHMETIC OPERATIONS
139:                    *              H AND L HOLD THE TABLE POINTER
140:                    *              B IS USED AS THE BIT COUNTER
141:                    *              D AND E HOLD THE NEXT TABLE ENTRY
142:                    *              C IS USED TO HOLD A SHIFTED REPLICA OF VALUE
143:                    *
144: 0200                       ORG    0200H             ; CONV ORIGIN
145: 0200 AF           CONV:    XRA    A                 ; CLEAR A
146: 0201 321D02                STA    TOTAL
147: 0204 321E02                STA    TOTAL+1           ; TOTAL := 0
148: 0207 0608                  MVI    B,08H             ; (B) = BITCOUNT = 8
149: 0209 3A6301                LDA    VALUE             ; GET BINARY VALUE
150: 020C 211F02                LXI    H,TABLE           ; INITIALISE TABLE POINTER
151: 020F 07           REPT4:   RLC                      ; ISOLATE ONE BIT IN CY
152: 0210 D21602       IF1:     JNC    ENIF              ; IF BIT = 0, DO NOTHING
153: 0213 CD2F02       ELSE1:   CALL   ADDBCD            ; ELSE ADD TO RUNNING TOTAL
154: 0216 23           ENIF:    INX    H
155: 0217 23                    INX    H                 ; POINT AT NEXT TABLE ENTRY
156: 0218 05                    DCR    B                 ; BITCOUNT := BITCOUNT - 1
157: 0219 C20F02       UNTIL4:  JNZ    REPT4             ; REPEAT UNTIL BITCOUNT = 0
158: 021C C9                    RET
159:                    *
160:                    * DATA AREA
161:                    *
162: 021D             TOTAL:    DS     2                 ; TWO LOCATIONS FOR TOTAL
163: 021F 25001250    TABLE:    DB     25H,00H,12H,50H
164: 0223 06300310              DB     06H,30H,03H,10H
165: 0227 01600080              DB     01H,60H,00H,80H            ; TABLE ENTRIES
166: 022B 00400020              DB     00H,40H,00H,20H
167:                    *
168:                    *
169:                    * SUBROUTINE ADDBCD
170:                    * EXECUTED IF ISOLATED BIT OF VALUE IS A 1
171:                    * ON ENTRY:
172:                    *              HL POINTS AT TABLE ENTRY TO ADD
173:                    * ON EXIT:
174:                    *              HL IS UNALTERED
175:                    *              TOTAL AND TOTAL+1 CONTAIN NEW RUNNING TOTAL
176:                    *
177:                    * STRUCTURE STATEMENT IMPLEMENTED IS:
178:                    *              TOTAL := TOTAL + NEXT TABLE ENTRY
179:                    *
180: 022F 4F           ADDBCD:  MOV    C,A               ; SAVE SHIFTED BINARY IN C
181: 0230 56                    MOV    D,M               ; GET MS BYTE OF TABLE ENTRY
182: 0231 23                    INX    H                 ; POINT TO LS BYTE
183: 0232 5E                    MOV    E,M               ; GET LS BYTE
184: 0233 2B                    DCX    H                 ; LEAVE HL UNALTERED
185: 0234 3A1D02                LDA    TOTAL             ; GET LS BYTE OF TOTAL
186: 0237 83                    ADD    E                 ; ADD LS BYTE OF TABLE ENTRY
187: 0238 27                    DAA                      ; CONVERT TO BCD
188: 0239 321D02                STA    TOTAL             ; UPDATE MS BYTE OF TOTAL
189: 023C 3A1E02                LDA    TOTAL+1           ; GET MS BYTE OF TABLE ENTRY
190: 023F 8A                    ADC    D                 ; ADD MS BYTES WITH ANY CARRY
191: 0240 27                    DAA                      ; CONVERT TO BCD
192: 0241 321E02                STA    TOTAL+1           ; UPDATE MS BYTE OF TOTAL
```

(Continued)

Figure 5.18 continued

```
193:   0244 79              MOV     A,C              ; RESTORE SHIFTED BINARY TO A
194:   0245 C9              RET
195:              *
196:              *    SUBROUTINE PRINT
197:              *    ================
198:              *    THIS SUBROUTINE PRINTS THE BCD CHARACTERS STORED IN TOTAL AND
199:              *    TOTAL+1.
200:              *
201:              *                STRUCTURE
202:              *                '''''''''
203:              *    BEGIN
204:              *        READ CONTENTS OF TOTAL AND TOTAL+1
205:              *        PRINT LEFT-HAND CHARACTER OF TOTAL+1
206:              *        PRINT A DECIMAL POINT
207:              *        PRINT RIGHT-HAND CHARACTER IN TOTAL+1
208:              *        PRINT LEFT-HAND CHARACTER OF TOTAL
209:              *        PRINT A CARRAIGE RETURN-LINE FEED
210:              *    END
211:              *
212:              *    REGISTER USAGE:
213:              *                  H AND L WILL BE LOADED WITH THE BCD NUMBER
214:              *                  ( MOST SIGNIFICANT IN H, LEAST SIGNIFICANT IN L)
215:              *                  A AND B ARE USED IN THE PCHAR ROUTINE
216:              *
217:   0250                 ORG     0250H            ; PRINT ORIGIN
218:   0250 2A1D02  PRINT:  LHLD    TOTAL            ; (L) = (TOTAL), (H) = (TOTAL+1)
219:   0253 7C              MOV     A,H              ; GET FIRST TWO CHARACTERS
220:   0254 CD6802          CALL    PRNLFT           ; PRINT THE LEFT ONE
221:              *
222:   0257 062E   PRNDEC: MVI     B,'.'            ; GET ASCII DECIMAL POINT
223:   0259 CD8902          CALL    PCHAR            ; PRINT IT
224:              *
225:   025C 7C              MOV     A,H              ; GET FIRST TWO CHARACTERS BACK
226:   025D CD7502          CALL    PRNRGT           ; PRINT THE RIGHT ONE
227:   0260 7D              MOV     A,L              ; GET LS TWO CHARACTERS
228:   0261 CD6802          CALL    PRNLFT           ; PRINT THE LEFT ONE
229:   0264 CD7E02          CALL    NEWL             ; PREPARE NEW LINE FOR OUTPUT
230:   0267 C9              RET
231:              *
232:              *    SUBROUTINE PRNLFT
233:              *    CALLED FROM 'PRINT' TO PRINT THE BCD CHARACTER WHICH,
234:              *    ON ENTRY, IS IN THE LEFT-HAND HALF OF REGISTER A.
235:              *
236:              *                STRUCTURE
237:              *                '''''''''
238:              *    BEGIN
239:              *        ZERO RIGHT-HAND FOUR BITS
240:              *        SHIFT REMAINING BITS FOUR PLACES RIGHT
241:              *        CONVERT TO ASCII BY ADDING 30H
242:              *        PRINT THE ASCII CHARACTER
243:              *    END
244:              *
245:   0268 E6F0   PRNLFT: ANI     0F0H             ; ZERO MS FOUR BITS
246:   026A 0F              RRC
247:   026B 0F              RRC                      ; SHIFT RIGHT FOUR PLACES
248:   026C 0F              RRC
249:   026D 0F              RRC
250:   026E C630            ADI     30H              ; CONVERT TO ASCII
251:   0270 47              MOV     B,A              ; STORE IN B
252:   0271 CD8902          CALL    PCHAR            ; PRINT ASCII CHARACTER
253:   0274 C9              RET
254:              *
255:              *    SUBROUTINE PRNRGT
256:              *    CALLED FROM 'PRINT' TO PRINT THE BCD CHARACTER WHICH,
```

(Continued)

Figure 5.18 continued

```
257:                         *  ON ENTRY, IS IN THE RIGHT-HAND HALF OF REGISTER A.
258:                         *
259:                         *                    STRUCTURE
260:                         *                    ''''''''''
261:                         *  BEGIN
262:                         *      ZERO LEFT-HAND FOUR BITS
263:                         *      CONVERT TO ASCII BY ADDING 30H
264:                         *      PRINT ASCII CHARACTER
265:                         *  END
266:                         *
267:   0275 E60F     PRNRGT: ANI      0FH              ; ZERO LEFT-HAND FOUR BITS
268:   0277 C630             ADI      30H              ; CONVERT TO ASCII
269:   0279 47               MOV      B,A              ; STORE IN B
270:   027A CD8902           CALL     PCHAR            ; PRINT ASCII CHARACTER
271:   027D C9               RET
272:                         *
273:                         *  SUBROUTINE NEWL
274:                         *  CALLED FROM 'PRINT' TO PREPARE A NEW LINE FOR SUBSEQUENT OUTPUT
275:                         *
276:                         *                    STRUCTURE
277:                         *                    ''''''''''
278:                         *  BEGIN
279:                         *      FETCH CARRAIGE RETURN ASCII CODE
280:                         *      PRINT IT
281:                         *      FETCH LINE-FEED ASCII CODE
282:                         *      PRINT IT
283:                         *  END
284:                         *
285:   027E 060D     NEWL:   MVI      B,0DH            ; ASCII FOR CARRAIGE-RETURN
286:   0280 CD8902           CALL     PCHAR            ; PRINT IT
287:   0283 060A             MVI      B,0AH            ; ASCII FOR LINE-FEED
288:   0285 CD8902           CALL     PCHAR            ; PRINT IT
289:   0288 C9               RET
290:                         *
291:                         *  SUBROUTINE PCHAR
292:                         *  CALLED FROM THE ABOVE ROUTINES TO SEND A CHARACTER TO THE CONSOLE
293:                         *  WHICH, ON ENTRY, MUST BE IN THE B REGISTER.
294:                         *
295:                         *                    STRUCTURE
296:                         *                    ''''''''''
297:                         *  BEGIN
298:                         *      REPEAT  (* UNTIL CONSOLE READY TO RECEIVE *)
299:                         *          READ STATUS BIT
300:                         *      UNTIL STATUS BIT = 1
301:                         *      SEND CHARACTER TO CONSOLE
302:                         *  END
303:                         *
304:                         *  PORT AND STATUS BIT ASSIGNMENTS FOR NORTH STAR
305:   0003 =        STATPT: EQU      03H              ; STATUS PORT NUMBER
306:   0002 =        CONSOL: EQU      02H              ; CONSOLE PORT NUMBER
307:   0001 =        STATBT: EQU      01H              ; STATUS BIT IS D0
308:                         *
309:   0289 DB03     PCHAR:  IN       STATPT           ; READ FROM STATUS PORT
310:   028B E601             ANI      STATBT           ; CHECK STATUS BIT
311:   028D CA8902   UNTIL5: JZ       PCHAR            ; REPEAT UNTIL CONSOLE READY
312:   0290 78               MOV      A,B              ; TRANSFER ASCII TO A
313:   0291 D302             OUT      CONSOL           ; SEND TO CONSOLE
314:   0293 C9               RET
315:                         *
316:   0294                  END
```

A>

Figure 5.18

```
            *  ALTERNATIVE VERSIONS OF THE MULTIPLICATION PROGRAM.
            *  ''''''''''''''''''''''''''''''''''''''''''''''''''''
            *
            *  REGISTER USAGE :-
            *                      A WILL ACCUMULATE PARTIAL PRODUCT (PARTPROD)
            *                      B WILL CONTAIN MULTIPLIER
            *                      C WILL CONTAIN MULTIPLICAND
            *
            *  VERSION 1
            *  ''''''''''
            *
0100                ORG    0100H
0100 3A1701 MULT1:  LDA    MPLIER
0103 47             MOV    B,A            ; (B) = MULTIPLIER
0104 3A1801         LDA    MCAND
0107 4F             MOV    C,A            ; (C) = MULTIPLICAND
0108 AF             XRA    A              ; (A) = PARTPROD = 0
            *
            *  INITIAL TEST ON MULTIPLIER
            *
0109 05             DCR    B              ; SUBTRACT 1 FROM MPLIER.
010A DA1301         JC     END1           ; CY = 1 MEANS MPLIER = 0, END.
010D 04             INR    B              ; OTHERWISE RESTORE MPLIER
            *
010E 81     LOOP1:  ADD    C              ; PARTPROD := PARTPROD + MCAND
010F 05             DCR    B              ; MPLIER := MPLIER - 1
0110 C20E01         JNZ    LOOP1          ; LOOP WHILE MPLIER > 0
0113 321901 END1:   STA    RESULT         ; STORE FINAL PRODUCT
0116 C9     CONT1:  RET                   ; STRUCTURE EXIT POINT
            *
            *  DATA FOR BOTH VERSIONS
            *
0117 03     MPLIER: DB     3              ; INITIAL VALUES. CHANGE
0118 04     MCAND:  DB     4              ; IN DDT WHEN TESTING
0119        RESULT: DS     1              ; RESULT WILL GO HERE
            *
            *  VERSION 2
            *  ''''''''''
            *
011A 3A1701 MULT2:  LDA    MPLIER         ; GET MULTIPLIER
011D FE00           CPI    00H            ; TEST FOR 0 MULTIPLIER
011F CA2D01         JZ     END2           ; END IF ZERO
0122 47             MOV    B,A            ; PREPARE, (B) = MULTIPLIER
0123 3A1801         LDA    MCAND          ; GET MULTIPLICAND
0126 4F             MOV    C,A            ; (C) = MULTIPLICAND
0127 AF             XRA    A              ; INITIAL PRODUCT = 0
0128 81     LOOP2:  ADD    C              ; PARTPROD := PARTPROD + MCAND
0129 05             DCR    B              ; MPLIER := MPLIER - 1
012A C22801         JNZ    LOOP2          ; WHILE MPLIER > 0, LOOP
012D 321901 END2:   STA    RESULT         ; STORE FINAL PRODUCT
0130 C9     CONT2:  RET                   ; STRUCTURE EXIT POINT
            *
0131               END
0131
001H USE FACTOR
END OF ASSEMBLY

A>
```

Figure 5.19   Two alternative versions of the multiplication program

```
            *  MULTIPLICATION BY REPEATED ADDITION
            *
            *  VERSION 3
            *  !!!!!!!!!
            *
            *  SAME REGISTER USAGE AS IN PREVIOUS VERSIONS
            *
0100              ORG     0100H
0100 3A1801 MULT3:   LDA     MPLIER          ; GET MULTIPLIER
0103 47          MOV     B,A             ; (B) = MULTIPLIER
0104 3A1901      LDA     MCAND           ; (A) = MULTIPLICAND = PARTPROD
0107 4F          MOV     C,A             ; (C) = MULTIPLICAND
            *
0108 05    LOOP3:   DCR     B               ; MPLIER := MPLIER - 1
0109 CA1401      JZ      END3            ; END IF MPLIER NOW 0
            *
            *  IF MPLIER WAS INITIALLY ZERO, CARRY WILL BE SET, TEST IT
            *
010C DA1301      JC      NOGO            ; NOGO IF CARRY SET
010F 81          ADD     C               ; PARTPROD := PARTPROD + MCAND
0110 C30801      JMP     LOOP3           ; RE-TEST
            *
0113 AF    NOGO:    XRA     A               ; FINAL PRODUCT IS ZERO HERE
0114 321A01 END3:   STA     RESULT          ; STORE FINAL PRODUCT
0117 C9    CONT3:   RET                     ; STRUCTURE EXIT POINT
            *
            *  DATA AREA
            *
0118 03    MPLIER:  DB      3
0119 04    MCAND:   DB      4
011A       RESULT:  DS      1
            *
011B              END
011B
000H USE FACTOR
END OF ASSEMBLY

A>
```

Figure 5.20   Another version of the multiplication program

5.10   Modify the structure and program of Question 5.9 to allow for a list comprising a maximum of 510 numbers – 255 odd and 255 even in any order.

5.11   A double-length (16-bit) number is stored, least significant byte first, in addresses DIVEND and DIVEND + 1. An 8-bit number is stored in another address labelled DIVSR. Write a program which divides the number in DIVEND and DIVEND + 1 by the number in DIVSR leaving the quotient and remainder in addresses labelled QUOT and REMDR, respectively. Division is achieved by repeatedly subtracting the divisor, in DIVSR, from the double-length dividend in DIVEND and DIVEND + 1. If the divisor is zero or the relative magnitudes of dividend and divisor are such that a proper 8-bit quotient cannot be generated, a location labelled OVFLOW (overflow) should be set to

01H or 02H, respectively, and the quotient and remainder locations should be cleared. If the division can proceed properly then OVFLOW should be set to zero.

Remember, first write a structure which precisely satisfies the program specification under all conditions. Begin writing code only after this structure has been thoroughly tested. Take your time!

5.12 The ADC program is to be modified in two respects:

1 The binary number is to be printed by a subroutine called PBIN.
2 A number of spaces is then to be printed, and then the decimal equivalent of the binary as before. The number of spaces to be printed is passed to a subroutine called SPACE, in register C.

Modify the main program and then write the PBIN and SPACE subroutines.

Chapter 6 Relocation and linking of object code

Objectives of this chapter *When you have completed studying this chapter you should be able to:*

1 *Understand the purpose of the CP/M utility, LOAD.*
2 *Appreciate the need for relocation and linking of object code modules in microprocessor system design.*
3 *Understand how relocatable loaders are required to change relocatable object code.*
4 *Appreciate the need for separate location counters during assembly.*
5 *Know of the Intel relocation and linking directives.*
6 *Know how a Universal MDS, such as the Futuredata system, employs a linkage editor to combine the functions of a linker and relocatable loader.*
7 *Appreciate the extra facilities provided by an MDS, when compared with a software development station, for system debugging.*

```
A>LOAD B:COMP2.HEX

FIRST ADDRESS 0100
LAST  ADDRESS 0118
BYTES READ      0019
RECORDS WRITTEN 01


A>B:COMP2

A>
```

Figure 6.1 Illustrating the CP/M LOAD utility and the effect of executing the program COMP 2

Q6.1

6.1 The need for relocation and linking

You may recall that when a CP/M .HEX file is loaded into memory before a debugging session begins, DDT converts the hexadecimal file contents to binary. Following this conversion, the program can be executed – it is an executable program. If it is already in executable form when DDT is called, the file containing it will have the .COM extension and DDT does not need to change it any way. Executable, .COM, files are created from .HEX files using the CP/M utility called LOAD. Once the .COM version of a file exists, it can be executed under CP/M by typing the file name (without the .COM extension) whenever the CP/M prompt is displayed. If the program ends in a RET or JMP 0000H instruction, control returns to CP/M once execution is finished.

Figure 6.1 shows what happens when the second version of the COMP program, COMP2.HEX, is first loaded and then executed. Since the program does not generate any console I/O, there is nothing to indicate that anything has happened during execution. Another program, however, may print operator messages or display measured values.

All the CP/M utilities we have used up to now are .COM files. They are designed to run under CP/M and return control to it when they have finished their task. They are no different in this respect from user-developed programs. They may not occupy the first 256 bytes of program memory (lowest execution address 0100H) and they must not overwrite the other memory-resident part of CP/M which starts at a fixed (known) address determined by the total amount of memory in the system.

This restriction presents us with a problem when we are developing programs for a standalone system which will not have CP/M in the background. Perhaps we are writing and testing programs which will eventually be loaded into ROM (or EPROM) and RAM in a system we are building from a microprocessor chip set. It is quite likely that our RAM/ROM chips will occupy addresses which do not correspond with the address band allocated to .COM files by CP/M. Admittedly we can test the logic of individual software modules by assembling and executing them at any address, but, having done that, we shall need to reassemble the whole program with the assembly origins corresponding with the absolute addresses of the RAMs and ROMs.

There is another problem, however, when we have to bind together a number of modules to make a complete working program. In our existing CP/M system, the only way of doing this is by combining them at source code level, either in the editor or by using another CP/M utility called PIP. It is quite likely that most modules will contain a mix of program and data segments which will have to be separated. Some of these will eventually go into EPROM, but not necessarily the same one, and some will go into RAM. When they have been separated, they will still have to work together as a complete program.

Not only are we faced with a formidable editing job, but very often when developing large segmented programs, we are not precisely sure of the eventual executing addresses of particular segments. Indeed, they may be different for different systems. What we need is some easy means of relocating object code modules and then linking them **Q6.2** together to make a complete program.

6.2 Relocating assemblers and loaders

At least part of our problem is solved if we use an assembler which generates relocatable object code. The term relocatable means that the object code can be relocated (moved) so that it can execute anywhere in memory, irrespective of its assembly addresses. The relocatable object code file contains relocation information, as well as the normal object code, which indicates which parts of the object code have to be changed if the module being assembled is loaded at an address which is not the same as the assembly origin. For example, if we assemble a program without an ORG statement in it, the first byte will be assigned to address 0000H and all the other bytes will follow on in successively higher addresses. JUMP and CALL instructions will all be referenced to this origin. We may, for instance, have an instruction such as JNZ 0014H in the source code. If the object code is to be relocated so that it is eventually loaded starting at 1000H, that jump instruction will have to be changed to JNZ 1014H to remain consistent with the new start address. The relocation information in the object code file will indicate where changes like this have to be made. When the program is eventually made absolute (converted to executable form), a relocating loader, rather than an absolute loader like LOAD, will be needed. The relocating loader will be supplied with the required load address and, as it reads the relocatable object

Q6.3, 6.4   code, it will make all the necessary changes.

6.3   The use of location counters during assembly

We have already looked at how the assembler assigns bytes of object code to particular addresses during assembly. It is sometimes helpful to think of the assembler as maintaining a location counter, the contents of which show where the next byte will be located. Once a byte has been assigned to an address, the contents of the location counter are incremented so that, like the program counter during execution, it keeps track of where we are in the assembly process. When an ORG statement is reached the ORG operand is loaded into the location counter and the effect of a DS statement is to add the DS operand to the counter contents.

To overcome this problem of separating out the ROMable parts of a program from those parts which will go into RAM, assemblers which produce relocatable object code often maintain more than one location counter. The Intel assembler, for example, has three location counters, one for absolute (non-relocatable) segments, one for relocatable program segments and one for relocatable data segments. By using one of three assembler directives, the appropriate location counter can be activated as if it were the only one in the system. At the end of assembly each of the different types of object code is formed into contiguous blocks which, in the case of the relocatable blocks, can be relocated to execute anywhere in memory and still stay in

Q6.5   touch with the other blocks.

6.4   The Intel relocation directives

The absolute directive, ASEG

Although the discussion is of relocation directives, code blocks assembled under this directive are absolute and not relocatable.

When the assembler reads an ASEG (absolute segment) directive in the source code file, it switches to the absolute location counter and assigns all following bytes of object code to specific (absolute) addresses until one of the other directives is read. A later occurrence of ASEG will switch the assembler back to the absolute location counter and the assignment process will continue in absolute mode as if the ASEG counter had always been in operation. Any ORG statement which is programmed while ASEG is active changes the ASEG location counter but not the other two.

The ASEG counter is the default location counter; that is to say, it is the one in operation when assembly begins. It may be needed when, for example, we are using interrupts. Wherever the rest of the program eventually resides, the interrupt service routines always start at fixed addresses between 0000H and 0038H. They are absolute!

The relocatable code directive, CSEG

The CSEG counter is activated when this directive is read from the source code file. It usually indicates that following program or fixed data segments will eventually be committed to ROM or EPROM. When it is used for the first time during assembly, the CSEG counter contains zero, but this can be changed, if necessary, by programming an ORG statement.

Various optional information can be entered in the opcode field of a CSEG statement. This extra information is stored with the object code and is used by two programs called LINK (the linker) and LOCATE (the relocatable loader) which are used to link together several object code modules and relocate them in memory when the whole program is made absolute. Typically, this extra information would indicate whether particular segments should start a new page boundary (be allocated to new ROM or EPROM) or whether it must be contained within a single page when relocated, or whether it can follow on from the previous CSEG program or data.

The relocatable data directive DSEG

This assembler directive activates the DSEG counter. The DSEG statement has exactly the same format as CSEG statements and, when read from the source code file, it is taken to mean (by convention) that the following program and data segments will be committed to RAM.

6.5 Program linkage directives

Very often separately assembled program modules access data or call subroutines which are not part of the module itself. Similarly, the module being assembled, or parts of it, may be referenced in other modules. Situations like this occur very frequently when modular programming techniques are used. Rather than requiring the programmer to insert dummy labels in the source code file just to resolve these address references, many assemblers provide one or more program linkage directives. These are used to inform the assembler of any instructions or data in this module which are accessible to any other module (define entry points), and also to inform the assembler of instructions or data which are referenced in this module but defined in another (external references).

The assembler will not be able to resolve external references at assembly time, but equally, it will not flag an undefined symbol error. The underlying assumption is that any external references will be made absolute when communicating modules are linked together. When the LINK program is called, the module names will be entered and the linker will make the necessary connections.

The Intel linkage directives of direct concern are PUBLIC and EXTRN.

The PUBLIC directive

This directive is used to declare a list of names (labels) attached to data or instructions in this module, which can be referenced from other modules. In other words, it declares the entry points. If, for example, we were to build a file containing a number of general-purpose subroutines (a library file), the name of each subroutine would be entered in the opcode field of a PUBLIC statement as:

```
PUBLIC    SUB1,SUB2,SUB3,...
```

When the library file is linked with another program which uses some or all of these subroutines, the linker resolves the references.

The EXTRN directive

In the calling program, SUB1, SUB2 and SUB3 will have been declared as external references using the EXTRN directive. The format of the EXTRN statement is:

```
EXTRN     SUB1,SUB2,SUB3,...
```

It informs the assembler of instructions or data which are referenced in this module but declared in another module. The assembler notes the external references and then adds linking information to the object code file which will be used by the linker to make the references absolute.

In effect, PUBLIC and EXTRN are handshaking directives used in communicating modules.

6.6 Alternative linkage and relocation directives

Other systems provide the same kind of linking and relocating facilities as the Intel system, but may use different mnemonics. For example, linking information is very often provided by the single directive GLOBAL (or GLBL) in both calling and called programs. Rather than declare external references and entry points in separate EXTRN and PUBLIC statements, both can be declared in the same GLBL statement. This is the case in the Futuredata Microprocessor Development System (MDS) operating system.

Q6.6

The same Futuredata system has two location counters which are activated by the (absolute) ASEG and (relocatable) RSEG directives. ASEG works in exactly the same way as the Intel ASEG directive, and RSEG combines the functions of the Intel CSEG and DSEG.

To illustrate how these directives might be used, let us reconsider our ADC program developed in the previous chapter. This time we shall assemble four separate modules, ADC, READ, CONV and PRINT, and include GLBL, ASEG and RSEG directives. For added clarity we will strip out most of the program code and concentrate on the linking and relocation directives.

Data are passed from READ to CONV (a binary value) and from CONV to PRINT (the BCD equivalent) and each of the subroutines is called from the main program. Our global references are therefore as shown in Table 6.1. Remember that declaring the label READ as global in the main program marks it as an external address reference (equivalent of Intel's EXTRN), and the same declaration in sub-routine READ marks the labelled instruction as an entry point (equivalent of Intel's PUBLIC). The linker will connect the two later. PCHAR and NEWL are declared as global because we want to begin building a package of general-purpose console I/O routines. It would be convenient if PCHAR and NEWL were available for any future programs we write which use console I/O.

Table 6.1

Module name	External references	Entry points
ADC	READ	
	CONV	
	PRINT	
READ		READ
		VALUE
CONV	VALUE	CONV
		TOTAL
PRINT	TOTAL	PRINT
		PCHAR
		NEWL

The code will be segmented as follows:

1   There will be an absolute code segment, defined in ADC, in which we will put dummy interrupt service routines for interrupts 6 and 7. (This was not part of the original ADC program but is included here to illustrate the use of the ASEG directive.) The first instruction in the program is at absolute address 0000H and is a jump to the start of the main program. This is needed in a standalone system because an 8080 RESET signal always starts program execution at 0000H. In a practical situation the instruction would probably be a jump to an initialisation routine which, for example, initialised the stack pointer, serial ports, etc.

2   The main code segment will eventually be relocated to start at address 1100H. This is the first address occupied by a 256×8 bit EPROM and address decoding logic on the prototype board will be designed to position the EPROM at that absolute address. The scattered code segments which have to be linked together before they are committed to EPROM will each be preceeded by a RSEG directive and then the word CODE*n*, where *n* is a number. Since there are four modules and each contain some code, *n* will range from 1 to 4. When the segments are eventually linked, the linker will be told the origin (1100H) and then the names of the various RSEG modules (CODE1, CODE2, etc) which have to be linked together.

3   Transient (variable) data like VALUE and TOTAL will be assigned to a RAM positioned at a starting address of C800H. Each of these data declarations will be preceeded by statement

```
 RSEG   RAMn
```

where, again, *n* is a number, this time, ranging from 1 to 2.

4   The look-up table will be located in a separate EPROM which occupies the address band from 1200H to 12FFH. This single relocatable segment will be labelled DATA1. It is expected that there will be much more fixed data to go in here by the time the whole system has been developed.

5   Finally, PCHAR and NEWL, the first entries in our console I/O library, will go into EPROM at address 8000H onwards. The relocatable segment for these routines is identified by the name LIBRY 1.

The four modules are listed in Figures 6.2 to 6.5.

Notice that this particular assembler has an unusual way of identifying hexadecimal numbers. It expects the number to be preceded by the letter X, and the number itself to be enclosed within apostrophes. Notice too how it deals with instructions like CALL READ when READ has been declared as a global (GLBL). The subroutine start address is temporarily entered as 0000H, but the extra

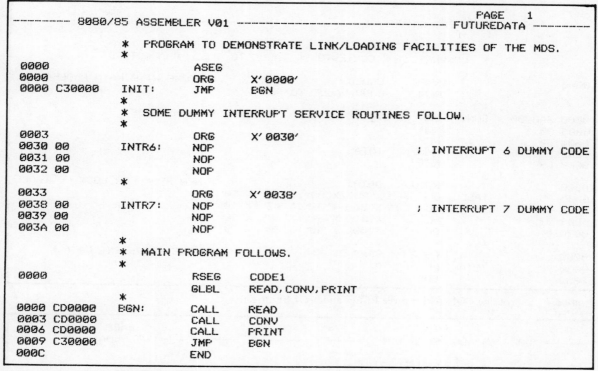

```
------------- 8080/85 ASSEMBLER V01 ----------------------------- PAGE    1
                                                                 FUTUREDATA -------------
                *    PROGRAM TO DEMONSTRATE LINK/LOADING FACILITIES OF THE MDS.
                *
0000                            ASEG
0000                            ORG       X'0000'
0000 C30000    INIT:            JMP       BGN
                *
                *    SOME DUMMY INTERRUPT SERVICE ROUTINES FOLLOW.
                *
0003                            ORG       X'0030'
0030 00        INTR6:           NOP                              ; INTERRUPT 6 DUMMY CODE
0031 00                         NOP
0032 00                         NOP
                *
0033                            ORG       X'0038'
0038 00        INTR7:           NOP                              ; INTERRUPT 7 DUMMY CODE
0039 00                         NOP
003A 00                         NOP
                *
                *    MAIN PROGRAM FOLLOWS.
                *
0000                            RSEG      CODE1
                                GLBL      READ,CONV,PRINT
                *
0000 CD0000    BGN:             CALL      READ
0003 CD0000                     CALL      CONV
0006 CD0000                     CALL      PRINT
0009 C30000                     JMP       BGN
000C                            END
```

Figure 6.2   The main program with an ASEG, GLBL and RSEG directive

```
------------- 8080/85 ASSEMBLER V01 ----------------------------- PAGE    1
                                                                 FUTUREDATA -------------
                *    SUBROUTINE READ
                *    READS AN 8-BIT NUMBER FROM THE ADC AND STORES IN 'VALUE'.
                *
0000                            RSEG      CODE2          ; STORED WITH MAIN PROGRAM
                                GLBL      READ,VALUE
                *
0000 00        READ:            NOP                      ; DUMMY CODE HERE
0001 00                         NOP
0002 00                         NOP
0003 C9                         RET
                *
0000                            RSEG      RAM1           ; TRANSIENT DATA
0000           VALUE:           DS        1
0001                            END
```

Figure 6.3   Subroutine PRINT with two RSEG and a GLBL directive

relocation information in the object code file will inform the linker of which subroutine was called so that the proper second and third bytes of the instruction can be entered.

The Futuredata linker actually combines the functions of LINK and LOCATE. When the four modules had been assembled, the linker

```
                                                        PAGE   1
------------ 8080/85 ASSEMBLER V01 ----------------------------- FUTUREDATA ----------

            *   SUBROUTINE CONV
            *   CONVERTS THE CONTENTS OF VALUE TO 4 BCD CHARACTERS.
            *
0000               RSEG     CODE3                ; STORE WITH MAIN PROGRAM
                   GLBL     CONV,VALUE,TOTAL
            *
0000 3A0000  CONV: LDA      VALUE                ; DUMMY CODE
0003 00            NOP
0004 00            NOP
0005 220000        SHLD     TOTAL
0008 C9            RET
            *
0000               RSEG     DATA1                ; NEW PROM FOR LOOK-UP TABLE
0000 25      TABLE: DC      X'25',X'00',X'12',X'50'
0004 06            DC       X'06',X'30',X'03',X'10'
0008 01            DC       X'01',X'60',X'00',X'80'
000C 00            DC       X'00',X'40',X'00',X'20'
            *
0000               RSEG     RAM2                 ; MORE TRANSIENT DATA
0000         TOTAL: DS      2
0002               END
```

Figure 6.4   Subroutine CONV with three RSEG and a GLBL directive

```
                                                        PAGE   1
------------ 8080/85 ASSEMBLER V01 ----------------------------- FUTUREDATA ----------

            *  SUBROUTINE PRINT
            *   PRINTS THE BCD CHARACTERS STORED IN TOTAL AND TOTAL+1.
            *
0000               RSEG  CODE4                    ; ADD TO EXISTING MAIN PROGRAM
                   GLBL  PRINT,TOTAL,PCHAR,NEWL
            *
0000 2A0000  PRINT: LHLD  TOTAL                   ; DUMMY CODE
0003 00            NOP
0004 00            NOP
0005 CD0000        CALL   PCHAR
0008 CD0100        CALL   NEWL
000B C9            RET
            *
0000               RSEG  LIBRY1                   ; CONSOLE I/O ROUTINES SEPARATE
0000 C9      PCHAR: RET
0001 C9      NEWL  RET
0002               END
```

Figure 6.5   Subroutine PRINT with two RSEG and a GLBL directive

was called by entering JL (jump-to-linker). After some preamble, the linker prompts for the names of the relocatable object code files which have to be linked and then for the name of an absolute code file which will contain the linked/relocated modules. It then prompts for the names of the relocatable segments contained in the input files and the absolute address to which the linked segments should be relocated. If we consider just the RAM and CODE segments of our program, the operator would supply this information in the form:

```
#ORG    X'C800'     -origin for relocation
RAM1                -segments to be linked
RAM2                -at that origin
#ORG    X'1100'     -linking CODEn segments
CODE1               -to execute at 1100H onwards
CODE2
CODE3
CODE4
```

When all the segments have been named in this way, the linker prints a memory map (Figure 6.6) showing the name of every RSEG, the input file it was read from, its absolute starting address and its length in bytes. (Notice that we have given our relocatable object code files the .R extension.) It may also be commanded to provide a linking reference list as shown in Figure 6.7. This shows the name of every disk file from which an RSEG was read, the name of every RSEG, its starting address and length, and all the global references. The entry point is the address at which program execution will begin.

6.7   Software/hardware testing in the MDS

When all the modules have been linked together, the next step is to test the complete program. The system debugger is called and the executable program is loaded into memory. At this stage the individual modules and the complete program have all been tested, but probably not at their eventual execution addresses. Our first concern is therefore to check that the modules have been properly linked. We can do this very easily by displaying the linked program on the console using the debugger D command.

Since the program is eventually intended to run in a standalone microprocessor system, the next important requirement is to check that the system hardware and software are properly integrated. The MDS in-circuit emulator (ICE) is designed for just this purpose. A cable links the MDS with a connector which plugs into the micro-processor socket in the target system. With this connection made, it is as though the full MDS debugging facility is encapsulated in the connector. We can, for example, execute our program in the MDS but run the system from the on-board clock. In this way the clock repetition rate and its rise and fall times can all be checked. Next we might execute our program in the MDS but direct I/O requests to ports in the target system and, later, have one part of the program executing in the MDS while another executes in the target system. Gradually more and more of the target system is brought into service, in much the same way as program modules were added to an expanding software package, until eventually the MDS is eliminated. At that point the program is committed to one or more EPROMs

```
                                                        PAGE    1
-------------- LINKAGE EDITOR V01 ------------------------ FUTUREDATA --------

ADDR   RSEG      FILE       LENGTH

C800   RAM1      READ.R     0001
C801   RAM2      CONV.R     0002
1100   CODE1     ADC.R      000C
110C   CODE2     READ.R     0004
1110   CODE3     CONV.R     0009
1119   CODE4     PRINT.R    000C
1200   DATA1     CONV.R     0010
8000   LIBRY1    PRINT.R    0002
```

Figure 6.6 The linker memory map

```
                                                        PAGE    2
-------------- LINKAGE EDITOR V01 ------------------------ FUTUREDATA --------


FILE         RSEG      ADDR LENGTH
ADC.R        CODE1     1100 000C

             GLOBALS
             CODE1     1100


FILE         RSEG      ADDR LENGTH
READ.R       CODE2     110C 0004
             RAM1      C800 0001

             GLOBALS
             CODE2     110C      RAM1    C800    READ    110C    VALUE   C800


FILE         RSEG      ADDR LENGTH
CONV.R       CODE3     1110 0009
             DATA1     1200 0010
             RAM2      C801 0002

             GLOBALS
             CODE3     1110      CONV    1110    DATA1   1200    RAM2    C801
             TOTAL     C801


FILE         RSEG      ADDR LENGTH
PRINT.R      CODE4     1119 000C
             LIBRY1    8000 0002

             GLOBALS
             CODE4     1119      LIBRY1  8000    NEWL    8001    PCHAR   8000
             PRINT     1119


ENTRY POINT 1100
```

Figure 6.7 The linker reference list

which are then plugged into sockets in the target system. In an MDS, committing program code to EPROM is just another debugger command.

Q6.7

6.8   Using software development stations for system development

In a few sentences we have summarised the essential difference between a microprocessor development system and a software development station. The difference is that the software development station provides no help in debugging a system. Even if we had an assembler which produced relocatable object code and a relocating linking loader, and were able to execute the program in the software development station without overwriting any part of the operating system, we could never be absolutely sure that the program will execute in the same way when running in the target system, because the hardware is different.

Loading program into EPROM from a software development station is not difficult. There are usually several EPROM programmers which are compatible with the more common software development stations and using them is no more complicated than issuing simple monitor commands and then operating a PROGRAM push-button. Debugging the target system from then on, however, is much more difficult.

On reflection, of course, this is not unexpected. An MDS will probably cost at least five times as much as a software development station, so it would be unreasonable to expect them to provide comparable facilities. So long as we appreciate the limitations of a software development station in system, as opposed to software, design it can be used in many more interesting projects.

Questions

6.1   Explain the purpose of the CP/M LOAD utility.

6.2   Explain the need for relocating and linking object code modules when developing software for standalone microprocessor systems.

6.3   Explain hos assemblers which produce relocatable object code differ from assemblers which produce absolute object code.

6.4   From your knowledge of the 8080 instruction set, list those instructions which may be changed when object code is relocated by a relocatable loader.

6.5   State the main reasons for having different location counters during assembly.

6.6   State the difference between entry points and external address references in program modules, and describe how the Intel and Futuredata assemblers provide for both.

6.7 Describe in broad outline the extra facilities provided by an MDS, as compared with a software development station, which are so useful for debugging microprocessor systems.

Chapter 7 Interfacing analogue plant with a microcomputer

Objectives of this chapter *After you have completed studying this chapter you should be able to:*

1 *Appreciate the need for analogue-to-digital and digital-to-analogue converters when analogue plant is monitored and controlled by a digital control system.*
2 *Appreciate and extend the typical hardware and software of these control systems.*
3 *Appreciate how interrupts can often be used to advantage to increase system efficiency.*
4 *Understand the organisation and operation of multichannel data-acquisition systems.*
5 *Understand how an interrupt-driven multichannel data-acquisition system could be implemented with various options.*

7.1 Introduction

Some of the interesting projects we referred to at the end of the last chapter are concerned with the control and monitoring of all sorts of analogue devices and systems. Several example programs have already been presented in which analogue values, assumed to have been read from analogue transducers, have been compared with limits (COMP – Chapters 2, 3 and 4) or printed on the console (ADC – Chapter 5). In this chapter we shall look more closely at analogue-to-digital and digital-to-analogue converters and the way in which they can be used to interface analogue plant with a microcomputer. In doing so we shall use some of the previously developed program modules, and, towards the end of the chapter, we shall see how interrupts could be used in a fairly typical real-time application.

7.2 Digital-to-analogue converters

For the digital systems engineer it is an unavoidable fact of life that the vast majority of natural systems are analogue. Inherent in digital systems is the discontinuity which exists between any two discrete (numerical) values. Analogue systems have no such discontinuities. Temperature, pressure and other physical parameters are continuous even though they may be recorded as sequences of numbers. Consequently when digital systems are employed in the control and monitoring of analogue plant, there is a need for an analogue–digital interface to convert analogue signals to digital format, and a digital–analogue interface to convert digital signals back to analogue. The problem is one of format conversion.

A digital-to-analogue converter (DAC) accepts a digital input and generates from it an analogue output which is directly proportional to the input. Typically the DAC output would drive some other device such as a display, a recorder, a servomotor or a valve. In continuous control applications, the DAC output is equivalent to the output of an analogue potentiometer. It may, for example, be the variable control signal which partially closes a valve or adjusts the speed of a motor. The equivalence between DAC and analogue potentiometer outputs is not complete, however, since the DAC output is not truly continuous. For instance, a 10-bit DAC has only 2^{10} (1,024) discrete analogue output values, whereas a potentiometer has an infinite number. If a continuous DAC output is required, then some filtering or integration will be needed.

The principle of DAC operation is illustrated in Figure 7.1. The digital input which is latched into the input register controls the setting of an array of analogue switches. Each switch connects either V_{ref} or 0 V to one side of a resistor. Since the resistors are weighted in

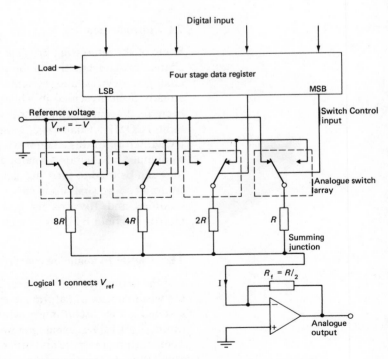

Figure 7.1　A binarily-weighted resistor network DAC

the same ratio as the binary digits which are controlling the switches, the total current flowing into the summing junction of the operational amplifier is directly proportional to the digital input. The operational amplifier converts this digitally controlled current to a voltage in the expectation that a voltage output is required.

With this 4-bit system only 2^4 (16) different output levels can be generated. The minimum output is 0 V and the maximum is:

$$(2^n - 1)FS/2^n \ \text{V}$$

where FS is referred to as the full-scale output, 10 V for example, and n is the number of bits. Notice that this maximum is less than FS by **Q7.1** the analogue equivalent of the least significant bit.

The resolution of a converter is the change in analogue output produced by a change in the least significant bit of the digital input. If the full scale output is fixed, then the resolution is clearly dependent upon the number of bits. It is common therefore to refer to the resolution of analogue-to-digital and digital-to-analogue converters **Q7.2** in terms of the number of bits.

The more common configuration of DAC network is shown in Figure 7.2. This $R/2R$ network has the same transfer function as the

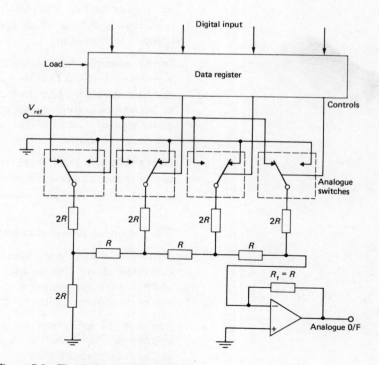

Figure 7.2 The R–$2R$ resistor network

weighted resistor network, i.e. it has the same input-output relationship, but the spread in resistor values of obviously much less. With only two resistor values, the manufacturing difficulties associated with matching widely differing values are avoided.

Typical DACs have 8-, 10- and 12-bit resolution although 14- and 16-bit resolution devices are available. They can be obtained quite easily if the accuracy requirements are not too stringent, and can be interfaced very easily with a microprocessor. To illustrate the ease with which interfacing can be achieved, a DAC will be used as a waveform generator.

7.3   Waveform generation using a DAC

There are two techniques by which a waveform may be generated:

1   Successive ordinate values can be calculated in the program and then sent to the DAC.
2   Ordinate values can be stored in a look-up table and retrieved from it as each new point is displayed.

The first method is suitable if the calculation is relatively straightforward. If it is not, the calculation time places a restriction upon how quickly the waveform can be generated and displayed – calculations of trigonometric functions, for example, may take several milliseconds during which time the display device cannot receive updated information.

In this example the requirement is to generate a simple triangular waveform. An 8-bit DAC is used so that 256 different ordinate values can be generated. The period of the waveform covers the generation of 511 values in total, with a change of direction occurring when the count reaches 0 and FF. The program is listed in Figure 7.3 and the connection diagram is shown in Figure 7.4.

Q7.3

Note that with a DAC there is usually no need to strobe data into the device input register – the port outputs can be connected directly to the analogue switches, if this is possible.

7.4   Analogue-to-digital converters

By adding an analogue comparator and some control logic, the DAC described above can be used as an analogue-to-digital converter (ADC) to convert analogue voltages to their digital equivalents. The system is shown in Figure 7.5.

The control logic may be designed to implement a successive-approximation ADC or a simple counting-type converter. In successive-approximation converters a series of digital values (approximations) are tried and at each stage the DAC output is

```
  1:
  2:
  3:               *   PROGRAM NAME FORM1
  4:               *   ====================
  5:               *
  6:               *   GENERATES A TRIANGULAR WAVEFORM AT THE OUTPUT OF A DAC.
  7:               *
  8:               *                 STRUCTURE
  9:               *                 '''''''''
 10:               *   BEGIN
 11:               *       AMPLITUDE := 0
 12:               *       REPEAT
 13:               *           REPEAT
 14:               *                 SEND AMPLITUDE
 15:               *                 AMPLITUDE := AMPLITUDE + 1
 16:               *           UNTIL AMPLITUDE = 255
 17:               *           REPEAT
 18:               *                 SEND AMPLITUDE
 19:               *                 AMPLITUDE := AMPLITUDE - 1
 20:               *           UNTIL AMPLITUDE = 0
 21:               *       UNTIL INFINITY
 22:               *   END.
 23:               *
 24:               *   OUTPUT PORT NUMBER IS FFH
 25:               *
 26: 00FF =        PORT:   EQU     0FFH
 27:               *
 28: 0100                  ORG     0100H           ; RUN UNDER CP/M
 29: 0100 AF       BGN:    XRA     A               ; AMPLITUDE = 0
 30:               *
 31:               *   GENERATE RISING SLOPE
 32:               *
 33: 0101 D3FF     REPT1:  OUT     PORT            ; SEND AMPLITUDE
 34: 0103 3C               INR     A               ; AMPLITUDE := AMPLITUDE + 1
 35: 0104 FEFF             CPI     0FFH            ; AMPLITUDE = 255 ?
 36: 0106 C20101   UNTIL1: JNZ     REPT1           ; REPEAT UNTIL YES
 37:               *
 38:               *   GENERATE FALLING SLOPE
 39:               *
 40: 0109 D3FF     REPT2:  OUT     PORT            ; SEND AMPLITUDE
 41: 010B 3D               DCR     A               ; AMPLITUDE := AMPLITUDE - 1
 42: 010C C20901   UNTIL2: JNZ     REPT2           ; REPEAT UNTIL AMPLITUDE = 0
 43: 010F C30101           JMP     REPT1           ; THEN START AGAIN
 44: 0112                  END

A>
```

Figure 7.3 A program that uses a DAC to generate a triangular waveform

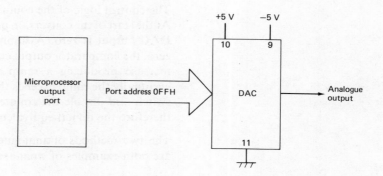

Figure 7.4 Connection diagram for the waveform generation programs. The DAC input is permanently enabled so that its output changes as a new value is sent to the output port

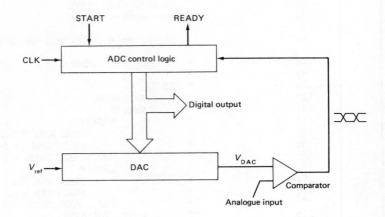

Figure 7.5 Showing how an ADC can be made from a DAC, an analogue comparator and some extra logic

compared with the analogue input. The result of that comparison indicates whether the trial value is too much or too little and a new number is tried. As the conversion proceeds the DAC input approximates more and more closely to the numerical equivalent of the analogue input. At the end of the conversion, the DAC digital input, and consequently its analogue output, are the best approximation which can be made to the amplitude of the analogue input.

When the conversion begins the first trial value is a 1 in the most significant bit position and zeros elsewhere, which produces a DAC output voltage of half full scale. The comparator output therefore indicates whether the analogue input is greater than or less than half full scale. If greater than half full scale the most significant bit is retained as a 1 but otherwise it is reset. In any event the next most significant bit is then turned on and a decision is made as to whether this should be a 1 or a 0. As the conversion proceeds every other bit of the digital input is tried and either retained or rejected. At the end of the conversion the DAC input is the ADC output. Figure 7.6

Q7.4 illustrates the procedure.

The control logic of the counting-type ADC is shown in Figure 7.7. At the start of the conversion process the counter is cleared so that the DAC output is zero. Assuming an analogue input of greater than zero, the comparator output enables the counter and so the count will increase producing a ramp voltage at the DAC output. When eventually the ramp exceeds the analogue input the comparator will switch and disable the counter. The number held in the counter is therefore the digital equivalent of the analogue input.

The two methods of analogue-to-digital conversion described here are both examples of what are known as direct voltage comparison

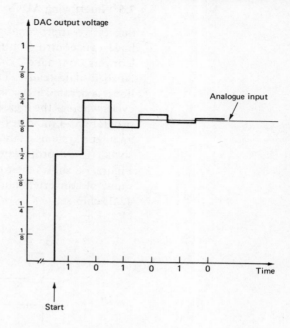

Figure 7.6 The conversion technique of a successive-approximation ADC

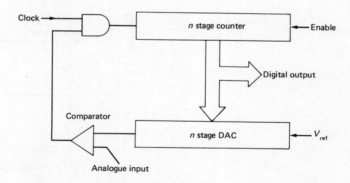

Figure 7.7 A counting-type ADC

methods. Other methods are voltage-to-time converters, which include the dual-slope technique commonly employed in digital volt-meters, and voltage-to-frequency converters. Although discussion of these methods is outside the scope of this book, they are well covered in references, some of which are listed at the end of the chapter.

7.5   Interfacing ADCs

Successive-approximation and counting-type converters typically have two control/status lines. The control line is usually labelled 'convert command', or something similar, and the status line is labelled 'data ready'. The signal imposed on the convert command line is generated in the user program to start the ADC on a conversion cycle, whereas the logic level on the data ready line is read by the user program and indicates that the ADC has finished. In our previous analogue systems example (Chapter 5) we called these lines, and the signals they propagate, CONVERT and READY, respectively. Figure 7.8 shows their relationship for the Analog Devices ADC-H range of converters and a system which uses the Ferranti ZN425E/424E chip set.

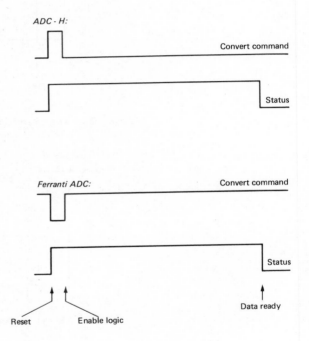

Figure 7.8   Typical ADC handshake signals

When relatively slow converters are used in analogue control/monitoring systems, the microprocessor, having started a conversion, may spend a significant amount of time waiting for the READY condition to become true. If there is other useful work to be done, it may be more sensible to connect the ADC READY line to the microprocessor interrupt input through some additional logic, and let the ADC interrupt when it has a value ready. This would free the microprocessor for other programmed tasks during the conversion period and eliminate the waiting time. However, the two criteria which must be considered when contemplating interrupt working are, whether there is other work to do, and then, whether there is sufficient time to do it in. If the ADC is sufficiently fast, the use of interrupts can actually reduce system efficiency.

7.6 Software-controlled analogue-to-digital conversion

The control logic of a successive-approximation ADC is required to generate a series of DAC inputs which progressively approximate closer and closer to a digital representation of the analogue input. If high speed is not a consideration, this control logic can be simulated in a program. All that is then required to make an ADC is a DAC and an analogue comparator. The technique is illustrated in Figure 7.9.

Conversion begins when a 1-to-0 change is detected at a START input. After that, the program generates the first number (approximation) and sends this to the DAC which is connected to an output port. A delay is then introduced to allow the comparator sufficient time to register the effect of this new number. (The comparator circuit used here includes a cheap, general-purpose 741-type operational amplifier and is consequently slow to operate.) If the comparator output is subsequently found to be a 1 this indicates that

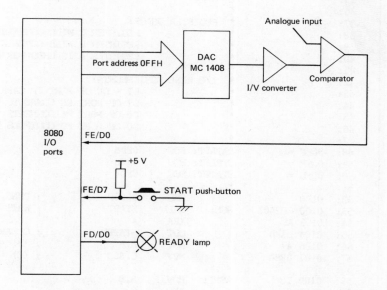

Figure 7.9 Hardware used with the software-controlled analogue-to-digital conversion programs

Figure 7.10

```
 1:
 2:
 3:                    *   PROGRAM NAME SOFT1
 4:                    *   ===================
 5:                    *
 6:                    *   THIS PROGRAM IS A SUCCESSIVE APPROXIMATION CONVERSION ROUTINE.
 7:                    *   IT IMITATES, IN SOFTWARE, THE CONTROL LOGIC OF A SUCCESSIVE
 8:                    *   APPROXIMATION ADC.
 9:                    *
10:                    *   THE TECHNIQUE AND THE HARDWARE USED ARE DESCRIBED IN THE TEXT.
11:                    *
12:                    *                   STRUCTURE
13:                    *                   :::::::::
14:                    *   BEGIN
15:                    *       REPEAT
16:                    *               WAIT FOR A START SIGNAL (SUBROUTINE)
17:                    *               EXTINGUISH THE READY LAMP
18:                    *               TRIAL := 80H
19:                    *               VALUE := 0
20:                    *               REPEAT   (* UNTIL TRIAL = 0 *)
21:                    *                       VALUE := VALUE + TRIAL
22:                    *                       SEND VALUE
23:                    *                       WAIT FOR COMPARATOR (SUBROUTINE)
24:                    *                       READ COMPARATOR OUTPUT
25:                    *                       IF COMPARATOR OUTPUT = 0 (* TOO LITTLE *) THEN
26:                    *                               DO NOTHING
27:                    *                       ELSE
28:                    *                               VALUE := VALUE - TRIAL
29:                    *                               SEND VALUE
30:                    *                       ENDIF
31:                    *                       TRIAL := TRIAL SHR 1   ( SHIFT 1 PLACE RIGHT )
32:                    *               UNTIL TRIAL = 0
33:                    *               LIGHT THE READY LAMP
34:                    *       UNTIL INFINITY
35:                    *   END.
36:                    *
37:                    *   REGISTER USAGE:
38:                    *                   REGISTER C WILL CONTAIN 'TRIAL'
39:                    *                   REGISTER B WILL CONTAIN 'VALUE'
40:                    *                   REGISTER A IS USED FOR ALL I/O
41:                    *
42:                    *   I/O LINE ASSIGNMENTS:
43:                    *                   D7 - D0 OF PORT FF CARRY THE DAC INPUT
44:                    *                   D7 OF PORT FE CONNECTS THE START PUSH-BUTTON
45:                    *                   D0 OF PORT FE CONNECTS THE COMPARATOR OUTPUT
46:                    *                   D0 OF PORT FD CONTROLS THE READY LAMP
47:                    *
48:  00FF =            DATAPT: EQU     0FFH
49:  00FE =            CTRLPT: EQU     0FEH
50:  00FD =            STATPT: EQU     0FDH
51:                    *
52:  0100                      ORG     0100H          ; RUNS UNDER CP/M
53:  0100 CD2A01       BGN:    CALL    START          ; WAIT FOR START SIGNAL
54:  0103 AF                   XRA     A
55:  0104 D3FD                 OUT     STATPT         ; CLEAR READY LAMP
56:  0106 47                   MOV     B,A            ; (B) = VALUE = 0
57:  0107 0E80                 MVI     C,80H          ; (C) = TRIAL = 80H
58:                    *
59:  0109 78           REPT:   MOV     A,B
60:  010A 81                   ADD     C
61:  010B 47                   MOV     B,A            ; VALUE := VALUE + TRIAL
62:  010C D3FF                 OUT     DATAPT         ; SEND VALUE
63:  010E CD3901                CALL    WAIT           ; WAIT FOR COMPARATOR
64:  0111 DBFE                 IN      CTRLPT
65:  0113 E601        IF1:     ANI     01H            ; CHECK COMPARATOR OUPUT
66:  0115 CA1D01       IF0:    JZ      ENIF           ; IF 0, DO NOTHING          (Continued)
```

Figure 7.10 continued

```
67:   0118 78      ELSE:    MOV    A,B
68:   0119 91               SUB    C
69:   011A 47               MOV    B,A          ; VALUE := VALUE - TRIAL
70:   011B D3FF             OUT    DATAPT       ; SEND VALUE
71:   011D 79      ENIF:    MOV    A,C
72:   011E 0F               RRC
73:   011F 4F               MOV    C,A          ; TRIAL := TRIAL / 2
74:   0120 D20901  UNTIL:   JNC    REPT         ; REPEAT UNTIL TRIAL = 0
75:                *
76:   0123 3E01             MVI    A,01H
77:   0125 D3FD             OUT    STATPT       ; LIGHT READY LAMP
78:   0127 C30001           JMP    BGN          ; REPEAT UNTIL INFINITY
79:                *
80:                *  SUBROUTINE START
81:                *  ================
82:                *
83:                *  THIS IS THE SAME SUBROUTINE AS WAS USED IN A PREVIOUS ADC PROGRAM.
84:                *  IT READS FROM A START PUSH-BUTTON AND RETURNS CONTROL TO THE MAIN
85:                *  PROGRAM ONLY IF THE PUSH-BUTTON IS FIRST RELEASED (LOGIC 1 READ)
86:                *  AND THEN PRESSED ( LOGIC 0 READ).
87:                *
88:                *               STRUCTURE
89:                *               '''''''''
90:                *  BEGIN
91:                *      REPEAT
92:                *           READ START INPUT
93:                *      UNTIL START = 1
94:                *      REPEAT
95:                *           READ START INPUT
96:                *      UNTIL START =0
97:                *  END
98:                *
99:   012A DBFE    START:   IN     CTRLPT       ; READ FROM CONTROL PORT
100:  012C E680             ANI    80H          ; CHECK START INPUT
101:  012E CA2A01  UNTIL2:  JZ     START        ; REPEAT UNTIL START = 1
102:  0131 DBFE    REPT3:   IN     CTRLPT       ; READ AGAIN
103:  0133 E680             ANI    80H          ; RE-CHECK START BIT
104:  0135 C23101  UNTIL3:  JNZ    REPT3        ; REPEAT UNTIL START = 0
105:  0138 C9               RET
106:                *
107:                *  SUBROUTINE WAIT
108:                *  ===============
109:                *
110:                *  THIS IS INCLUDED SO THAT THE SLOW-TO-OPERATE COMPARATOR HAS
111:                *  SUFFICIENT TIME TO REGISTER THE EFFECT OF THE MOST RECENTLY
112:                *  TRIED VALUE.
113:                *
114:                *               STRUCTURE
115:                *               '''''''''
116:                *  BEGIN
117:                *      READ DELAYPARAMETER
118:                *      REPEAT
119:                *           DELAYPARAMETER := DELAYPARAMETER - 1
120:                *      UNTIL DELAYPARAMETER = 0
121:                *  END.
122:                *
123:  1000 =        DLYPAR:  EQU    1000H
124:                *
125:  0139 110010   WAIT:    LXI    D,DLYPAR     ; READ DELAYPARAMETER
126:  013C 1D       REPT4:   DCR    E
127:  013D C23C01            JNZ    REPT4
128:  0140 15                DCR    D            ; DELAYPARAMETER := DELAYPARAMETER - 1
129:  0141 C23C01  UNTIL4:   JNZ    REPT4        ; REPEAT UNTIL DELAYPARAMETER = 0
130:  0144 C9                RET
131:                *
132:  0145                   END
```

Figure 7.10   A software-controlled successive-approximation ADC

the approximation is too large and the bit is changed to a 0, otherwise it stays at a 1. As explained before, the next step is to try the next most significant bit and continue in this fashion until all bits have been tried and tested. The program and its structure are listed in Figure 7.10.

Although this system works well enough, you will appreciate that it should only be used when costs have to be cut to a minimum and speed is of little or no importance. For most of the time the program is simulating the action of a standard integrated circuit. In many applications the use of a dedicated ADC would significantly increase

Q7.5   the rate at which data could be acquired.

7.7   The need for delay routines

Delay routines were introduced in Chapter 5 as an example of a REPEAT-UNTIL structure, and the technique was used in the previous program to allow a slow-speed comparator time to operate. Many of the programs which we study from now on will need delay routines to provide variable time delays between successive programmed actions. Very often, accurate time delays are not needed – the requirement is for a brief pause before continuing. Even in situations like this, however, we need to be sure that the pause has not been too brief, or unnecessarily extended. Some understanding of how to generate predictable time delays is therefore important.

Delays are produced by counting. The standard REPEAT-UNTIL format of a delay routine is:

```
Load a number into a register
REPEAT
        Decrement the register contents
UNTIL the register contains zero
```

Quite clearly the time spent in executing the loop depends on two things:

1   The number initially loaded into the register.
2   The time taken to subtract 1 from the contents of a register and then test for zero.

The first of these factors is controlled by the programmer while the second is a function of the system in which the program runs.

In 8080, 8085 and Z80 systems, instruction execution times are expressed as a number of T-states, or just states. A state is the period of the master clock which synchronises all activity in the micro-processor. One state is one clock cycle. In the delay routine two instructions, DCR and JNZ, are mainly responsible for the delay. The DCR instruction decrements the contents of a register and the

JNZ tests the Z flag following the DCR. If the Z flag is not set (register does not contain zero), program control jumps back to decrement the register once more.

How then can the programmer, knowing the required delay, choose a number to store in the register?

First consider the execution times of DCR and JNZ instructions. The master clock frequency in our system, a North Star Horizon micro-computer, is 4 MHz which means that one state lasts for 0.25 μs. The DCR and JNZ instructions execute in 4 and 10 states, respectively, so that, running through the two-instruction sequence just once, will take $14 \times 0.25 = 3.5$ μs. Since the number is decremented before the first test for zero is made, the starting number which produces the longest delay is 00H (256 decimal) and the number corresponding with the shortest delay is 01H. Consequently the maximum delay is,

$$256 \times 14 \times 0.25 = 896 \text{ μs}$$

If longer delays than this are needed, we must, somehow, start with a larger number or add to the number of clock cycles inside the loop by inserting NOP instructions between the DCR and JNZ. For every added NOP, we increase the number of clock cycles by 4.

If we decide to use a larger number it will have to go in a register pair and the instruction sequence will need to be:

1   Store a 16-bit number in a register pair.
2   Decrement the register pair.
3   Jump to 2 if not zero.

Unfortunately this will not work because, when the contents of an 8080 register pair are decremented to zero, the Z flag is not affected. Consequently the JNZ instruction will not test the proper condition. The way round this problem, once the register pair has been initialised, is to treat the pair as separate 8-bit registers. We already know that when the contents of an 8-bit register are reduced to zero by decrementing, the Z flag is set, so our new delay routine will be programmed as:

1   Store a 16-bit number in a register pair.
2   Decrement the least significant byte. (4)
3   Jump is not zero to 2. (10)
4   Decrement the most significant byte. (4)
5   Jump if not zero to 2. (10)
6   Stop.

The numbers in brackets are the number of clock cycles needed to execute each instruction. If we refer to the least significant byte of the 16-bit number as LSCONS and the most significant byte as MSCONS (both having maximum values of 256), the total time to execute steps

2 to 5 is:

$$\left[\begin{array}{l} (\text{LSCONS} \times 14) + (\text{MSCONS} \times 14) \\ \qquad + (\text{MSCONS} - 1)(256 \times 14) \end{array} \right] \times 0.25 \; \mu s$$

For very accurate time delays we will have to add the time taken to load the register pair, call the subroutine and return, but in most cases these additional times will be negligible compared with the loop execution time.

Using this technique the maximum delay which can be produced in a North Star Horizon is 0.23 s, which corresponds with a hexadecimal constant of 0000. A delay constant of 0101 produces delay of 7 µs. For even longer delays than 0.23 s, at 24-bit (3-byte) number will be needed and this will be decremented until all 24 bits are 0. There is theoretically no limit to the amount of delay we can produce.

Q7.6

7.8   A single-channel data-logging system

The ADC which will be used in the following programs is shown in Figure 7.11. Although slow, it can be constructed for a few pounds, and with it we can study a number of interesting analogue interfacing applications. Of immediate concern is a single-channel monitoring system.

A single analogue input is periodically sampled and the measured value compared with pre-set high and low limits. As each sample is taken the value is printed on the console and if an alarm condition is detected, a high or low alarm lamp is flashed. The operation of the program can be summarised as:

1   Read an 8-bit value from an ADC output.
2   Convert to a BCD number in the range 0.00 and 5.00 V.
3   Print the BCD number on the console.
4   Compare the binary value with high and low limits.
5   Flash an appropriate alarm lamp if either limit is exceeded.

It is clear that our previously developed subroutines READ, CONV, PRINT and COMP are directly applicable here. The only new requirement is for a subroutine called FLASH which will turn one or other of the alarm lamps on and off in the event of an out-of-limits value being read. There are also, however, some minor modifications to be made to READ and PRINT.

The new program specification states that, when an alarm condition exists, the value should be printed and an alarm lamp should be flashed once. Without waiting for the START signal, a new measurement cycle should begin immediately and, if the alarm condition persists, the new, but still out-of-limits, value should overwrite the old (no intervening line feed) and the lamp should be flashed once

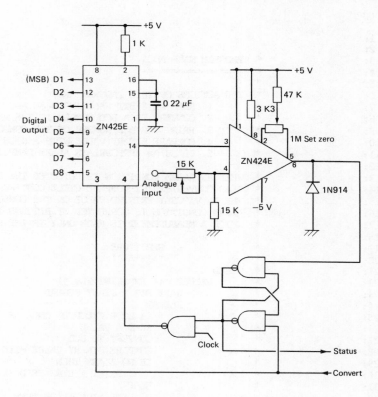

Figure 7.11   An ADC using the Ferranti ZN425E/424E chip set

again. In this way, the lamp and the displayed value flash continually until the fault is corrected. At that point, a line feed is printed and the next, within limits, value is displayed on a new line. Operation is now back to normal with the next sample taken only when the START condition is satisfied.

The new main program, without the subroutines, is called ADC3 and is listed in Figure 7.12. The supporting hardware is shown in Figure 7.13. Notice that the high and low alarm lamps are connected to D7 and D6 of output port number 0FEH. On entry to the subroutine FLASH, listed in Figure 7.14 with its delay routine, register A has one or other of these bits set depending upon which alarm condition exists.

Q7.7

7.9   Interrupt-driven ADC control programs

The technique in which a program reads continually the logic level on the ADC READY line is generally referred to as polling, although the term is more usually applied in systems in which service demands

Figure 7.12

```
 1:
 2:
 3:                    *   PROGRAM NAME ADC3.
 4:                    *   ================
 5:                    *
 6:                    *   THE ACTIONS OF THIS PROGRAM ARE:
 7:                    *        1. READ AN 8-BIT VALUE FROM AN ADC OUTPUT
 8:                    *        2. CONVERT TO A BCD NUMBER IN THE RANGE 0.00 TO 5.00
 9:                    *        3. PRINT THE BCD NUMBER ON THE CONSOLE
10:                    *        4. COMPARE BINARY VALUE WITH A HIGH AND LOW LIMIT
11:                    *        5. FLASH AN APPROPRIATE ALARM LAMP IF EITHER LIMIT EXCEEDED
12:                    *
13:                    *   WHEN AN ALARM CONDITION IS DETECTED THE PROGRAM REPEATS THE
14:                    *   READ-CONVERT-PRINT-COMPARE CYCLE CONTINUOUSLY, OVERWRITTING
15:                    *   THE PREVIOUSLY PRINTED VALUE ON THE CONSOLE SCREEN. WHEN THE
16:                    *   ALARM CONDITION IS CORRECTED IT RETURNS TO THE MAIN LOOP IN
17:                    *   WHICH A MEASUREMENT IS MADE ONLY IF THE START INPUT IS ACTIVATED.
18:                    *
19:                    *                   STRUCTURE
20:                    *                   '''''''''
21:                    *   BEGIN
22:                    *      REPEAT   (* INDEFINITELY *)
23:                    *           WAIT FOR A START SIGNAL
24:                    *           REPEAT
25:                    *                (* LOOP EXECUTED ONCE IF NO ALARM, CONTINUALLY IF ALARM *)
26:                    *                READ A VALUE
27:                    *                CONVERT TO BCD
28:                    *                COMPARE BINARY VALUE WITH LIMITS
29:                    *                IF NO ALARM THEN
30:                    *                     PRINT A LINE FEED (START NEW LINE)
31:                    *                ELSE
32:                    *                     IF HIGH ALARM THEN
33:                    *                          FLASH HIGH ALARM LAMP ONCE
34:                    *                     ELSE
35:                    *                          FLASH LOW ALARM LAMP ONCE
36:                    *                     ENDIF
37:                    *                ENDIF
38:                    *                PRINT CARRAIGE RETURN
39:                    *                PRINT BCD VALUE
40:                    *           UNTIL NO ALARM
41:                    *      UNTIL INFINITY
42:                    *   END.
43:                    *
44:                    *   NOTE - THE FOLLOWING PREVIOUSLY DEVELOPED SUBROUTINES ARE USED:
45:                    *        1.  START IS AS LISTED IN FIG. 5.11
46:                    *        2.  READ IS AS LISTED IN FIG. 5.11 WITH START DELETED
47:                    *        3.  CONV IS AS LISTED IN FIG. 5.13
48:                    *        4.  PRINT IS AS IN FIG. 5.16 WITH THE CALL NEWL DELETED
49:                    *        5.  COMP IS AS LISTED IN FIG. 4.19
50:                    *
51: 0100                       ORG     0100H              ; RUNS UNDER CP/M
52: 0100 CD4601  BGN:  CALL    START              ; WAIT FOR START PUSHBUTTON
53: 0103 CD4701  REP:  CALL    READ               ; READ A VALUE
54: 0106 CD4801        CALL    CONV               ; CONVERT TO BCD
55: 0109 CD4901        CALL    COMP               ; COMPARE BINARY WITH LIMITS
56:                    *                                    (Continued)
```

Figure 7.12 continued

```
57:                         *  ON RETURN FROM COMP, REGISTER B CONTAINS AN ALARM CODE
58:                         *
59:  010C 78                        MOV     A,B             ; GET ALARM CODE
60:  010D 324201                    STA     ALMCDE          ; SAVE IT TEMPORARILY
61:  0110 FE00      IFALRM: CPI     00H             ; ANY ALARM ?
62:  0112 C21D01                    JNZ     ALARM           ; ALARM IF ALMCDE NOT ZERO
63:                         *
64:  0115 060A      NOALRM: MVI     B,0AH           ; LINE FEED CODE
65:  0117 CD4B01                    CALL    PCHAR           ; PRINT IT
66:  011A C32F01                    JMP     CRET            ; THEN A CARRAIGE RETURN
67:                         *
68:  011D FE02      ALARM:  CPI     02H             ; CHECK FOR HIGH ALARM
69:  011F CA2A01                    JZ      HALRM           ; FLASH HI-ALARM LAMP
70:                         *
71:  0122 3E41      LALRM:  MVI     A,41H           ; ELSE, MUST BE LO-ALARM
72:  0124 CD4C01                    CALL    FLASH           ; FLASH THE LAMP
73:  0127 C32F01                    JMP     CRET            ; RETURN CARRAIGE
74:                         *
75:  012A 3E81      HALRM:  MVI     A,81H
76:  012C CD4C01                    CALL    FLASH           ; FLASH LAMP
77:                         *
78:  012F 060D      CRET:   MVI     B,0DH           ; CARRAIGE RETURN CODE
79:  0131 CD4B01                    CALL    PCHAR           ; PRINT IT
80:  0134 CD4A01                    CALL    PRINT           ; PRINT BCD CHARACTERS
81:                         *
82:  0137 3A4201    TSTALM: LDA     ALMCDE          ; GET ALARM CODE BACK
83:  013A FE00              CPI     00H             ; WAS THERE AN ALARM ?
84:  013C C20301            JNZ     REP             ; YES, REPEAT CYCLE
85:  013F C30001            JMP     BGN             ; NO, WAIT FOR START SIGNAL
86:                         *
87:  0142          ALMCDE: DS      1               ; TEMPORARY STORAGE FOR ALARM CODE
88:                         *
89:                         *  DEFINING LIMITS AND VALUE LOCATION HERE.
90:                         *  FOR COMP TO WORK PROPERLY VALUE, HLMT AND LLMT MUST BE SUCCESSIVE
91:                         *  MEMORY LOCATIONS. THE DEFINITIONS ARE DELETED FROM COMP.
92:                         *  LIMITS ARE CHOSEN AS FOLLOWS:
93:                         *      HIGH LIMIT = 4.00 VOLTS
94:                         *      LOW LIMIT  = 1.00 VOLTS
95:                         *  BOTH ARE APPROXIMATE.
96:                         *
97:  0143          VALUE:  DS      1               ; RESERVED FOR BINARY VALUE
98:  0144 CC       HLMT:   DB      0CCH            ; APPROXIMATELY 4.00 VOLTS
99:  0145 33       LLMT:   DB      033H            ; APPROXIMATELY 1.00 VOLTS
100:                        *
101:                        *  EXTERNAL REFERENCES DEFINED HERE TO SURPRESS ERROR MESSAGES.
102:                        *  THEY ARE DELETED WHEN MODULES ARE LINKED TOGETHER.
103:                        *
104: 0146 C9       START:  RET                     ; DUMMY SUBROUTINE CODE
105: 0147 C9       READ:   RET
106: 0148 C9       CONV:   RET
107: 0149 C9       COMP:   RET
108: 014A C9       PRINT:  RET
109: 014B C9       PCHAR:  RET
110: 014C C9       FLASH:  RET                     ; LISTED IN FIGURE 7.14
111:                        *
112: 014D                  END
```

Figure 7.12   The main, ADC3, program

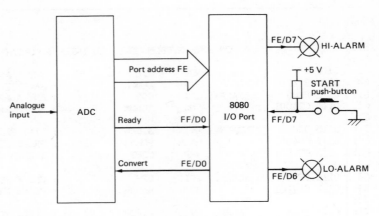

Figure 7.13   Hardware for the ADC3 program

from a number of separate input lines have to be satisfied. The program polls the READY input and when it is logically true, a value is read. The other way of servicing a peripheral device, such as an ADC, is to use the interrupt capability of the microprocessor. A conversion is initiated from the user program or some external timing circuit, and then the ADC is left to complete its task. When the conversion is complete, the ADC interrupts the executing program and a new value is read and processed just as before. Before discussing this type of system, however, it may be helpful to remind you of the way in which an 8080 handles interrupts.

Interrupt handling in the 8080

Interrupt requests from 8080 peripherals are only granted if the interrupt enable flag, INTE, is set. Following a system reset, the flag will be reset, and it can only be set by executing an enable interrupts (EI) instruction. A peripheral can then interrupt the executing program by taking the processor INT line high. When that happens, the processor completes the current instruction, resets the interrupt enable flag, and then, instead of fetching the next programmed instruction, it generates an INTA (interrupt acknowledge) signal. In reply, the interrupting peripheral is expected to supply a restart, RST, instruction. As far as the processor is concerned, fetching a restart instruction from a peripheral is no different from fetching the next programmed instruction from memory, except that the contents of the program counter are not incremented – it still contains the next *programmed* instruction address.

Assuming that the instruction supplied is a restart (and it need not be), the processor saves the program counter contents on the stack (as it would for a normal CALL instruction), and then jumps to a restart

```
 1:
 2:
 3:                         *    SUBROUTINE FLASH
 4:                         *    ================
 5:                         *
 6:                         *    ON ENTRY TO THIS SUBROUTINE REGISTER A HAS D6 OR D7
 7:                         *    SET DEPENDING UPON WHICH ALARM LAMP, HI-ALARM OR LO-ALARM
 8:                         *    RESPECTIVELY, IS TO BE FLASHED. IT ALSO HAS D0 SET SINCE THE
 9:                         *    HIGH AND LOW ALARM LAMPS ARE CONNECTED TO THE SAME PORT AS THE ADC
10:                         *    CONVERT LINE. A 1 TO 0 CHANGE ON THIS LINE WOULD START THE ADC OFF
11:                         *    AGAIN.
12:                         *
13:                         *                    STRUCTURE
14:                         *                    '''''''''
15:                         *    BEGIN
16:                         *         LIGHT LAMP
17:                         *         DELAY
18:                         *         EXTINGUISH THE LAMP
19:                         *         DELAY
20:                         *    END.
21:                         *
22:    0000 D3FE            FLASH:  OUT      OUTPRT         ; LIGHT THE LAMP
23:    0002 CD0D00                  CALL     DELAY          ; DELAY
24:    0005 E601                    ANI      01H            ; CLEAR THE LAMP DRIVE BIT
25:    0007 D3FE                    OUT      OUTPRT         ; EXTINGUISH THE LAMP
26:    0009 CD0D00                  CALL     DELAY          ; DELAY
27:    000C C9                      RET
28:                         *
29:    00FE =              OUTPRT: EQU      0FEH           ; LAMP PORT ADDRESS
30:                         *
31:                         *    SUBROUTINE DELAY
32:                         *    ================
33:                         *
34:                         *    STANDARD 16-BIT DELAY ROUTINE WHICH USES D AND E
35:                         *
36:    000D 110010          DELAY:  LXI      D,DLYPAR       ; READ DELAY PARAMETER
37:    0010 1D              AGAIN:  DCR      E
38:    0011 C21000                  JNZ      AGAIN
39:    0014 15                      DCR      D
40:    0015 C21000                  JNZ      AGAIN
41:    0018 C9                      RET
42:                         *
43:    1000 =              DLYPAR: EQU      1000H
44:                         *
45:    0019                        END
```

Figure 7.14   The FLASH and DELAY subroutines

address. The actual destination of that jump is indicated by a 3-bit number imbedded in the restart instruction code itself. Using three bits allows for 8 different restart addresses to be selected – RST0 to RST7 – although it would be somewhat restrictive if these addresses were consecutive. If this were the case, programs which service an interrupting peripheral, called interrupt service routines, could only contain one, 1-byte, instruction. For this reason the restart number is fitted into the restart opcode as shown below:

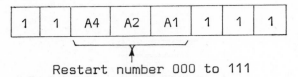

| 1 | 1 | A4 | A2 | A1 | 1 | 1 | 1 |

Restart number 000 to 111

When the processor reads this restart instruction it saves the next programmed instruction address, as already explained, and loads the program counter with:

| 0 | 0 | 0 | 0 | 0 | 0 | 0 | 0 | 0 | 0 | A4 | A2 | A1 | 0 | 0 | 0 |

The next instruction is therefore fetched from hexadecimal address 0, 8, 10, 18, 20, 28, 30, or 38 with seven unoccupied addresses between each restart address. This is sufficient space for very short interrupt service routines, or for a JMP instruction which transfers control to a longer instruction sequence somewhere else in memory. At the end of the interrupt service routine, a RET instruction will reload the program counter with the address of the instruction which would have been executed had the interrupt not occurred. If further interrupts are to be accepted, an EI instruction is programmed just before the RET, and if the interrupt service routine is itself interruptable, the EI instruction is programmed much earlier on in the interrupt service routine.

Peripheral interrupt hardware

There are several 8080-compatible integrated circuits which are designed to interface interrupting peripherals. In our system, the device used is the popular 8212, 8-bit I/O port register which contains an interrupt service request flip-flop. The simplified logic diagram of the 8212 is shown in Figure 7.15.

Although not immediately obvious from the logic diagram, four general observations must be made before considering 8212 applications:

1   When $\overline{\text{CLR}}$ is activated, all eight latches are reset and the service request flip-flop is set.
2   The latch outputs follow the inputs for as long as the clock (CLK) input is high. At the negative-going edge of CLK the input data are latched.
3   The output buffers are enabled when EN is a 1. When EN is 0 the outputs are tristate.
4   The service request flip-flop is reset by the negative-going edge of the strobe input, STB.

When an interrupt-driven I/O system is used, the output of the

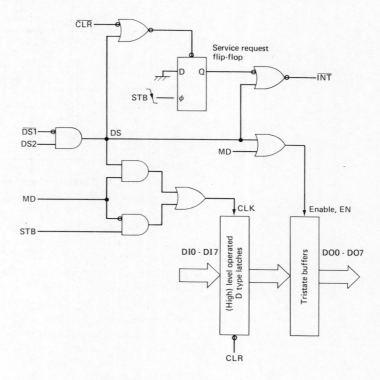

Figure 7.15 The 8212 8-bit I/O port

service request flip-flop is connected, through some extra logic circuitry, to the INT input of the 8080.

The mode of the 8212 is set by the mode (MD) input. If $MD = 0$ the input (to the processor) mode is selected. The logic diagram of the 8212 can now be redrawn as shown in Figure 7.16.

In the input mode the peripheral takes STB high to load data into the D-type latches. At the negative-going edge of STB the service request flip-flop is reset which takes $\overline{INT}$ low, thereby signalling to the processor that the port requires service. In responding to the service request, the processor activates DS2 and $\overline{DS1}$ which enables the tristate buffers and sets the service request flip-flop. At the end of the read cycle $\overline{INT}$ returns high and the transfer is complete. If STB is connected to the V_{cc} supply line (logic 1) then the latches are permanently enabled. The processor can then read input data at any time but interrupt working is never possible since the service request flip-flop must always stay set.

In output mode ($MD = 1$) the 8212 logic diagram can be redrawn as shown in Figure 7.17. For output, we shall use the device as a simple

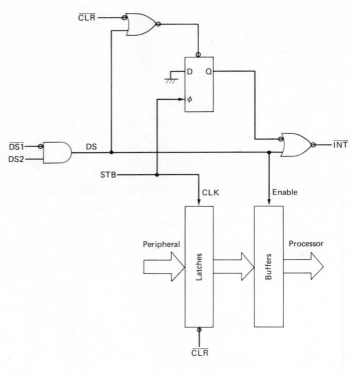

Figure 7.16   The 8212 in input mode (MD = 0)

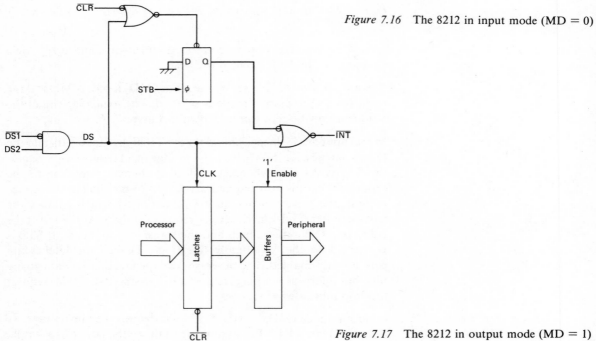

Figure 7.17   The 8212 in output mode (MD = 1)

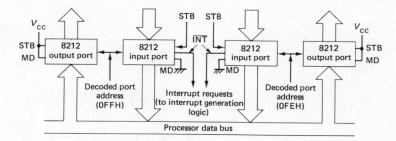

Figure 7.18 The I/O system used for all programs that use interrupts. Port FF interrupt request line corresponds with RST 1 and port FE corresponds with RST 2 (see next figure)

latch with STB connected permanently to logic 1 and $\overline{INT}$ not connected at all. When an OUT instruction is executed, the processor sends data to the port by imposing data on the data bus and the port address code on the lower half of the address bus. Data are then latched into the port register at the end of the OUT instruction when DS changes from 1 to 0.

The 8212 data sheet shows several other ways in which the device may be configured but these need not concern us. For the interrupt service routine examples which follow, our system provides us with four 8212s in total, two connected as input (interrupting) ports and two as output ports. One input port and one output port share a common address and the four devices are connected as shown in Figure 7.18.

With this hardware system we can service peripherals as follows:

1   To send data, just execute an OUT instruction to one of two port addresses (0FEH or 0FFH).
2   To interrupt from an input port, take STB high and then low. Data are latched into the port register and an interrupt is generated at the high-to-low transition. Cancel the interrupt request and read any input data, by executing an IN, from 0FEH or 0FFH, instruction.

Processor interrupt hardware

Having generated an interrupt request at an input port, the next requirement is to properly present this to the 8080 and provide some means of forming the RST instruction code when the interrupt is accepted. Figure 7.19 shows a fairly simple way of doing this. The 8 interrupt request lines, from a maximum of 8 interrupting peripherals, are labelled $\overline{VI0}$ to $\overline{VI7}$ which corresponds with the labelling used in the S100 bus specification. The 8-stage latch to which these inputs are connected is transparent (outputs connected directly to the inputs) so long as the enabling input $\overline{INTA}$ is a 1. This

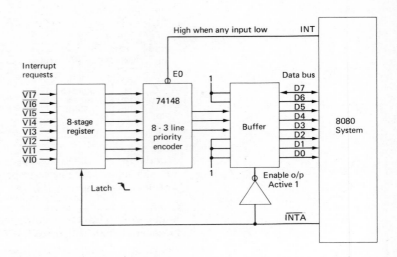

Figure 7.19 A simple way of generating RST instruction codes when interrupt requests appear

situation exists until the processor takes $\overline{\text{INTA}}$ low when acknowledging an interrupt request.

When one or more of the interrupt request lines go low, the 74148 priority encoder output, labelled EO, goes high and a processor interrupt request is generated. At that point the main 3-line output of the 74148 is a binary number which indicates the highest priority interrupting input. $\overline{\text{VI7}}$ has the highest (of all) priority, and $\overline{\text{VI0}}$ the lowest, so if we use VI1 and VI2 and they are simultaneously activated, the 74148 output will be 010 showing that $\overline{\text{VI2}}$ (interrupt 2) is the highest priority pending interrupt. Having a higher priority means that interrupt 2 will be serviced before interrupt 1.

When the interrupt request is acknowledged ($\overline{\text{INTA}} = 0$), the input latch is disabled but the proper RST instruction code has already been formed and is now connected to the processor data bus through the tristate buffer. The processor reads this instruction code and **Q7.8** proceeds to service the interrupt as already described.

An interrupt example

To demonstrate how interrupts can be handled in programs which run under CP/M, we will write a simple program which includes an interrupt service routine. The main (interruptable) program will flash a lamp at a constant rate. When an interrupt occurs the lamp will be flashed ten times at one-eighth of the normal flash rate. After that the previous, interrupted, flash rate will be resumed.

When interrupt working is adopted in CP/M systems there are a number of things to be aware of:

1 The restarts, RST 0, RST 6 and RST 7 are used by CP/M and cannot be used by your programs. The other five restarts, 1 to 5, are available and correspond with the prioritised interrupt lines,

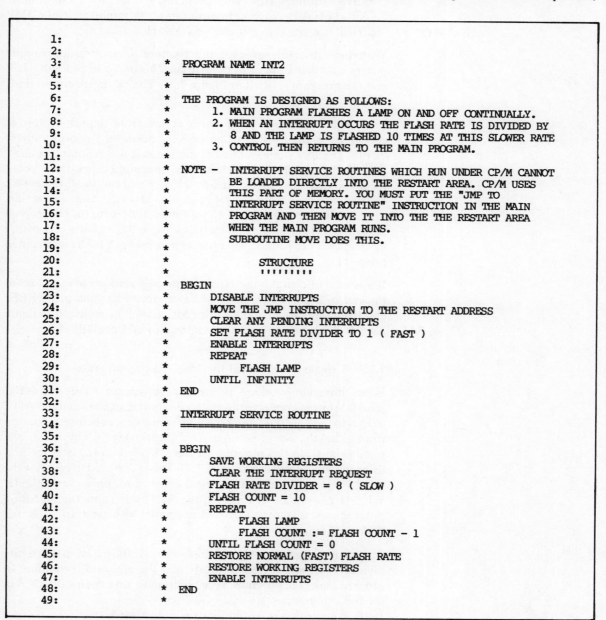

```
1:
2:
3:          *    PROGRAM NAME INT2
4:          *    ================
5:          *
6:          *    THE PROGRAM IS DESIGNED AS FOLLOWS:
7:          *         1. MAIN PROGRAM FLASHES A LAMP ON AND OFF CONTINUALLY.
8:          *         2. WHEN AN INTERRUPT OCCURS THE FLASH RATE IS DIVIDED BY
9:          *            8 AND THE LAMP IS FLASHED 10 TIMES AT THIS SLOWER RATE
10:         *         3. CONTROL THEN RETURNS TO THE MAIN PROGRAM.
11:         *
12:         *    NOTE -   INTERRUPT SERVICE ROUTINES WHICH RUN UNDER CP/M CANNOT
13:         *             BE LOADED DIRECTLY INTO THE RESTART AREA. CP/M USES
14:         *             THIS PART OF MEMORY. YOU MUST PUT THE "JMP TO
15:         *             INTERRUPT SERVICE ROUTINE" INSTRUCTION IN THE MAIN
16:         *             PROGRAM AND THEN MOVE IT INTO THE THE RESTART AREA
17:         *             WHEN THE MAIN PROGRAM RUNS.
18:         *             SUBROUTINE MOVE DOES THIS.
19:         *
20:         *                 STRUCTURE
21:         *                 '''''''''
22:         *    BEGIN
23:         *         DISABLE INTERRUPTS
24:         *         MOVE THE JMP INSTRUCTION TO THE RESTART ADDRESS
25:         *         CLEAR ANY PENDING INTERRUPTS
26:         *         SET FLASH RATE DIVIDER TO 1 ( FAST )
27:         *         ENABLE INTERRUPTS
28:         *         REPEAT
29:         *              FLASH LAMP
30:         *         UNTIL INFINITY
31:         *    END
32:         *
33:         *    INTERRUPT SERVICE ROUTINE
34:         *    =========================
35:         *
36:         *    BEGIN
37:         *         SAVE WORKING REGISTERS
38:         *         CLEAR THE INTERRUPT REQUEST
39:         *         FLASH RATE DIVIDER = 8 ( SLOW )
40:         *         FLASH COUNT = 10
41:         *         REPEAT
42:         *              FLASH LAMP
43:         *              FLASH COUNT := FLASH COUNT - 1
44:         *         UNTIL FLASH COUNT = 0
45:         *         RESTORE NORMAL (FAST) FLASH RATE
46:         *         RESTORE WORKING REGISTERS
47:         *         ENABLE INTERRUPTS
48:         *    END
49:         *
```

Figure 7.20 Structure of the INT2 program

$\overline{VI1}$ to $\overline{VI5}$. The restart addresses are 0008H, 0010H, 0018H, 0020H and 0028H.

2 CP/M will not allow you to load any code into addresses below 0100H. Consequently it is necessary to load the restart addresses with JMP instructions which transfer control to the interrupt service routines, from your program. We have used a subroutine called MOVE, early on in our example program, to load a JMP INTR1 instruction into address 0008H.

Q7.9

With these observations made, the structure of our interrupt example program, called INT2, can be written. This is shown in Figure 7.20 and the program is listed in Figure 7.21. The hardware connections are shown in Figure 7.22.

The single interrupt input, which comes from a push-button, is connected to the STB input of the 8212 positioned at port address 0FFH. The $\overline{INT}$ output of this device is connected to interrupt line 1 ($\overline{VI1}$ in Figure 7.19) so that when the interrupt occurs, the selected restart address is 0008H. At this address will be the JMP INTR1 instruction put there by subroutine MOVE. Since a restart instruction is just like a CALL, the return address to the interrupted program will be on top of the stack, so a RET at the end of the interrupt service routine will transfer control back to the interrupted program.

Q7.10, 7.11

If a second interrupt is used (refer to the self-assessment questions at the end of this chapter) this will be connected to input port 0FEH, and from there to $\overline{VI2}$. Subroutine MOVE will be modified so that a JMP INTR2 instruction will be moved to address 0010H.

7.10 A single channel, real-time data-logging program

When interrupt working is used to service an ADC, the ADC READY line is connected to the STB input of an 8212 and the ADC output to the 8212 data inputs. A conversion can, as before, be started from within the user program or it may be triggered-off by an external timing signal. In this program we have decided on the later method using the timing circuit of Figure 7.23. This is designed to generate the negative-going pulse which starts a conversion, once every minute. When a conversion is finished, the ADC interrupts the executing program and a value is read and compared with arbitrarily selected limits as before.

The main program is only required to slowly flash a lamp (flash rate divider = 8), and thereby indicate that the program is running. In order to make the program more realistic we have changed ADC3 in the following respects:

1 A value which is within limits is not printed.

2 If an out-of-limits value is read, the program should speed-up the

```
 1:
 2:
 3:                       *  PROGRAM NAME INT2
 4:                       *  ==================
 5:                       *
 6:  0100                    ORG     0100H
 7:  0100 F3      MAIN:      DI                      ; DISABLE INTERRUPTS
 8:  0101 CD1201             CALL    MOVE            ; LOAD UP RESTART AREA
 9:  0104 DBFF               IN      0FFH            ; CLEAR ANY PENDING INTERRUPT
10:  0106 3E01               MVI     A,01H
11:  0108 325C01             STA     DIVIDR          ; FLASH RATE DIVIDER = 1 (FAST)
12:  010B FB                 EI                      ; SWITCH ON INTERRUPTS
13:  010C CD3901   LOOP:     CALL    FLASH           ; FLASH LAMP
14:  010F C30C01             JMP     LOOP            ; AND AGAIN
15:                       *
16:  0112 3EC3     MOVE:     MVI     A,0C3H          ; JMP INSTRUCTION OP-CODE
17:  0114 320800             STA     0008H           ; INTO RST 1 START ADDRESS
18:  0117 211E01             LXI     H,INTR1         ; REMAINDER OF JMP INSTRUCTION
19:  011A 220900             SHLD    0009H           ; INTO ADDRESSES 09 AND 0A
20:  011D C9                 RET                     ; RESTART AREA INITIALISED
21:                       *
22:  011E F5      INTR1:     PUSH    PSW             ; REMEMBER WHERE WE ARE
23:  011F E5                 PUSH    H
24:  0120 DBFF               IN      0FFH            ; CLEAR INTERRUPT REQUEST
25:  0122 3E08               MVI     A,08H
26:  0124 325C01             STA     DIVIDR          ; FLASH RATE DIVIDER = 8 (SLOW)
27:  0127 060A               MVI     B,0AH           ; INITIALISE FLASH COUNTER
28:                       *
29:  0129 CD3901   AGAIN:    CALL    FLASH           ; FLASH AT NEW RATE
30:  012C 05                 DCR     B               ; DECREMENT FLASH COUNT
31:  012D C22901             JNZ     AGAIN           ; REPEAT UNTIL FLASH COUNT = 0
32:                       *
33:  0130 3E01               MVI     A,01H
34:  0132 325C01             STA     DIVIDR          ; NORMAL FLASH RATE (FAST)
35:  0135 E1                 POP     H               ; RESTORE REGISTER STATUS
36:  0136 F1                 POP     PSW
37:  0137 FB                 EI                      ; SWITCH ON INTERRUPTS AGAIN
38:  0138 C9                 RET                     ; AND RETURN TO INTERRUPTED PROG
39:                       *
40:  0139 3E01     FLASH:    MVI     A,01H           ; SET LAMP BIT
41:  013B D3FF               OUT     0FFH            ; SWITCH ON THE LAMP
42:  013D CD4701             CALL    DELAY           ; DELAY FOR A WHILE
43:  0140 AF                 XRA     A               ; RESET LAMP BIT
44:  0141 D3FF               OUT     0FFH            ; SWITCH OFF LAMP
45:  0143 CD4701             CALL    DELAY           ; DELAY FOR A WHILE LONGER
46:  0146 C9                 RET                     ; NOW RETURN
47:                       *
48:  0147 2A5A01   DELAY:    LHLD    FRATE           ; GET EXISTING FLASH RATE
49:  014A 3A5C01             LDA     DIVIDR          ; GET FLASH RATE DIVIDER
50:  014D 2D       MORE:     DCR     L               ; DECREMENT LS BYTE
51:  014E C24D01             JNZ     MORE            ; UNTIL ITS ZERO
52:  0151 25                 DCR     H               ; DECREMENT MS BYTE
53:  0152 C24D01             JNZ     MORE            ; UNTIL THAT TOO IS ZERO
54:  0155 3D                 DCR     A               ; DECREMENT MULTIPLYING FACTOR
55:  0156 C24D01             JNZ     MORE            ; REPEAT UNTIL TOTAL DELAY GONE
56:  0159 C9                 RET                     ; RETURN - DELAY TIME OVER
57:                       *
58:  015A FFFF     FRATE:    DW      0FFFFH          ; NORMAL FLASH RATE
59:  015C          DIVIDR:   DS      1               ; FLASH RATE DIVIDER IN HERE
60:  015D                    END
```

Figure 7.21   INT2 program listing

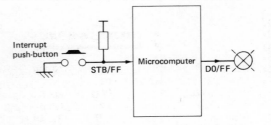

Figure 7.22 Hardware connections for the INT2 program

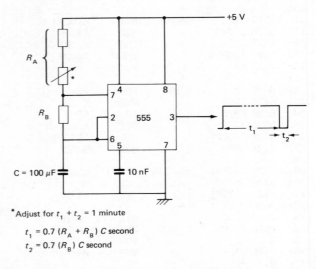

*Adjust for $t_1 + t_2$ = 1 minute

$t_1 = 0.7 (R_A + R_B) C$ second

$t_2 = 0.7 (R_B) C$ second

Figure 7.23 Using a 555 timer chip to generate an accurate 1 minute pulse

flash rate and print a message of the form:

HIGH ALARM AT 02:54 HOURS - MEASURED VALUE

WAS 4.38

3 If the alarm condition still exists one minute later, the same message should be printed, with the time updated, on a new line.

4 When the alarm condition is cleared, the flash rate should return to normal.

There are only two extra requirements in this program. Firstly we must be able to print a message on the screen, and secondly, we have to maintain a run-time clock so that, when an alarm condition arises, we can print the time at which it occurred.

The first extra requirement is not difficult to satisfy. All we need is a character string defined in a DB statement and a means of accessing the characters one-by-one so that they can be sent to the PCHAR subroutine in register B. A general-purpose message print (MESP)

```
 1:
 2:
 3:                      *    SUBROUTINE MESP
 4:                      *    ================
 5:                      *
 6:                      *    THIS SUBROUTINE IS USED TO PRINT A CHARACTER STRING ON THE
 7:                      *    CONSOLE. ON ENTRY THE START ADDRESS OF THE STRING MUST BE
 8:                      *    CONTAINED IN THE D AND E REGISTER PAIR. ALSO, THE STRING
 9:                      *    MUST END IN A NULL (00H).
10:                      *
11:                      *               STRUCTURE
12:                      *               '''''''''
13:                      *    BEGIN
14:                      *        READ THE FIRST CHARACTER
15:                      *        WHILE CHARACTER <> NULL DO
16:                      *        BEGIN
17:                      *            PRINT THE CHARACTER
18:                      *            READ THE NEXT CHARACTER
19:                      *        END
20:                      *    END
21:                      *
22:    0000 1A           MESP:   LDAX    D           ; GET CHARACTER FROM STRING
23:    0001 FE00                 CPI     00H         ; TEST FOR NULL
24:    0003 C8                   RZ                  ; RETURN IF NULL
25:    0004 47                   MOV     B,A
26:    0005 CD0C00               CALL    PCHAR       ; OTHERWISE PRINT IT
27:    0008 13                   INX     D           ; BUMP STRING POINTER
28:    0009 C30000               JMP     MESP        ; AND GET NEXT CHARACTER
29:                      *
30:                      *    RE-DEFINE SUBROUTINE PCHAR FOR THE SAKE OF THE ASSEMBLER
31:                      *
32:    000C C9           PCHAR:  RET                 ; DUMMY CODE - REMOVE LATER
33:                      *
34:    000D                      END
```

Figure 7.24   MESP – the subroutine used to print console messages

subroutine can be written and added to the other console I/O routines like NEWL and PCHAR. The MESP structure and its listing are given in Figure 7.24.

If MESP is easy to understand, the run-time clock part of the program requires a little more thought.

Maintaining a run-time, or real-time, clock

The typical alarm message shown earlier had the time printed in the form:

    HOURS : MINUTES

Clearly, when the program starts, HOURS and MINUTES should both be zero. Every minute after that, the minutes should be increased by 1. Since the whole point of maintaining the clock is so that the time can be printed, it is sensible that we should define one location called MINS which contains a number in the range 0 to 59, and another called HOURS which contains another number in the range 0 to 23. It is equally sensible that we should hold these numbers in BCD form so that when they need to be printed, we can use the PRNLFT and PRNRGT subroutines developed in Chapter 5.

Two possibilities exist when we think about advancing the time. Since the ADC will interrupt at one-minute intervals, we can up-date the HOURS/MINS locations whenever an interrupt occurs. Alternatively we could connect our timing circuit to a second interrupt line and program a second interrupt service routine just to maintain the clock. On reflection, this alternative seems to be somewhat extravagant, so we shall plump for the first idea. If we particularly wanted to use a second interrupt, then a useful addition to our system could be a STATUS button which, when pressed, interrupted to report on how long the program has been running and the number of alarms that had been recorded so far. Since interrupt service routines are virtually independent programs we can add this facility later. Without the addition however, our system now appears as shown in Figure 7.25.

Maintaining a run-time clock can be programmed in an instruction sequence which, when the ADC interrupts, does the following:

```
BEGIN
        MINS: = MINS+1
        CONVERT (MINS) TO BCD
        IF MINS = 60 THEN
                MINS: = 0
                HOURS: = HOURS+1
                CONVERT (HOURS) TO BCD
                IF HOURS = 24 THEN
                        HOURS: = 0
                ELSE
                        DO NOTHING
                ENDIF
        ELSE
        DO NOTHING
        ENDIF
END
```

Printing the time, now that HOURS and MINS contain BCD numbers, is hardly any different from printing the BCD measured value which, you will remember, was held in TOTAL and TOTAL +

Q7.12   1 after the CONV subroutine was executed.

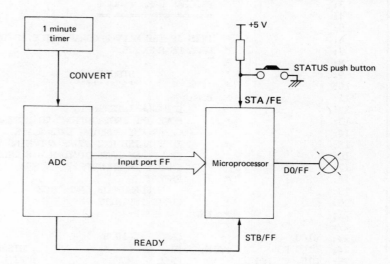

Figure 7.25   Hardware for the program ADC4. The STATUS push-button is not needed for this program but may be needed for any future example

The main program

Let us now put together our interrupt-driven single-channel data logging program. Apart from moving the jump instructions to the restart area, the initialisation part of the program will also have to set the contents of HOURS and MINS to zero. We have described the program operation below and listed it in Figure 7.26:

```
BEGIN   (*Main program*)
        DISABLE INTERRUPTS
        MOVE JMP INSTRUCTIONS TO RESTART AREA
        CLEAR ANY PENDING INTERRUPTS
        MINS: = 0
        HOURS: = 0
        SET FLASH RATE DIVIDER TO 8 (SLOW)
        ENABLE INTERRUPTS
        REPEAT
                FLASH THE LAMP ON AND OFF
        UNTIL INFINITY
END
```

Flashing the lamp on and off is achieved in the same FLASH/ DELAY subroutines used before.

The ADC interrupt service routine

The ADC interrupt service routine must up-date the run-time clock

```
 1:
 2:
 3:                    *   PROGRAM NAME : ADC4
 4:                    *   ========================
 5:                    *
 6:                    *   THIS IS THE MAIN PROGRAM WHICH IS INTERRUPTED WHEN THE ADC
 7:                    *   DEMANDS SERVICE.
 8:                    *
 9:                    *                   STRUCTURE
10:                    *                   '''''''''
11:                    *   BEGIN
12:                    *        DISABLE INTERRUPTS
13:                    *        MOVE JMP INSTRUCTIONS TO RESTART AREA
14:                    *        CLEAR ANY PENDING INTERRUPTS
15:                    *        INITIALISE RTC HOURS AND MINS TO ZERO
16:                    *        SET FLASH RATE DIVIDER = 8 (SLOW RATE)
17:                    *        ENABLE INTERRUPTS
18:                    *        REPEAT
19:                    *             FLASH THE LAMP ONCE
20:                    *        UNTIL INFINITY
21:                    *   END
22:                    *
23:   0100                     ORG     0100H
24:   0100 F3          MAIN:   DI                       ; DISABLE INTERRUPTS
25:   0101 CD1B01              CALL    MOVE             ; FILL UP THE RESTART AREA
26:   0104 DBFF                IN      0FFH             ; CLEAR ANY PENDING INTERRUPTS
27:   0106 DBFE                IN      0FEH
28:   0108 AF                  XRA     A
29:   0109 323001              STA     MINS             ; MINS := 0
30:   010C 323101              STA     HOURS            ; HOURS := 0
31:   010F 3E08                MVI     A,08H
32:   0111 323201              STA     DIVIDR           ; FLASH RATE DIVIDER = 8
33:   0114 FB                  EI                       ; ENABLE INTERRUPTS
34:   0115 CD3301      LOOP:   CALL    FLASH            ; FLASH THE LAMP
35:   0118 C31501              JMP     LOOP             ; AND AGAIN
36:                    *
37:                    *   SUBROUTINE MOVE
38:                    *   ===============
39:                    *
40:                    *   THIS FILLS UP THE RESTART AREA WITH THE JMP TO INTERRUPT
41:                    *   SERVICE ROUTINE INSTRUCTIONS.
42:                    *   THE ADC READY LINE IS CONNECTED TO  THE STB INPUT OF PORT
43:                    *   FF WHICH CORRESPONDS WITH RESTART 1. THE JUMP AT RESTART
44:                    *   2 IS PROVIDED FOR FUTURE EXPANSION.
45:                    *
46:   011B 3EC3        MOVE:   MVI     A,0C3H           ; JMP OP-CODE
47:   011D 320800              STA     0008H            ; RESTART 1
48:   0120 321000              STA     0010H            ; RESTART 2
49:   0123 213401              LXI     H,ADCINT         ; ADC INTERRUPT ROUTINE
50:   0126 220900              SHLD    0009H            ; START ADDRESS TO 0009/A
51:   0129 213501              LXI     H,INTR2          ; INTERRUPT 2 START
52:   012C 221100              SHLD    0011H            ; ADDRESS TO 0011/2
53:   012F C9                  RET
54:                    *
55:                    *   THE FOLLOWING LABELS ARE DEFINED FOR THE BENEFIT OF THE
56:                    *   ASSEMBLER. THEY WILL BE REMOVED WHEN MODULES ARE LINKED TOGETHER
57:                    *
58:   0130            MINS:   DS      1
59:   0131            HOURS:  DS      1
60:   0132            DIVIDR: DS      1
61:   0133 C9         FLASH:  RET
62:   0134 C9         ADCINT: RET
63:   0135 C9         INTR2:  RET
64:                    *
65:   0136                    END
```

Figure 7.26   The program ADC4 which sets up the restart area ready for an interrupt and flashes a lamp

as well as read the value and compare it with high and low limits. Its structure is quite straightforward, however:

```
BEGIN    (*Servicing the RTC and ADC*)
         SAVE ALL THE REGISTERS USED
         UPDATE THE RTC
         READ THE VALUE
         COMPARE VALUE WITH LIMITS
         IF EITHER LIMIT EXCEEDED THEN
                 SET FLASH RATE DIVIDER = 1 (FAST)
                 REPORT ALARM CONDITION
         ELSE
                 SET FLASH RATE DIVIDER = 8 (SLOW)
         ENDIF
         RESTORE THE REGISTERS
         ENABLE INTERRUPTS
END
```

Considering the requirements of this program one-by-one, it is reasonably clear that a subroutine called UPDATE, programmed as explained earlier, could take care of updating the run-time clock. Reading the ADC output and storing it in VALUE will be an IN instruction followed by a STA. The IN instruction will also clear the interrupt request. The, by now familiar, COMP subroutine compares the contents of VALUE with upper and lower limits and returns a non-zero value in register B if either limit is exceeded. Only then do we change the flash rate and report the alarm condition. If there is no existing alarm condition the flash rate divider is reset to 8 and, after restoring the registers and switching on the interrupt enable flag, return is made to the interrupted program. The flash rate divider may already be 8 of course, but setting it to 8 again will do no harm.

Before going on we should perhaps list this interrupt service routine and the new subroutine UPDATE. The interrupt service routine is called ADCINT as shown in Figure 7.27 and UPDATE is listed in Figure 7.28.

Reporting an alarm condition

This subroutine will be called REPORT. It is called if either alarm condition exists and is required to:

1 Convert the binary contents of VALUE to an equivalent voltage and leave the result in TOTAL and TOTAL + 1.
2 If the high limit has been exceeded it should call MESP to print the word HIGH. Otherwise it should print the word LOW.
3 It should then print the words ALARM AT
4 followed by the BCD contents of HOURS and MINS with a colon between the two numbers.

```
 1:
 2:
 3:                   *   ADC INTERRUPT SERVICE ROUTINE
 4:                   *   ========================
 5:                   *
 6:                   *   EVERY MINUTE THE ADC INTERRUPTS AND THIS INTERRUPT SERVICE
 7:                   *   ROUTINE IS EXECUTED.
 8:                   *
 9:                   *                 STRUCTURE
10:                   *                 '''''''''
11:                   *   BEGIN  (* SERVICING THE ADC AND RTC *)
12:                   *       SAVE THE REGISTERS
13:                   *       UPDATE THE RTC
14:                   *       READ THE VALUE, AND IN SO DOING CANCEL THE INTERRUPT REQUEST
15:                   *       COMPARE VALUE WITH THE LIMITS
16:                   *       IF EITHER LIMIT EXCEEDED THEN
17:                   *              SET FLASH RATE DIVIDER = 1 (FAST)
18:                   *              REPORT ALARM CONDITION
19:                   *       ELSE
20:                   *              SET FLASH RATE DIVIDER = 8 (SLOW)
21:                   *       ENDIF
22:                   *       RESTORE THE REGISTERS
23:                   *       RE-ENABLE INTERRUPTS
24:                   *   END
25:                   *
26:   0000 F5         ADCINT: PUSH   PSW              ; SAVE THE REGISTERS
27:   0001 C5                 PUSH   B
28:   0002 CD2A00             CALL   UPDATE           ; UPDATE THE RTC
29:   0005 DBFF               IN     0FFH             ; READ ADC O/P - CLEAR INTERRUPT
30:   0007 322C00             STA    VALUE            ; STORE IN VALUE
31:   000A CD2B00             CALL   COMP             ; COMPARE VALUE WITH LIMITS
32:   000D 78                 MOV    A,B              ; GET ALARM CODE, IF ANY
33:   000E FE00               CPI    00H              ; CHECK FOR AN ALARM
34:   0010 CA2100             JZ     OK               ; ALARM CODE=0 MEANS OK
35:   0013 322F00     ALARM:  STA    ALMCDE           ; OTHERWISE SAVE ALARM CODE
36:   0016 3E01               MVI    A,01H
37:   0018 322D00             STA    DIVIDR           ; FLASH RATE DIVIDER = 1
38:   001B CD2E00             CALL   REPORT           ; REPORT ALARM STATUS
39:   001E C32600             JMP    TIDY             ; NOW TIDY UP
40:   0021 3E08       OK:     MVI    A,08H
41:   0023 322D00             STA    DIVIDR           ; FLASH RATE DIVIDER = 8
42:   0026 C1         TIDY:   POP    B                ; RESTORE REGISTERS
43:   0027 F1                 POP    PSW
44:   0028 FB                 EI                      ; ENABLE INTERRUPTS
45:   0029 C9                 RET
46:                   *
47:                   *   LABELS DEFINED FOR THE ASSEMBLER
48:                   *
49:   002A C9         UPDATE: RET                     ; SEPARATE SUBROUTINE
50:   002B C9         COMP:   RET                     ; SEPARATE SUBROUTINE
51:   002C            VALUE:  DS     1                ; DEFINED IN COMP
52:   002D            DIVIDR: DS     1                ; DEFINED IN FLASH/DELAY
53:   002E C9         REPORT: RET                     ; SEPARATE SUBROUTINE
54:   002F            ALMCDE: DS     1                ; USED BY THIS ROUTINE
55:                   *
```

Figure 7.27   The interrupt service routine executed when ADC4 is interrupted

```
 1:
 2:
 3:             *   SUBROUTINE NAME : UPDATE
 4:             *   ========================
 5:             *
 6:             *   THIS SUBROUTINE UPDATES A REAL-TIME CLOCK AT 1 MINUTE INTERVALS.
 7:             *   THE TIMING SIGNAL, WHICH ALSO TRIGGERS OFF AN ADC, IS PROVIDED
 8:             *   FROM AN EXTERNAL CIRCUIT.
 9:             *   ONLY REGISTER A IS USED.
10:             *
11:             *                    STRUCTURE
12:             *                    '''''''''
13:             *   BEGIN
14:             *        MINS := MINS + 1
15:             *        CONVERT (MINS) TO BCD
16:             *        IF MINS = 60 THEN
17:             *             MINS := 0
18:             *             HOURS := HOURS + 1
19:             *             CONVERT (HOURS) TO BCD
20:             *             IF HOURS = 24 THEN
21:             *                  HOURS := 0
22:             *             ELSE
23:             *                  DO NOTHING
24:             *             ENDIF
25:             *        ELSE
26:             *             DO NOTHING
27:             *        ENDIF
28:             *   END.
29:             *
30:   0000 3A2500   UPDATE: LDA    MINS      ; GET CURRENT MINUTES
31:   0003 C601             ADI    01H       ; MINS := MINS + 1
32:   0005 27               DAA              ; CONVERT TO BCD
33:   0006 322500           STA    MINS      ; UPDATE MINUTES
34:             *
35:   0009 FE60    TST60:  CPI    60H       ; TEST FOR 60 MINUTES
36:   000B C22400           JNZ    TIMEOK    ; IF NOT 60, TIME OK
37:   000E AF               XRA    A
38:   000F 322500           STA    MINS      ; IF 60, MINS := 0
39:   0012 3A2600           LDA    HOURS     ; GET CURRENT HOURS
40:   0015 C601             ADI    01H       ; HOURS := HOURS + 1
41:   0017 27               DAA              ; CONVERT TO BCD
42:   0018 322600           STA    HOURS     ; UPDATE HOURS
43:             *
44:   001B FE18    TST24:  CPI    24        ; TEST FOR 24 HOURS
45:   001D C22400           JNZ    TIMEOK    ; IF NOT 24, TIME OK
46:   0020 AF               XRA    A
47:   0021 322600           STA    HOURS     ; IF 24, HOURS := 0
48:   0024 C9      TIMEOK: RET              ; RETURN WITH CLOCK UP-DATED
49:             *
50:   0025        MINS:   DS     1         ; CLOCK MAINTAINED HERE
51:   0026        HOURS:  DS     1
52:             *
```

Figure 7.28 UPDATE – the subroutine which updates the run-time clock when ADCINT is executed

5   Then it should print the words MEASURED VALUE WAS
6   and finally print the contents of TOTAL and TOTAL + 1 with a decimal point between them, and then a carriage-return-line feed.

The text parts of the complete report will be stored as the following string constants:

```
MESSHI:   DB    'HIGH',00H
MESSLO:   DB    'LOW',00H
MESS1 :   DB    'ALARM',00H
MESS2 :   DB    'MEASURED VALUE WAS',00H
```

Notice that each part of the message ends in a 00, NULL, byte. You will remember that all character strings printed by MESP must end in a NULL.

The structure of this part of the complete program is just:

```
BEGIN   (*Reporting*)
        CONVERT BINARY VALUE TO BCD (CONV)
        IF HIGH ALARM THEN
                PRINT MESSHI
        ELSE
                PRINT MESSLO
        ENDIF
        PRINT MESS1
        PRINT TIME
        PRINT MESS2
        PRINT MEASURED VALUE
        PRINT CARRIAGE-RETURN-LINE FEED
END
```

The REPORT subroutine is listed in Figure 7.29. It calls two new subroutines called PRNTME (print time) and PRNVAL (print value) which are very similar to our original PRINT subroutine. The main difference is that the PRNLFT and PRNRGT subroutines have been deleted and grouped instead with the other console I/O routines in a library file called CONSOL.LIB. This library file contains nothing new but is listed in the Appendix should you need to refer to it. PRNTME and PRNVAL are listed in Figures 7.30 and 7.31.

We can picture the complete software package as shown in Figure 7.32. An interrupt can occur at any point in the LOOP part of the main program and, when it does occur, the interrupt service routine is executed. If an alarm condition is detected, subroutine REPORT is called. This, in turn, calls PRNTME and PRNVAL, and the three subroutines use the console I/O library to report the prevailing alarm condition.

The form of this alarm report is shown in Figure 7.33. This was

```
  1:
  2:
  3:                        *   SUBROUTINE REPORT
  4:                        *   ==================
  5:                        *
  6:                        *   CALLED FROM ADCINT WHEN AN ALARM CONDITION IS DETECTED
  7:                        *
  8:                        *                    STRUCTURE
  9:                        *                    '''''''''
 10:                        *   BEGIN
 11:                        *        SAVE ANY REGISTERS USED HERE
 12:                        *        CONVERT BINARY VALUE TO BCD
 13:                        *        IF HIGH ALARM THEN
 14:                        *             PRINT 'HIGH'
 15:                        *        ELSE
 16:                        *             PRINT 'LOW'
 17:                        *        ENDIF
 18:                        *        PRINT MESS1
 19:                        *        PRINT TIME
 20:                        *        PRINT MESS2
 21:                        *        PRINT MEASURED VOLTAGE
 22:                        *        PRINT NEWL
 23:                        *        RESTORE THE REGISTERS
 24:                        *   END
 25:                        *
 26:     0000 C5            REPORT: PUSH    B               ; SAVE THE REGISTERS
 27:     0001 D5                    PUSH    D
 28:     0002 E5                    PUSH    H
 29:     0003 CD6000                CALL    CONV            ; CONVERT VALUE TO BCD
 30:     0006 3A6100                LDA     ALMCDE          ; GET ALARM CODE
 31:     0009 FE02                  CPI     02H             ; CHECK FOR HIGH ALARM
 32:     000B C21700                JNZ     LALRM
 33:     000E 113600        HLRM:   LXI     D,MESSHI
 34:     0011 CD6200                CALL    MESP            ; PRINT 'HIGH'
 35:     0014 C31D00                JMP     REST
 36:     0017 113C00        LALRM:  LXI     D,MESSLO
 37:     001A CD6200                CALL    MESP            ; ELSE PRINT 'LOW'
 38:     001D 114100        REST:   LXI     D,MESS1
 39:     0020 CD6200                CALL    MESP            ; PRINT 'ALARM AT'
 40:     0023 CD6300                CALL    PRNTIME         ; PRINT TIME
 41:     0026 114B00                LXI     D,MESS2
 42:     0029 CD6200                CALL    MESP            ; PRINT 'MEASURED VALUE WAS'
 43:     002C CD6400                CALL    PRNVAL          ; PRINT BCD VALUE
 44:     002F CD6500                CALL    NEWL            ; THEN A NEW LINE
 45:     0032 E1                    POP     H               ; RESTORE THE REGISTERS
 46:     0033 D1                    POP     D
 47:     0034 C1                    POP     B
 48:     0035 C9                    RET                     ; AND RETURN
 49:                        *
 50:                        *   MESSAGES FOLLOW:
 51:                        *
 52:     0036 4849474820MESSHI: DB      'HIGH ',00H
 53:     003C 4C4F572000MESSLO: DB      'LOW ',00H
 54:     0041 414C41524DMESS1:  DB      'ALARM AT ',00H
 55:     004B 2D4D454153MESS2:  DB      '-MEASURED VALUE WAS ',00H
 56:                        *
 57:                        *   EXTERNAL REFERENCES DEFINED FOR THE BENEFIT OF THE ASSEMBLER
 58:                        *
 59:     0060 C9            CONV:   RET                     ; SEPARATE SUBROUTINE
 60:     0061               ALMCDE: DS      1               ; DEFINED IN ADCINT
 61:     0062 C9            MESP:   RET                     ; DEFINED IN CONSOL.LIB
 62:     0063 C9            PRNTIME: RET                    ; SEPARATE SUBROUTINE
 63:     0064 C9            PRNVAL: RET                     ; SEPARATE SUBROUTINE
 64:     0065 C9            NEWL:   RET                     ; DEFINED IN CONSOL.LIB
 65:                        *
```

Figure 7.29 The REPORT subroutine

```
 1:
 2:
 3:                  *   SUBROUTINE PRNTME
 4:                  *   ==================
 5:                  *
 6:                  *   CALLED WHEN IT IS REQUIRED TO PRINT THE TIME WHICH IS
 7:                  *   STORED AS BCD NUMBERS IN LOCATIONS LABELLED HOURS AND MINS.
 8:                  *
 9:                  *                 STRUCTURE
10:                  *                 '''''''''
11:                  *   BEGIN
12:                  *       GET CONTENTS OF HOURS AND MINS
13:                  *       PRINT LEFT HAND CHARACTER OF HOURS
14:                  *       PRINT THE RIGHT HAND CHARACTER OF HOURS
15:                  *       PRINT A COLON
16:                  *       PRINT THE LEFT HAND CHARACTER OF MINS
17:                  *       PRINT THE RIGHT HAND CHARACTER OF MINS
18:                  *   END
19:                  *
20:  0000 2A1900     PRNTME: LHLD   MINS          ; (L) = MINS, (H) = HOURS
21:  0003 7C                 MOV    A,H           ; GET HOURS
22:  0004 CD1B00             CALL   PRNLFT        ; PRINT LEFT HAND CHARACTER
23:  0007 7C                 MOV    A,H           ; RESTORE HOURS
24:  0008 CD1C00             CALL   PRNRGT        ; PRINT RIGHT HAND CHARACTER
25:  000B 063A               MVI    B,':'
26:  000D CD1D00             CALL   PCHAR         ; PRINT A COLON
27:  0010 7D                 MOV    A,L           ; GET MINUTES
28:  0011 CD1B00             CALL   PRNLFT        ; PRINT LEFT HAND CHARACTER
29:  0014 7D                 MOV    A,L           ; RESTORE MINUTES
30:  0015 CD1C00             CALL   PRNRGT        ; PRINT RIGHT HAND CHARACTER
31:  0018 C9                 RET                  ; AND RETURN
32:                  *
33:                  *   EXTERNAL REFERENCES
34:                  *
35:  0019            MINS:   DS     2             ; DEFINED IN UPDATE
36:  001B C9         PRNLFT: RET                  ; DEFINED IN CONSOL.LIB
37:  001C C9         PRNRGT: RET                  ; DEFINED IN CONSOL.LIB
38:  001D C9         PCHAR:  RET                  ; DEFINED IN CONSOL.LIB
39:                  *
```

Figure 7.30   The PRNTME subroutine which prints out the current run-time when called

Q7.13   produced by connecting a variable d.c. voltage to the ADC input and then adjusting it so that alarm conditions can be simulated.

7.11   Multichannel data-acquisition systems

So far our discussion has been restricted to systems with only one analogue input. A realistic data acquisition/monitoring system would have many analogue inputs, some of which represented measured temperatures and others pressures or rates-of-flow, etc. Each system parameter would probably have a different set of limits and before a value was printed it would be necessary to convert it to a decimal number in the appropriate range. A temperature, for example may vary from 20°C to 100°C whereas a pressure may range

```
 1:
 2:
 3:                  *    SUBROUTINE PRNVAL
 4:                  *    ==================
 5:                  *
 6:                  *    PRINTS A NUMBER IN THE RANGE 0.00 TO 5.00 STORED AS BCD NUMBERS
 7:                  *    IN TWO LOCATIONS LABELLED TOTAL AND TOTAL+1.
 8:                  *
 9:                  *                    STRUCTURE
10:                  *                    '''''''''
11:                  *    BEGIN
12:                  *         READ CONTENTS OF TOTAL AND TOTAL+1
13:                  *         PRINT LEFT HAND CHARACTER OF TOTAL+1 (MS CHARACTER)
14:                  *         PRINT RIGHT HAND CHARACTER OF TOTAL+1
15:                  *         PRINT A DECIMAL POINT
16:                  *         PRINT LEFT HAND CHARACTER OF TOTAL (LS CHARACTER)
17:                  *    END
18:                  *
19:   0000 2A1500    PRNVAL: LHLD    TOTAL        ; (L) = TOTAL, (H) = TOTAL+1
20:   0003 7C                MOV     A,H          ; GET MS CHARACTERS
21:   0004 CD1700            CALL    PRNLFT
22:   0007 062E              MVI     B,'.'
23:   0009 CD1900            CALL    PCHAR        ; PRINT A DECIMAL POINT
24:   000C 7C                MOV     A,H          ; RESTORE MS CHARACTERS
25:   000D CD1800            CALL    PRNRGT
26:   0010 7D                MOV     A,L          ; GET LS CHARACTERS
27:   0011 CD1700            CALL    PRNLFT
28:   0014 C9                RET
29:                  *
30:                  *    EXTERNAL REFERENCES
31:                  *
32:   0015           TOTAL:  DS      2            ; DEFINED IN CONV
33:   0017 C9        PRNLFT: RET                  ; DEFINED IN CONSOL.LIB
34:   0018 C9        PRNRGT: RET                  ; DEFINED IN CONSOL.LIB
35:   0019 C9        PCHAR:  RET                  ; DEFINED IN CONSOL.LIB
36:                  *
```

Figure 7.31 The PRNVAL subroutine which prints the measured value when called from REPORT

from 5 to 25 p.s.i. It would make little sense to measure a temperature and then print it as 2.5 V as we have been doing.

What this means of course, is that the CONV subroutine will need to access several different look-up tables and not just the one we have provided so far. When a particular measurement is made we will need to find out the start address of the look-up table which corresponds with the parameter being measured. Equally if different limits apply, we will need to compile a table of limits and pick out the appropriate set for each type of measurement. A set of limits would comprise two numbers which we would store in the HLMT and LLMT addresses before calling the COMP subroutine.

Even with all that however, the necessary program changes are not that difficult to incorporate. Since we always have a known number of different transducers and different limits, we can handle the problem. As we shall see, choosing between one of a number of look-

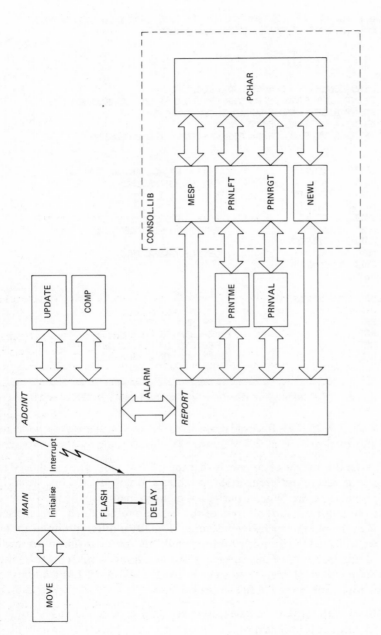

Figure 7.32   Organisation of ADC4 software

```
LOW ALARM AT 00:21-MEASURED VALUE WAS 0.39
LOW ALARM AT 00:41-MEASURED VALUE WAS 0.91
HIGH ALARM AT 01:00-MEASURED VALUE WAS 4.05
HIGH ALARM AT 01:01-MEASURED VALUE WAS 4.14
HIGH ALARM AT 01:02-MEASURED VALUE WAS 4.26
LOW ALARM AT 01:36-MEASURED VALUE WAS 0.75
```

Figure 7.33   Typical ADC4 printout

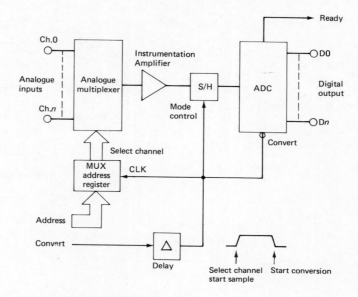

Figure 7.34 A classical data-acquisition system

up tables and limit sets is the software equivalent of selecting one of a number of analogue inputs for measurement.

In a classical data-acquisition system, these analogue inputs (transducer outputs) are connected as shown in Figure 7.34. Each of them is connected to an input of an analogue multiplexer. The multiplexer, or MUX, is a device which can be pictured as a rotary switch having several inputs but only one output. As the switch rotates, each input is connected in turn to the output and becomes the prevailing analogue input. Clearly the number of different analogue inputs which can be handled depends on the size of the switch, and, if necessary, we might have to provide a two-level arrangement in which several switch outputs become inputs to another switch. This technique would be similar to the way in which telephone calls from many sources are routed through a telephone exchange to a single destination.

The analogue multiplexer in our microprocessor-controlled data-acquisition system is not a mechanical switch but another integrated circuit. We can represent it as shown in Figure 7.35. Apart from the analogue input channels, it has a number of channel-select lines to which are applied the binary-coded number of the selected channel. When this code is changed, the multiplexer should, ideally, switch from one input to another in zero time and present zero series resistance and offset voltage to the selected input. In addition, each analogue switch should have infinite off, i.e. open, resistance and there should be no crosstalk between channels.

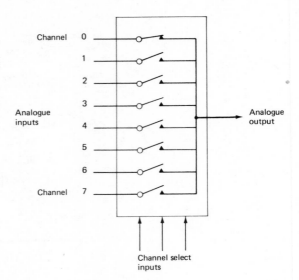

Figure 7.35   Explanatory diagram for an analogue multiplexer. The 3-bit number on the channel select lines identifies the switch which will be closed and consequently the analogue input that will be connected to the analogue output

How nearly a practical multiplexer approaches this ideal specification is, as always, largely a matter of cost. The multiplexer we shall use is the CD4051, 8-channel device, which costs less than £1 (at 1980 prices) and is far from ideal. Nevertheless, it is perfectly adequate for our purpose, which is to demonstrate the principles of multichannel data-acquisition systems.

Of the remaining components in Figure 7.34, the instrumentation, or signal conditioning, amplifier is needed to translate the range of transducer output voltages so that it coincides with the range of voltages which can be handled by the ADC. If the system includes many different transducers, it may be necessary to install amplifiers at each analogue input rather than use just the single amplifier at the multiplexer output. It all depends on the application, but it is fairly certain that we shall need at least one amplifier for one or more of the following reasons:

1   To boost the signal level.
2   To buffer the input signal (provide a high input impedance and a low output impedance).
3   To convert a current output to a voltage.
4   To extract a differential measurement signal from common mode interference.

The sample and hold circuit (S/H) in Figure 7.34 may or may not be necessary. If the amplitude of the selected analogue input is likely to change by more than the resolution of the ADC during the conversion period, then we need a sample and hold circuit. What it does is to track the changing analogue input when in the sample mode, and then, just before the conversion starts, i.e. at the sample instant, it switches to hold mode in which it effectively disconnects the analogue input by retaining (holding) the latest analogue input amplitude. During conversion therefore, the ADC input is constant and its eventual digital output corresponds with the analogue input at the sample instant.

Establishing the need, or otherwise, for a sample and hold circuit is done by considering the ADC conversion time in relation to the rate of change of analogue input. Consider, for example, a 10-V, 10-bit ADC with a conversion time of 50 μs. The resolution of this device is $10\,V/2^{10}$ which is approximately 10 mV. We will be able to do without a sample and hold circuit provided that the analogue signal amplitude is not likely to change by as much as 10 mV in any 50-μs period. If it changes faster than this, and we do not use a sample and hold circuit, the digital output could be meaningless.

If the highest frequency component in the analogue input signal is ω rad s^{-1} and its peak-to-peak amplitude is 10 V, then we can write,

$$V_{in} = 5 \sin \omega t$$

The maximum rate of change of this voltage occurs when it crosses through zero and is given by,

$$\left. \frac{dV_{in}}{dt} \right|_{max} = 5\omega \cos \omega t = 5\omega \ V \ s^{-1}$$

This must be less than 10 mV in 50 μs. In other words:

$$5\omega < 10 \times 10^{-3}/50 \times 10^{-6}$$

Therefore

$$\omega < 40 \text{ rad } s^{-1} \text{ or } f < 6.366 \text{ Hz}$$

Q7.15   If the input frequency is any greater than this, then we shall need a sample and hold circuit or, maybe, a faster ADC.

Alternative data-acquisition system organisation

The alternative way of making data-acquisition systems is to convert each analogue signal to a digital form at the transducer location and then transmit digital signals. A practical system which is organised in this way is shown in Figure 7.36. The voltage-to-frequency converters simply translate the amplitude of the analogue signal to a pulse train

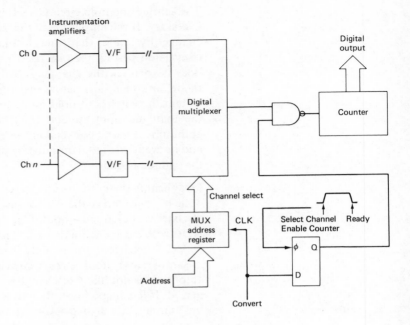

Figure 7.36 An alternative data-acquisition system

of proportional frequency. By counting the number of pulses received in a fixed time period, the digital equivalent of each analogue input can, therefore, be determined.

Notice that the analogue multiplexer is now replaced by a digital multiplexer. As each channel is selected the counter is enabled for a fixed time period and, at the end of this time, the number in the counter is read by the microprocessor. If a 12-stage counter is used, the maximum input voltage should produce a count of 4,095.

The main advantage of this alternative system, compared with the classical system discussed earlier, is that the analogue data are transmitted digital form from remote transducers to the main system. Digital signals have a higher noise immunity than analogue signals and can be transmitted over long lines without suffering irreversible deterioration.

A multichannel data acquisition program

To illustrate the way in which a multichannel monitoring system may be engineered, we need only make minor changes to the hardware and software of our single-channel system. The new hardware arrangement is shown in Figure 7.37.

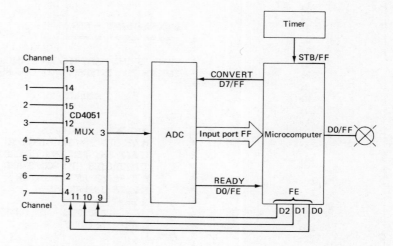

Figure 7.37 Hardware for the DAS1 program

From this you will see that the real-time clock input is the only interrupt used. The main program flashes a lamp on and off, but, once every minute, it is interrupted by the timing signal. The clock is then updated and each of the eight channels are sampled and compared with the limits. A complete cycle is summarised in Figure 7.38. You will note that the main program is exactly the same as ADC4 which was listed earlier. However some of the I/O lines have been reassigned as follows:

STB of input port FE	– RTC interrupt (INTR2)
Data lines of input port FF	– ADC output
D0 to D2 of output port FE	– MUX channel select lines
D7 of output port FF	– ADC 'CONVERT' input
D0 of output port FF	– the lamp
D0 of input port FE	– ADC 'READY' line

There are several statements in the interrupt service routine structure which need some explanation. Selecting a channel, for instance, is achieved by sending a channel address code (000 to 111) to the multiplexer on the designated lines of output port FE. After that it is necessary to wait for the multiplexer to register this change of conditions before starting a new conversion. If we do not include some waiting time at this point, the ADC input will be changing during the conversion and its eventual output will be irrelevant. As you will see later, we have chosen to execute the delay routine while the multiplexer is settling down. This gives it more than enough time to stabilise the ADC input, but there is no particular need to tune this system so that it acquires values as rapidly as possible.

```
 1:
 2:
 3:        *    PROGRAM NAME : DAS1
 4:        *    ================
 5:        *
 6:        *    THIS IS THE MAIN PROGRAM WHICH IS INTERRUPTED WHEN THE RTC
 7:        *    INTERRUPT (INTERRUPT 2) OCCURS.
 8:        *
 9:        *                   STRUCTURE
10:        *                   ''''''''''
11:        *    BEGIN
12:        *         DISABLE INTERRUPTS
13:        *         MOVE JMP INSTRUCTIONS TO RESTART AREA
14:        *         CLEAR ANY PENDING INTERRUPTS
15:        *         INITIALISE RTC HOURS AND MINS TO ZERO
16:        *         SET FLASH RATE DIVIDER = 8 (SLOW RATE)
17:        *         ENABLE INTERRUPTS
18:        *         REPEAT
19:        *                 FLASH THE LAMP ONCE
20:        *         UNTIL INFINITY
21:        *    END
22:        *
23:        *    INTERRUPT SERVICE ROUTINE 2
24:        *    ==============================
25:        *
26:        *    THIS PROGRAM IS EXECUTED WHEN A RTC INTERRUPT OCCURS.
27:        *    AFTER THE CLOCK HAS BEEN UPDATED IT CHECKS 8 INPUT CHANNELS
28:        *    AND COMPARES THE MEASURED VALUES WITH LIMITS. IF ANY
29:        *    CHANNEL IS IN AN ALARM CONDITION IT PRINTS AN ALARM MESSAGE
30:        *    AND CHANGES THE MAIN PROGRAM FLASH RATE.
31:        *
32:        *                   STRUCTURE
33:        *                   ''''''''''
34:        *    BEGIN
35:        *         SAVE ALL THE REGISTERS
36:        *         CANCEL THE INTERRUPT REQUEST
37:        *         UPDATE THE CLOCK
38:        *         SET UP SLOW CLOCK RATE ( DON'T EXPECT ANY ALARMS )
39:        *         CHANNEL NUMBER = 7
40:        *         REPEAT
41:        *             SELECT CHANNEL
42:        *             WAIT FOR MULTIPLEXER AND ADC INPUT TO SETTLE
43:        *             PULSE THE ADC
44:        *             WAIT FOR THE ADC TO FINISH
45:        *             READ A VALUE
46:        *             COMPARE VALUE WITH LIMITS
47:        *             IF EITHER ALARM CONDITION EXISTS THEN
48:        *                 SET UP FAST FLASH RATE
49:        *                 INFORM OF ALARM CONDITION
50:        *             ELSE
51:        *                 DO NOTHING
52:        *             ENDIF
53:        *             CHANNEL NUMBER := CHANNEL NUMBER -1
54:        *         UNTIL CHANNEL NUMBER IS NEGATIVE
55:        *         RESTORE REGISTERS
56:        *         RE-ENABLE INTERRUPTS
57:        *    END
58:        *
```

Figure 7.38   The structure of DAS1 and its interrupt service routine

```
 1:
 2:
 3:                    *   SUBROUTINE INFORM
 4:                    *   ===============
 5:                    *
 6:                    *   THIS SUBROUTINE IS CALLED WHEN AN ALARM CONDITION IS DETECTED
 7:                    *   ON ONE OF THE 8 INPUT CHANNELS.
 8:                    *   IT JUST INFORMS THE MAINTENANCE STAFF ABOUT THE ALARM
 9:                    *
10:                    *                    STRUCTURE
11:                    *                    '''''''''
12:                    *   BEGIN
13:                    *        CONVERT BINARY VALUE TO A VOLTAGE
14:                    *        IF THE ALARM CONDITION WAS HIGH THEN
15:                    *             PRINT 'HIGH'
16:                    *        ELSE
17:                    *             PRINT 'LOW'
18:                    *        ENDIF
19:                    *        PRINT 'ALARM ON CHANNEL NO. '
20:                    *        PRINT CHANNEL NUMBER
21:                    *        PRINT 'AT '
22:                    *        PRINT TIME
23:                    *        PRINT ' - VALUE '
24:                    *        PRINT VALUE
25:                    *        PRINT CARRAIGE RETURN-LINE FEED
26:                    *   END
27:                    *
28:  0000 CD6A00       INFORM: CALL    CONV            ; CONVERT BINARY TO VOLTAGE
29:  0003 3A6B00               LDA     ALMCDE          ; GET ALARM CODE
30:  0006 FE02                 CPI     02H             ; CHECK FOR HIGH ALARM
31:  0008 C21400               JNZ     LALRM
32:  000B 113900       HALRM:  LXI     D,MESSHI
33:  000E CD6C00               CALL    MESP            ; PRINT 'HIGH'
34:  0011 C31A00               JMP     REST
35:  0014 113F00       LALRM:  LXI     D,MESSLO
36:  0017 CD6C00               CALL    MESP            ; PRINT 'LOW'
37:  001A 114400       REST:   LXI     D,MESS1
38:  001D CD6C00               CALL    MESP            ; PRINT 'ALARM ON CHANNEL NO.
39:  0020 CD6900               CALL    PCHAN           ; PRINT CHANNEL NUMBER
40:  0023 115A00               LXI     D,MESS2
41:  0026 CD6C00               CALL    MESP            ; PRINT 'AT'
42:  0029 CD6D00               CALL    PRNIME          ; PRINT TIME
43:  002C 115F00               LXI     D,MESS3
44:  002F CD6C00               CALL    MESP            ; PRINT '- VALUE'
45:  0032 CD6E00               CALL    PRNVAL          ; PRINT VALUE
46:  0035 CD6F00               CALL    NEWL            ; START A NEW LINE
47:  0038 C9                   RET
48:                    *
49:                    *   MESSAGES
50:                    *
51:  0039 4849474820MESSHI:  DB      'HIGH ',00
52:  003F 4C4F572000MESSLO:  DB      'LOW ',00
53:  0044 414C41524DMESS1:   DB      'ALARM ON CHANNEL NO. ',00
54:  005A 2041542000MESS2:   DB      ' AT ',00
55:  005F 202D205641MESS3:   DB      ' - VALUE ',00
56:                    *
57:                    *   EXTERNAL REFERENCES
58:                    *
59:  0069 C9           PCHAN:  RET                     ; SEE SELF ASSESSMENT QUESTIONS
60:  006A C9           CONV:   RET
61:  006B             ALMCDE: DS      1
62:  006C C9           MESP:   RET
63:  006D C9           PRNIME: RET
64:  006E C9           PRNVAL: RET
65:  006F C9           NEWL:   RET
66:                    *
67:                    *
```

Figure 7.39   The INFORM subroutine

```
 1:
 2:
 3:                         *   INTERRUPT SERVICE ROUTINE 2
 4:                         *   ==========================
 5:                         *
 6:   0000 F5      INTR2:    PUSH    PSW             ; SAVE REGISTERS
 7:   0001 C5                PUSH    B
 8:   0002 D5                PUSH    D
 9:   0003 E5                PUSH    H
10:   0004 DBFE              IN      0FEH            ; CANCEL INTERRUPT REQUEST
11:   0006 CD4600            CALL    UPDATE          ; UPDATE THE CLOCK
12:   0009 3E08              MVI     A,08H
13:   000B 324700            STA     DIVIDR          ; SET UP SLOW FLASH RATE
14:   000E 3D                DCR     A
15:   000F 324500  SELECT:   STA     CHANNL          ; CHANNEL NUMBER = 7
16:   0012 D3FE              OUT     0FEH            ; SELECT CHANNEL
17:                         *
18:   0014 CD4800  SAMPLE:   CALL    PULSE           ; PULSE ADC CONVERT LINE
19:   0017 DBFE    WAIT:     IN      0FEH            ; READ THE READY BIT
20:   0019 E601              ANI     01H             ; CHECK IT
21:   001B C21700            JNZ     WAIT            ; WAIT IF NOT ZERO
22:                         *
23:   001E DBFF              IN      0FFH            ; READ VALUE
24:   0020 324900            STA     VALUE           ; STORE VALUE
25:   0023 CD4A00            CALL    COMP            ; COMPARE WITH LIMITS
26:   0026 78                MOV     A,B             ; GET ALARM CODE, IF ANY
27:   0027 FE00              CPI     00H             ; CHECK IT
28:   0029 CA3700            JZ      OK              ; OK IF ITS ZERO
29:                         *
30:   002C 324400  ALARM:    STA     ALMCDE          ; STORE ALARM CODE
31:   002F 3E01              MVI     A,01H
32:   0031 324700            STA     DIVIDR          ; SET UP FAST FLASH RATE
33:   0034 CD4B00            CALL    INFORM          ; TELL ABOUT ALARM CONDITION
34:                         *
35:   0037 3A4500  OK:       LDA     CHANNL          ; GET CHANNEL NUMBER BACK
36:   003A 3D                DCR     A
37:   003B C20F00            JNZ     SELECT          ; TO SELECT IF MORE TO DO
38:   003E E1                POP     H               ; OTHERWISE RESTORE REGISTERS
39:   003F D1                POP     D
40:   0040 C1                POP     B
41:   0041 F1                POP     PSW
42:   0042 FB                EI                      ; ENABLE INTERRUPTS
43:   0043 C9                RET                     ; AND RETURN
44:                         *
45:                         *   EXTERNAL REFERENCES DEFINED FOR THE ASSEMBLER
46:                         *
47:   0044          ALMCDE:  DS      1
48:   0045          CHANNL:  DS      1
49:   0046 C9       UPDATE:  RET
50:   0047          DIVIDR:  DS      1
51:   0048 C9       PULSE:   RET
52:   0049          VALUE:   DS      1
53:   004A C9       COMP:    RET
54:   004B          INFORM:  DS      1
55:                         *
```

Figure 7.40   The DAS1 interrupt service routine code. Its structure is given in Figure 7.38

Controlling the ADC is a matter of taking its CONVERT line low and then back high again. You will remember that our original PULSE subroutine did just this, and so we have used it again but slightly modified it to take account of the fact that the CONVERT I/O line is different. After PULSE comes the usual wait for the ADC to finish and then the READ-COMP operations.

If, after reading and comparing with the limits, any input is found to be in an alarm condition, the flash rate is increased and an alarm message is printed on the console. Printing is carried out in the INFORM subroutine and a typical message is:

`HIGH ALARM ON CHANNEL NO.3 AT 01:50 - VALUE 4.2`

This is much the same sort of message as was printed before, except that now we need to identify the channel number. You will not be surprised to see that INFORM, listed in Figure 7.39, has much in common with REPORT.

When all the channels have been measured and the error messages printed, the main program is re-entered with the flash rate indicating whether or not an alarm condition was detected on the last scan. The interrupt service routine which achieves all of this is listed in Figure 7.40.

Q7.16

Testing the program

Almost all the code needed here has been tested and used repeatedly in other programs so there are not likely to be many software problems. For testing the multichannel hardware of the system the simple circuit of Figure 7.41 was used. Each of the potentiometers

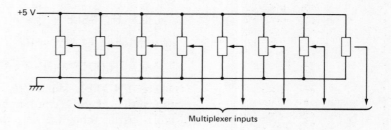

Figure 7.41 A simple test circuit for simulating transducers with their signal-conditioning amplifiers. All potentiometers are 50 kΩ

simulates a transducer and its signal-conditioning amplifier, but now alarm conditions can be easily produced by adjusting a potentiometer rather than the actual parameter being measured. Typical results from this program are given in Figure 7.42.

```
HIGH ALARM ON CHANNEL NO.  7 AT 00:06 - VALUE 4.20
HIGH ALARM ON CHANNEL NO.  7 AT 00:09 - VALUE 4.01
LOW ALARM ON CHANNEL NO.  4 AT 00:10 - VALUE 0.55
LOW ALARM ON CHANNEL NO.  4 AT 00:11 - VALUE 0.63
LOW ALARM ON CHANNEL NO.  4 AT 00:12 - VALUE 0.81
LOW ALARM ON CHANNEL NO.  4 AT 00:13 - VALUE 0.91
LOW ALARM ON CHANNEL NO.  0 AT 00:14 - VALUE 0.00
LOW ALARM ON CHANNEL NO.  1 AT 00:27 - VALUE 0.55
LOW ALARM ON CHANNEL NO.  1 AT 00:28 - VALUE 0.77
HIGH ALARM ON CHANNEL NO.  1 AT 00:32 - VALUE 4.62
HIGH ALARM ON CHANNEL NO.  2 AT 00:34 - VALUE 4.08
HIGH ALARM ON CHANNEL NO.  3 AT 00:36 - VALUE 4.32
LOW ALARM ON CHANNEL NO.  5 AT 00:38 - VALUE 0.12
LOW ALARM ON CHANNEL NO.  5 AT 00:39 - VALUE 0.94
HIGH ALARM ON CHANNEL NO.  6 AT 00:42 - VALUE 4.62
LOW ALARM ON CHANNEL NO.  6 AT 00:44 - VALUE 0.94
```

Figure 7.42   Typical results produced by DAS1

Accessing different look-up tables and limit values

Assuming that we had eight different transducers measuring eight different parameters, then it is quite likely that we would have eight different look-up tables and eight different sets of limits. The only way of knowing which is the relevant table and limits, is by referring to the channel number. When a single look-up table was used, its address was loaded into the H,L register pair just before the first bit in VALUE was examined. With our eight different look-up tables we need to replace the

```
LXI  H,TABLE  ;get table start address
```

instruction in CONV, with

```
CALL  FNDTBL  ;get relevant table start address
```

where FNDTBL stands for 'find table'. On return from the subroutine, H and L contain the start address of the relevant look-up table, just as though it were the only one in the system.

Subroutine FNDTBL is listed in Figure 7.43 and, except to say that it illustrates very nicely the use of the DW pseudo-op, we leave it without further comment. We could also write a subroutine called FNDLMT (find limits) which located the appropriate limit set for a particular measurement. Having found them it would store the two numbers in HLMT and LLMT just before the main part of COMP was executed. This final program of the chapter is offered as a student exercise.

Q7.17

References

7.1 E. L. Zuchs, 'Principles of data acquisitions and conversions' (the first of a five-part series), *Digital Design*, Vol. 9(5), (May 1979).

7.2 D. Aldridge, *Analog-to-digital Conversion Techniques with the M6800 Microprocessor System*, Motorola Application Note AN757.

7.3 R. Isaacson, *Converters for Use with Microprocessors*, Burr-Brown Application Note.

7.4 *ADC-H Series Data Sheet*, Analog Devices.

7.5 ZN425E Data Sheet, Ferranti Ltd.

Figure 7.43

```
 1:
 2:
 3:              *   SUBROUTINE NAME FNDTBL
 4:              *   =======================
 5:              *
 6:              *   THIS SUBROUTINE IS USED TO GET THE ADDRESS OF ONE OF 8 LOOK-UP
 7:              *   TABLES INTO H AND L SO THAT SUBROUTINE CONV HAS THE CORRECT
 8:              *   DATA TO WORK ON. EACH LOOK-UP TABLE CONTAINS A LIST OF NUMBERS
 9:              *   WHICH REPRESENT THE ACTUAL EQUIVALENT OF EACH BIT OF AN 8-BIT
10:              *   NUMBER.
11:              *
12:              *               STRUCTURE
13:              *               '''''''''
14:              *   BEGIN
15:              *       TRIAL TABLE NO. = 7
16:              *       GET ACTUAL TABLE NO.  (SAME AS CHANNEL NUMBER)
17:              *       POINT AT ADDRESS OF TRIAL TABLE
18:              *       WHILE TRIAL TABLE NO. <> ACTUAL TABLE NO. DO
19:              *       BEGIN
20:              *           POINT AT NEXT TABLE ADDRESS
21:              *           TRIAL TABLE NO. = TRIAL TABLE NO. - 1
22:              *       END
23:              *       GET TABLE ADDRESS
24:              *   END
25:              *
26:  0100                     ORG     0100H           ; FOR TESTING
27:  0100 0607    FNDTBL: MVI B,07H           ; TRIAL TABLE NO. = 7
28:  0102 3A2701          LDA     CHANNL          ; ACTUAL TABLE NO. TO A
29:  0105 211701          LXI     H,ADDTBL        ; POINT AT TABLE 7 ADDRESS
30:  0108 B8      TRYAGN: CMP     B               ; COMPARE TRIAL WITH ACTUAL
31:  0109 CA1201          JZ      GOTIT           ; IF THE SAME YOU'VE GOT IT
32:  010C 23              INX     H               ; ELSE POINT AT NEXT ADDRESS
33:  010D 23              INX     H
34:  010E 05              DCR     B               ; TRIAL TABLE NO. DECREMENTED
35:  010F C30801          JMP     TRYAGN          ; AND TRY AGAIN
36:              *
37:  0112 5E      GOTIT:  MOV     E,M             ; GET LS HALF OF ADDRESS
```

(Continued)

```
Figure 7.43 continued
38:  0113 23         INX     H
39:  0114 56         MOV     D,M             ; THEN MS HALF
40:  0115 EB         XCHG                    ; ADDRESS INTO H,L
41:  0116 C9         RET                     ; ALL READY FOR CONV
42:            *
43:            *  AT 'RET' H AND L CONTAIN THE PROPER LOOK-UP TABLE START ADDRESS.
44:            *
45:  0117 0010  ADDTBL: DW    TABLE7          ; TABLE 7 ADDRESS
46:  0119 0012         DW     TABLE6
47:  011B 0014         DW     TABLE5
48:  011D 0016         DW     TABLE4
49:  011F 0018         DW     TABLE3
50:  0121 001A         DW     TABLE2
51:  0123 001C         DW     TABLE1
52:  0125 001E         DW     TABLE0
53:            *
54:            *  FOR TESTING, IMAGINE THAT TABLES ARE LOCATED AT THE FOLLOWING ADDRESSES.
55:            *
56:  0127 03   CHANNL: DB     03H             ; CHANGE IN DDT
57:  1000             ORG     1000H
58:  1000 00   TABLE7: NOP
59:  1200             ORG     1200H
60:  1200 00   TABLE6: NOP
61:  1400             ORG     1400H
62:  1400 00   TABLE5: NOP
63:  1600             ORG     1600H
64:  1600 00   TABLE4: NOP
65:  1800             ORG     1800H
66:  1800 00   TABLE3: NOP
67:  1A00             ORG     1A00H
68:  1A00 00   TABLE2: NOP
69:  1C00             ORG     1C00H
70:  1C00 00   TABLE1: NOP
71:  1E00             ORG     1E00H
72:  1E00 00   TABLE0: NOP
73:            *
74:  1E01             END
```

Figure 7.43　The FNDTBL subroutine

Questions

7.1　An equivalent circuit diagram of the DAC register network shown in Figure 7.1 is given in Figure 7.44. The output voltage is given by the formula,

$$V_0 = -\tfrac{1}{2}(V_1 + \tfrac{1}{2}V_2 + \tfrac{1}{4}V_3 + \tfrac{1}{8}V_4)$$

Each of the input voltages is either 0 or –5 V depending upon whether the digital input to the controlling switch is 0 or 1. Tabulate the 16 possible combinations of digital input, and against each record the corresponding DAC output voltage.

7.2　Define the term 'resolution' when applied to an ADC or DAC.

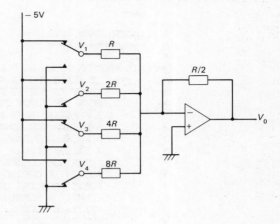

Figure 7.44 An equivalent circuit for the weighted-resistor DAC network

7.3 Write a program which can be used with the circuit shown in Figure 7.4 to generate the following waveform:

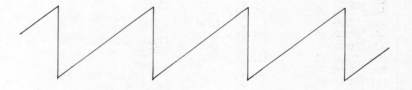

7.4 A 4-bit successive-approximation ADC converts an analogue input of 3/8ths the full-scale input to an equivalent digital output. Write down the successive numbers which are generated during the conversion process.

7.5 Write a program that can be used with the circuit of Figure 7.9 to initiate a counting-type ADC.

7.6 Use the formula given in the text to calculate the 4-character hexadecimal numbers which would produce delays of 0.1 s and 75 µs.

7.7 It is required that the START subroutine called from ADC3 should only return control to the main program when the START push-button is first released and then a 0 to 1 change is detected. Write a structure for the subroutine.

7.8 Discuss the way in which the 8080 handles interrupts and the hardware which could be used to generate the necessary information needed by the microprocessor to locate the appropriate interrupt service routine.

```
 1:
 2:
 3:              *    PROGRAM NAME INT3
 4:              *    ========================
 5:              *
 6:              *    THIS PROGRAM WORKS AS FOLLOWS:
 7:              *         1. IT READS FROM A SINGLE INPUT AND, FOR AS LONG AS THE
 8:              *            INPUT IS A 1 IT KEEPS AN LAMP PERMANENTLY SWITCHED ON.
 9:              *         2. WHEN THE INPUT CHANGES TO A 0 THE LAMP FLASHES.
10:              *         3. A FLASHING LAMP IS INTERPRETED AS AN ALARM CONDITION,
11:              *            AND WHEN THE CONDITION IS ACKNOWLEDGED BY OPERATING AN
12:              *            ACKNOWLEDGE PUSH BUTTON, THE FLASH RATE IS REDUCED BY
13:              *            A FACTOR OF 8.
14:              *         4. AFTER SOME CORRECTIVE MEASURE HAS BEEN TAKEN, A RE-TRY
15:              *            BUTTON IS OPERATED. THIS CAUSES THE PROGRAM TO READ
16:              *            AGAIN FROM THE INPUT AND, IF IT IS NOW A 1, THE LAMP IS
17:              *            TURNED ON PERMANENTLY. IF THE ALARM CONDITION STILL
18:              *            EXISTS HOWEVER, THE LAMP IS AGAIN FLASHED AT
19:              *            THE FAST RATE.
20:              *
21:              *    THE ACKNOWLEDGE AND RE-TRY BUTTONS ARE CONNECTED TO INTERRUPT INPUTS.
22:              *
23:              *                    STRUCTURE
24:              *                    ''''''''''
25:              *    BEGIN
26:              *        REPEAT
27:              *            LIGHT THE LAMP
28:              *            REPEAT
29:              *                    READ THE INPUT
30:              *            UNTIL INPUT = 0
31:              *            FLASH RATE DIVIDER  = 1  ( FAST )
32:              *            RE-TRY = 0
33:              *            REPEAT
34:              *                    FLASH THE LAMP
35:              *            UNTIL RE-TRY = 1
36:              *        UNTIL INFINITY
37:              *    END.
38:              *
39:              *    INTERRUPT SERVICE ROUTINE NO. 1
40:              *    ================================
41:              *
42:              *    BEGIN  (* AFTER ACKNOWLEDGE BUTTON HAS BEEN PRESSED *)
43:              *        FLASH RATE DIVIDER = 8  ( SLOW )
44:              *    END.
45:              *
46:              *    INTERRUPT SERVICE ROUTINE NO. 2
47:              *    ================================
48:              *
49:              *    BEGIN  (* AFTER RE-TRY BUTTON HAS BEEN PRESSED *)
50:              *        RE-TRY = 1
51:              *    END.
52:              *
```

Figure 7.45 A suitable structure for the program specified in Question 7.10

7.9 Explain why interrupt service routine instructions cannot be loaded directly into the restart area when programs using interrupts are run under CP/M. Describe a technique which can be used to overcome this problem.

7.10 A program reads a single input from a switch and for as long as the switch connects a 1, a lamp is permanently illuminated. When the switch is changed over so that a logic 0 alarm condition is connected, the program should rapidly flash the lamp on and off. (A suitable FLASH/DELAY routine is listed as part of Figure 7.21.)

When the operator acknowledges the alarm condition by operating an ACCEPT push-button this generates an interrupt. The interrupt service routine slows down the flash rate by a factor of 8 and then the interrupted part of the main program is re-entered.

Having, hopefully, corrected the fault the operator pushes a RE-TRY button. This generates another different interrupt which causes the main program to retest the alarm input. If no alarm condition now exists the lamp should be held on permanently once again. If the fault has not cleared, the lamp should resume flashing at the fast rate so that the operator will need to operate ACCEPT and RE-TRY as explained above.

A suggested program structure is given in Figure 7.45 and the connection diagram in Figure 7.46. Write and test the program which implements the structure using RST 1 and RST 2. Note that the MOVE subroutine is only needed if your program runs under CP/M. If you can load instructions directly into the restart area then do so.

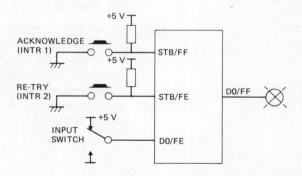

Figure 7.46   Connection diagram used with the program INT3

7.11 A main program is normally in an endless loop doing nothing. When an interrupt occurs (interrupt 1) a lamp is flashed slowly on and off from within the interrupt service routine. When a second interrupt occurs (interrupt 2), the lamp is turned off and control returns to the main program.

Write and test a program for the system. Notice that this is an example of one interrupt service routine interrupting another.

7.12   Write a program called RTC which, once every minute, prints the message

"RUNTIME = "

and then the time. The clock is updated when an interrupt occurs but in between interrupts the main program does nothing useful.

7.13   The program ADC4 and its hardware are to be modified so that when a STATUS button, connected to interrupt 2 input, is operated a message such as

RUNTIME = 01:50, TOTAL ALARM COUNT SO FAR 0003

is printed. Explain how the main program will need to be modified and write a suitable interrupt service routine and a subroutine called PRNALM which prints out the error, or alarm, count.

7.14   A data acquisition system has 64 inputs and uses a number of 8-line to 1-line multiplexers to select one of these inputs for measurement. Draw a block diagram which shows how the multiplexers would be connected.

7.15   Explain why a sample and hold circuit may be needed in a data acquisition system. How would you determine whether or not one was necessary?

7.16   The program DAS1 prints the channel number when an alarm message is printed. Write a suitable subroutine called PCHAN which would be used for this purpose.

7.17   Section 7.11 referred to a program called FNDLMT which used the channel number to locate high and low limits for the particular measurement being made. Assuming that those limits are stored in pairs, with the low limit value at the lowest address, but that pairs could be scattered around anywhere in memory, write a program which finds the appropriate limits and stores the low limit value in LLMT and the high value in HLMT.

Chapter 8 Stepping motors

Objectives of this chapter *When you have completed studying this chapter you should be able to:*

1 *Appreciate the advantages of using stepping motors in open-loop position control systems.*
2 *Understand the operation of the three most common types of stepping motor.*
3 *Understand the terms used to describe the stepping motor characteristics and performance.*

In this and the following chapter we shall discuss stepping motors: how they work, how they can be interfaced with microprocessor systems and how they can be used to advantage in position control systems. We shall also explain the terms used to describe their performance so that the information contained on data sheets can be properly assessed.

This chapter is concerned with the construction and operation of stepping motors, and the next with the problems of interfacing them with microprocessor systems.

8.1 Introduction

All rotating electric motors consist essentially of a stator, a rotor and some windings. When a conventional electric motor is switched on the rotor rotates continuously until the power is switched off again. Stepping motor action differs from this because, even when the motor is switched on, the shaft remains stationary until a step pulse is sent to the motor. When the stepping motor drive circuit receives a step pulse it drives the rotor through a precise angle, or step, and then stops until the next step pulse is received. Consequently, provided that the maximum permissible motor load is not exceeded, the total angular displacement of the shaft is equal to the step angle multiplied by the number of pulses supplied. This relationship is further simplified by saying that the shaft position is directly proportional to the number of step pulses supplied since the step angle for any particular stepping motor is fixed.

The majority of stepping motors have step angles in the range 0.45 to 90° with the most common configuration, particularly for machine tool applications, being 1.8° per step (200 steps per revolution). The positional error at each step is typically ±5% but this obviously depends on the motor. The important point to note here is that this error is not cumulative; irrespective of the number of pulses supplied, the final positional accuracy is always within ±5% of one step.

For accurate linear rather than rotational positioning, the motor shaft can be coupled to a leadscrew and nut. The relationship between the displacement and the number of step pulses is then:

$$\text{Linear displacement} = \frac{\text{Number of step pulses}}{\text{Steps per revolution}} \times \text{Pitch of leadscrew}$$

If the leadscrew has a pitch of 0.2 inch/revolution (5 tpi) and the motor step angle is 1.8°, then each step pulse produces a linear travel of 0.001 inch. You will appreciate that such an arrangement would find immediate application in automatic lathes, milling and drilling machines, X-Y coordinate tables and positioning mechanisms of all sorts.

The major advantage that stepping motors have over alternative drive systems is that control can be open loop. This means that there is no need for displacement transducers or complicated feedback (closed loop) control systems. All that is required is an electronic counter which counts drive pulses as they are sent to the motor. This counter can be built into the software if the motor is controlled from a microprocessor, or it may be an independent logic circuit. At any point in the operating cycle the number in the counter is a measure of angular or linear displacement from a datum position. Furthermore, the rate at which drive pulses are supplied determines the rotational or linear speed of travel so that velocity and acceleration can also be

Q8.1   controlled without feedback.

8.2   Stepping motor principles

The three common types of stepping motor are variable reluctance, permanent magnet and hybrid motors. Fundamentally they are the same kind of device but their different characteristics, which result from different methods of construction, are important when choosing a stepping motor for a particular application. A brief review

Q8.2   of stepping motor principles is therefore of value.

The variable reluctance (VR) stepping motor

This type of stepping motor has a cylindrical soft-iron rotor with longitudinal slots machined along the surface of the cylinder. The slots occur at precise angular intervals around the circumference of the cylinder so that when viewed end-on it looks like a toothed wheel.

The rotor is mounted inside a stator which also has teeth projecting inwards towards the rotor. Predictable movement of the rotor is ensured by making the number of stator teeth different to the number of rotor teeth. In Figure 8.1 for example, in which the longitudinal slots are somewhat exaggerated, the stator has 8 teeth and the rotor only 6. This means that when two stator teeth are aligned with two rotor teeth all the other teeth must be misaligned by at least 15°.

Unlike the rotor, the stator teeth have coils wound on them. When these windings are connected in turn to a d.c. supply, the stator teeth behave like individual electromagnets attracting the closest rotor tooth. By properly sequencing the order in which these windings are energised, the rotor can be made to step from one position in which one pair of teeth are aligned to a different position in which a different pair are aligned. For example, if the stator coils labelled A (phase A) in Figure 8.1 are energised, the rotor will align itself with the stator field as shown in the diagram. If now the d.c. supply is switched to phase D, the rotor will step in an anticlockwise direction through the step angle of 15°. Had the supply been switched to B instead of D the rotor would have stepped through the same angle but in the opposite direction. The drive sequence for clockwise rotation is therefore A, B, C, D, A, etc., and for anticlockwise rotation it is A, D, C, B, A, etc. VR motors are manufactured with step angles which range from 1.8 to 15°. From the above description you will appreciate that if the step angle is to be reduced the number of stator and rotor teeth must be increased. This is certainly true but there are other ways of reducing the step angle such as changing the winding configuration and excitation sequence.

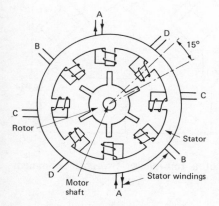

Figure 8.1 Basic four-phase variable reluctance stepping motor

Q8.3

VR motors can be operated at high speed but are most suitable for use with light loads. Since the rotor of a VR motor has practically no residual magnetism, there is no magnetic force to hold the rotor in position when the stator supply is switched off. Such a force exists in other types of stepping motor and is known as detent or residual torque. It is often a very useful motor characteristic.

Q8.4

Another drawback with this type of motor is that the rotor has little inherent inertia. This means that when the rotor is stepped it tends to oscillate about the new position before finally coming to rest. Although evident in other types of stepping motor, this phenomenon is much more severe in VR-type motors.

The permanent magnet (PM) stepping motor

The permanent magnet stepping motor consists of a radially

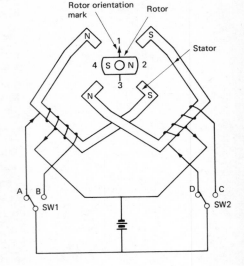

Phases energised	Rotor position No.	Direction
A, D	1	
A, C	2	
B, C	3	
B, D	4	
A, D	1	

Figure 8.2 Operating principle of a four-phase, two-pole permanent magnet stepping motor

magnetised permanent magnet rotor and a wound stator. Its action is illustrated in the much simplified diagram of Figure 8.2.

With the switches in the positions shown, phases A and D are energised so that the rotor aligns itself at position 1. If now SW2 is changed over so that phase C is energised, the magnetic field in that arm of the stator is reversed. The change in direction of the magnetic field pulls the rotor through 90° in a clockwise direction so that it now lines up at position 2. To continue the clockwise rotation, SW1 is switched to B, then SW2 is switched to D and finally, to complete one revolution, SW1 is switched back to A. If the switching sequence is reversed the rotor moves in an anti-clockwise direction.

Although the step angle of this motor is 90°, half-step operation would be possible if the switches had a third position which, when selected, turned off both stator phases. For example, assume that the rotor is aligned as shown in Figure 8.2 and then SW2 is switched to this third position in which phases C and D are both de-energised. The only magnetic field now acting on the rotor is generated by the A/B stator windings and the direction of that field will pull the rotor through 45° to a position midway between positions 1 and 2. When phase C is subsequently energised the rotor will complete a full step by aligning itself at position 2.

In Table 8.1, which summarises the switching sequences for full- and

Table 8.1 *Switching sequence for half and full-step operation of a four-phase stepping motor*

Full step					Half step				
Step	Phase				Step	Phase			
	A	B	C	D		A	B	C	D
1	1	0	0	1	1	1	0	0	1
2	1	0	1	0	2	1	0	0	0
3	0	1	1	0	3	1	0	1	0
4	0	1	0	1	4	0	0	1	0
1	1	0	0	1	5	0	1	1	0
					6	0	1	0	0
					7	0	1	0	1
					8	0	0	0	1
					1	1	0	0	1

half-step operation, a 1 indicates that a phase is energised and a 0 that a phase is de-energised.

Note that most types of stepping motors can be operated in half-step mode. It is not just a characteristic of permanent magnet motors.

The hybrid stepping motor

Combining some of the characteristics of permanent magnet motors and others of variable reluctance motors, the hybrid stepping motor is the third main type of stepping motor. It is sometimes called a permanent magnet or hybrid (permanent magnet) stepping motor because its rotor is an axially magnetised cylindrical permanent magnet. Attached at each end of the rotor are gear-like hubs which, typically, have 50 teeth. These hubs are deliberately misaligned so that the teeth at the north end of the magnet are exactly 180° out of phase with the teeth at the south end. The photograph of Figure 8.3 shows the rotor construction quite clearly.

Figure 8.3   The rotor of a 200 steps/revolution permanent magnet (hybrid) type stepping motor. *(Photo courtesy of Sigma Instruments Inc., USA)*

Figure 8.4   The stator comprises eight poles, each with five teeth protruding from the pole face. The stator windings are clearly shown. *(Photo courtesy of Sigma Instruments Inc., USA)*

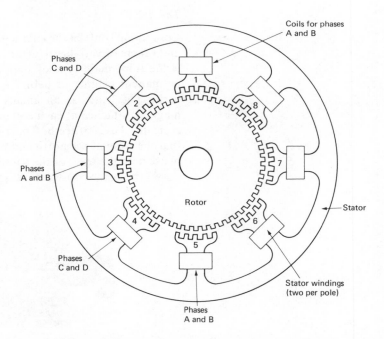

Figure 8.5   Stator/rotor configurations for 200 steps/revolution hybrid stepping motors

Each of the eight stator poles also has teeth cut into their face as shown in the photograph of Figure 8.4. Figure 8.5 shows the alignment of rotor and stator teeth at one end of the rotor.

As before, the rotor of a hybrid stepping motor is made to move, one step at a time, by properly sequencing the stator drive currents. To explain in more detail, assume initially that phase A is energised so that the teeth on stator poles 1 and 5 are south poles and those on 3 and 7 are north poles. Considering just the north end of the rotor, this means that the teeth of poles 1 and 5 will attract rotor teeth and the teeth of poles 3 and 7 will repel them. At the south end of the rotor the situation is exactly reversed. In other words the rotor will align itself with the stator field as shown in Figure 8.5. Note that in this position the stator and rotor teeth at positions 2, 4, 6 and 8 are 90°, or one-quarter of a rotor pitch, out of alignment.

Now imagine that phase C or D is energised. Depending upon which of the even-numbered poles become north poles and which become south poles, the rotor will move in a clockwise or anticlockwise direction through $\frac{1}{4}$ of a rotor tooth pitch. If there are 50 teeth on the rotor, that movement is the equivalent of 1/200th of a revolution, so that Figure 8.5 actually relates to the popular 200 steps/revolution hybrid motor.

Practical four-phase hybrid motors have their stator windings connected as shown in Figure 8.6. With this winding configuration, the switching sequences already listed in Table 8.1 are used for half- and full-step operation. The main characteristics of this motor are,

1 Because the rotor is a permanent magnet there is always some detent or residual torque.
2 If accelerated from low speed the motor can operate at speeds up to 30,000 steps per second.
3 Positional resolution is good since, in half-step mode, the step angle is only 0.9°.

Of all the stepping motors the hybrid type is probably the most common and is widely used in all kinds of linear and angular positioning systems.

Figure 8.6 Stator windings for standard four-phase hybrid stepping motors. Phases A,B and C,D each constitute bifilar windings on alternate stator poles

Q8.5

8.3 Stepping motor terminology

At this point in the discussion it is appropriate to define some of the terms used to describe stepping motor behaviour.

Static and holding torque

When a stepping motor reaches a step position its rotor is held stationary by the magnetic field developed in the energised stator

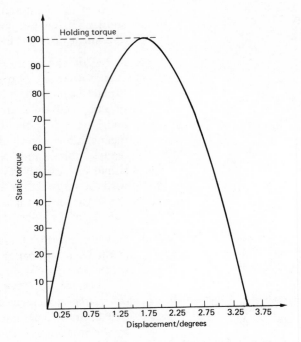

Figure 8.7   Variation of static torque with displacement angle

windings. If an attempt is made to rotate the motor shaft by hand the magnetic field will oppose the rotation. The external force needed to overcome the magnetic pull is called the static torque and it is a function of the displacement angle. Figure 8.7 shows the relationship between static torque and the displacement angle for a 200 steps/ revolution hybrid motor. The maximum value of the static torque is called the holding torque.

Dynamic torque

Even when operated at low speed, the useful torque which a stepping motor can develop is always less than the holding torque. At 50 steps per second for example, the dynamic torque available to overcome frictional forces and the total load inertia is typically 80% of the holding torque. As speed increases the torque reduces as shown in Figure 8.8. The reason for this reduction is that the stator windings are inductive. When the proper d.c. supply is connected to an inductor, the current builds up gradually towards its rated value. If the winding currents are switched on and off too rapidly the rated current is never reached and so the motor develops less than its low-speed torque. Increasing the switching rate reduces the average current, and therefore the torque, still further.

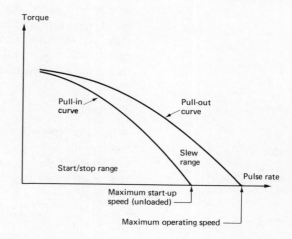

Figure 8.8 Dynamic characteristics of a stepping motor

Pull-in rate

When a stepping motor which is at rest receives a step pulse it must develop sufficient torque to overcome all retarding forces and rotate the shaft through the step angle before the next step pulse is received. If the total load inertia is too great or, conversely, the maximum torque which the motor can develop is too little, or the step pulses are applied too rapidly, the motor will not be able to keep up with the demanded speed. If this happens the one-to-one correspondence between the number of command pulses and the number of steps taken is lost. For a given load on the motor the maximum speed at which the motor will start without losing steps is called the pull-in rate. The relationship between motor torque and the pull-in rate is the inner curve of Figure 8.8.

Pull-out rate

When a motor is already running, the speed, or step rate, can be gradually increased to a point where the motor can only just drive the load at the demanded speed. Any further increase in demanded speed will result in lost steps. This critical step rate is called the pull-out rate and is obviously a function of the motor torque. The graph which relates speed and pull-out rate is called the pull-out curve. It is the outer curve in Figure 8.8.

Slew range

The area bounded by the pull-in and pull-out curves of Figure 8.8 is called the slew range. When operating within this range the motor cannot be stopped, started or reversed without losing steps. If high-speed operation is required the motor must be gradually accelerated from standstill to the required slew rate and then decelerated to a speed within the pull-in curve before being stopped. This drive technique is called ramping.

Resonance

When a step pulse is applied to a stepping motor the rotor accelerates towards the next step position and invariably overshoots it. As shown in Figure 8.9, the rotor response to a single step command is similar to that of an under-damped second-order system (LCR circuit) when a

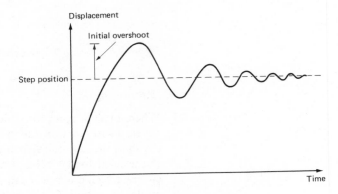

Figure 8.9   Rotor response to a single step input

step voltage is applied. At certain critical step rates this overshoot can lead to oscillation of the rotor so that the motor runs erratically or even reverses. Various forms of electronic and mechanical dampers are available to minimise this effect but, apart from increasing the cost of the system, the less complex of them also increase the load on the motor thereby reducing the useful torque which can be developed. If a stepping motor is found to resonate at certain step rates the cheapest effective solution is not to operate at these speeds. Acceleration through resonance to the required operating speed is acceptable provided that the resonance range is cleared within a pulse or two.

Q8.6

8.4   Stepping motor drives

Fundamentally, a stepping motor is driven from one step position to the next by switching a d.c. power supply from one set of stator windings to another. The simplest, and cheapest, way of driving stator windings is with a single drive transistor as shown in Figure 8.10(a). When the transistor is turned on the supply voltage V_1 is just sufficient to produce the rated winding current, and when the

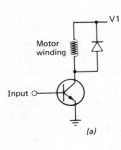

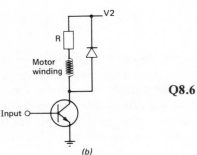

Figure 8.10 Drive circuits for a single stator winding. The added resistance in circuit *(b)* reduces the winding time constant and therefore permits faster switching rates

transistor is turned off, the diode provides a path through which the current can decay without damaging the transistor.

This circuit is perfectly adequate so long as the interval between successive drive pulses is not less than the winding time constant, L/R. At higher step rates than this the torque reduces because the rated winding currents are never reached.

The most common way of increasing the motor torque at high speeds is to connect a resistor in series with each winding and increase the supply voltage so that the steady-state current again reaches the rated value; see Figure 8.10(b). The added resistance reduces the effective winding time constant so that the rated current is established more quickly allowing the motor to be operated at higher speed. This technique of adding resistance in series with the stator windings is used in the standard unipolar drive circuit shown in Figure 8.11. Since phases A and B or C and D are never switched on at the same time, a single resistance can be shared by each pair of phases.

Bipolar drive circuits, similar to the one shown in Figure 8.12, are said to produce between 20 and 40% more torque than unipolar drives at low speed, but require two power supplies. They are also

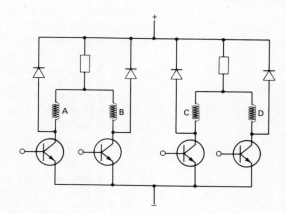

Figure 8.11   Unipolar drive circuit for four-phase hybrid type stepping motor

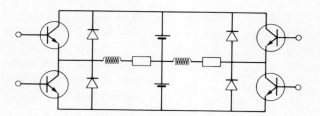

Figure 8.12   Typical bipolar stepping motor drive circuit

more expensive than unipolar drives. A third way of driving stepping motors, used when optimum motor performance is required, is to use a d.c. chopper circuit to supply the motor windings. At the beginning of every step pulse the driver supplies a high voltage to rapidly build up the winding current. Just before the rated current is exceeded the supply is switched off and the current begins to decay. When the current has fallen to, typically, 90% of the rated current, the supply is switched on again. This drive method gives improved high-speed performance without the need for series resistance. Inevitably

Q8.7   however, it is also more expensive than simpler circuits.

8.5   Selecting stepping motors

From the foregoing discussion it should be clear that the torque developed by a stepping motor is heavily dependent upon the drive circuit. In any application the motor torque must be sufficient to drive a load which is characterised in terms of total load inertia and frictional losses. Also relevant when selecting motors for particular applications are the step angle, the time to accelerate the load from rest to the rated speed and the rated speed itself. When all these system parameters are known, standard formulae, which are often included on manufacturer's data sheets [8.7, 8.8], are used to calculate how much torque is actually needed to drive the load under specified conditions. Having decided upon that, a motor/driver combination which will supply that torque can be selected by referring to the relevant torque-speed curves.

You should appreciate however, that matching stepping motors with mechanical loads is not a precise procedure. It is always prudent to treat calculated figures as a rough guide and then select a motor with more than adequate capability.

8.6   Stepping motor application areas

In recent years the applications of stepping motors have expanded mainly because digital control systems have become predominant and the stepping motor is essentially a digital device. With open-loop control possible, applications cover all types of position control, speed control, timing and remote control systems. In the computing field stepping motors are used in paper tape readers, printers, floppy disk head drives and X-Y plotters. In mechanical engineering they are used in engine speed control systems to regulate fuel flow, and in numerically controlled machine tool drives. There are also applications in medical electronics and a whole variety of other scientific and engineering activities.

As microprocessor system engineers, we are interested in them because many systems have been implemented, and new systems proposed, in which stepping motors are controlled from microprocessors. The interface techniques employed and the form of the controlling software are therefore directly relevant.

References and bibliography

8.1 W. F. Waller (Editor), *Electronic Data Library: Volume 2 – Servomechanisms*, Morgan-Grampian (1969).

8.2 IEE Conference Publication No. 136, *Small Electrical Machines*, IEE London (1976).

8.3 ERA Technical Seminar Publication ERA 78-101, *Selecting Small Motors for Control Applications*, Leatherhead (1979).

8.4 P. Giacomo, 'A stepping motor primer', *Byte* (February and March, 1979).

8.5 A. Hughes, 'High speed operation of stepping motors', *Electronics and Power* (October 1978).

8.6 W. Riggs, 'Small stepping motors meet varied application requirements', *Computer Design (USA)*, (February 1978).

8.7 *SIGMA Stepping Motors, Synchronous Motors, Electronic Drivers and Controls – Data Catalogue*, Unimatic Engineers Ltd, 122 Granville Road, London NW2.

8.8 *Slo-syn; Synchronous/Stepping Motor Data Catalogue*, Superior Electric Nederland BV, The Hague, Netherlands. Also T1 Supplies.

Questions

8.1 State the main advantage of using stepping motors in angular and linear positioning systems.

8.2 What are the three main types of stepping motor?

8.3 Describe how a variable reluctance stepping motor works.

8.4 Define detent, or residual, torque in a stepping motor.

8.5 Briefly describe the operation and construction of the industry-standard, 200 steps/revolution hybrid stepping motor.

8.6 Define the following terms when used to describe particular stepping motor characteristics:

1 Static torque.   4 Maximum pull-out rate.
2 Dynamic torque.   5 Slew range.
3 Maximum pull-in rate. 6 Resonance.

8.7 Explain why the torque developed by a stepping motor reduces as the operating speed increases and suggest two ways in which the torque/speed curve could be improved.

Chapter 9 Interfacing stepping motors

Objectives of this chapter *When you have completed studying this chapter you should be able to:*

1 *Understand the hardware/software alternatives of sequencing the drive to the stator windings of a stepping motor.*
2 *Write programs to drive a stepping motor at a constant rate in either direction.*
3 *Appreciate the need for ramping when driving stepping motors, and the difficulty of achieving uniform acceleration and deceleration.*

9.1 Introduction

Having read through Chapter 8 you will know that a stepping motor is driven from one step position to the next by switching a d.c. supply from one set of stator windings to another. For a standard 4-phase motor having phases labelled A, B, C and D, the stator excitation sequences for half- and full-step operation were listed in Table 8.1. Since the generation of these sequences is a straightforward logic design problem they can be generated either in a control program (software) if the motor is to be directly controlled from a microprocessor, or dedicated logic can be designed to generate the sequence (hardware). In both cases level conversion circuits are needed to amplify the low-power logic levels so that rated winding currents can be achieved. The two alternatives are illustrated in Figure 9.1 (overleaf).

9.2 The software solution

If the software solution is adopted, four lines of an output port are connected directly to four drive transistors which supply the stator windings, and the excitation sequence is either stored with the program code in a table of numbers, or calculated step-by-step. When the sequence is held in a table, the motor is stepped-on one position by retrieving the next number from the table and sending it to the output port. For instance, if the four phases are connected to the least

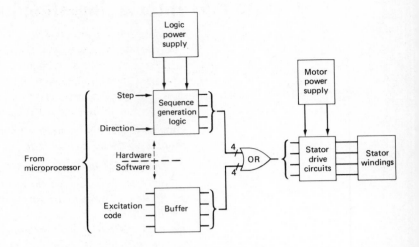

Figure 9.1 Two alternative ways of generating the stator drive sequence for a four-phase stepping motor

significant four lines of an 8-bit output port, the table may contain the following hexadecimal numbers:

Phase	A	B	C	D	Hexadecimal
Port line	D3	D2	D1	D0	table contents
	1	0	0	1	09
	1	0	1	0	0A
	0	1	1	0	06
	0	1	0	1	05

Since data lines D7 to D4 are not used in the sequence generation program the most significant hexadecimal character of each table entry could be anything. We have arbitarily assumed that it is zero.

Notice that the table is circular in the sense that the next table entry after 05 is 09. To step the motor in a clockwise direction the table is traversed from top to bottom, and to step in the opposite direction the table is traversed from bottom to top.

Pausing here to think about the program which accesses this table, you may, properly, come to the conclusion that it is not as simple as we have implied. Your first thought may be to initialise the H,L register pair to the start address of the table and then increment (HL) when accessing the next table entry. The obvious problem is how to make the table appear circular and, having solved that problem, what happens when the direction of travel is reversed? Undoubtedly several different solutions could be found but the software is now

Q9.1 becoming more complex than we would like.

9.3 The hardware solution

A much more common way of controlling stepping motors is to use external hardware to generate the excitation sequence. The microprocessor controls this hardware by supplying a step signal which advances the sequence generator from one state to the next, and a direction signal which determines the order in which successive states are generated. Figure 9.2 illustrates two ways in which this hardware could be provided.

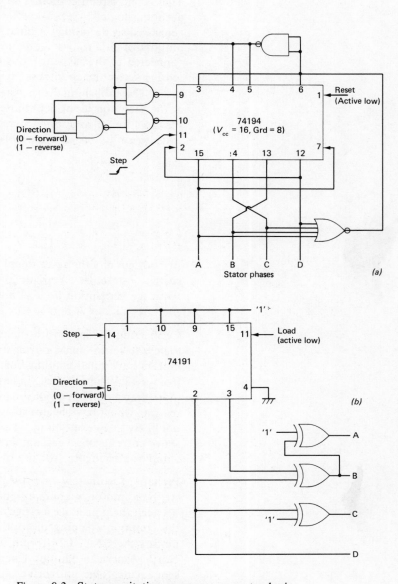

Figure 9.2 Stator excitation sequence generator logic

The first circuit uses a bidirectional shift register (74194) to generate the sequence. When the shift register is reset the parallel load data inputs (pins 3, 4, 5 and 6) are set to 1001 and the mode control inputs (pins 9 and 10) are programmed for parallel load. The first step pulse loads 1001 into the shift register which switches on phases A and D. Thereafter the direction signal determines whether this pattern will be shifted right or left, and therefore whether the motor will step clockwise or anti-clockwise, when further step pulses are applied.

The second circuit combines an up-down counter (74191) with some decoding logic (7486). The four states in the full-step sequence are generated by decoding the binary number at the least significant two outputs of this four-stage counter. In this case the reset signal is connected to the asynchronous load terminal (pin 11) so that when load is active the counter is preset to 1111. This switches on phases A and D establishing the first step position. After that the logic level at the direction input determines the count direction and therefore the direction of rotation. The relationship between the counter state and the excitation state is recorded in the following table:

Pin 2	Pin 3	A	B	C	D
1	1	1	0	0	1
0	0	1	0	1	0
0	1	0	1	1	0
1	0	0	1	0	1
1	1	1	0	0	1

In both circuits the reset signal would normally be the output of a switch-on-reset (R-C) circuit so that when power is first applied, the sequence generation logic is automatically reset to the state which energises phases A and D.

Connecting the logic with the motor is the circuit which translates logic levels into higher-power stator drive signals. Some low-torque motors have rated winding currents of 200 mA or less and operate from a 12 V supply. For these motors the drive circuit need be no more than a number of Darlington drivers (Figure 9.3), although for reasons which have been explained before, such an arrangement is not likely to give optimum performance. Larger motors operate with stator currents of several ampères so that their drive circuits are more complex and involve the use of discrete power transistors.

Perhaps fortunately for the microprocessor systems engineer, stepping motor manufacturers and other electronics companies between them produce a range of interface cards and chips to suit all the common stepping motors. For low-torque, four-phase hybrid motors the SAA 1027 16-pin integrated circuit available from the North American Phillips Corporation contains all the necessary sequencing logic and drive circuits. More powerful motors need compatible drive cards.

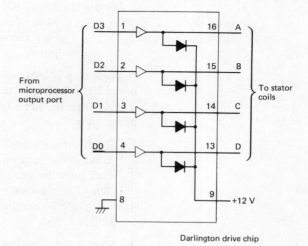

Figure 9.3   Drive circuit for low-power stepping motors showing four of the (typically) seven drivers in a 16-pin chip

Drive cards and chips make the task of interfacing stepping motors with microprocessors relatively easy because the control program is only required to generate step and direction signals. Rotational speed is set by the rate at which step pulses are generated and if acceleration and deceleration are necessary it is just a matter of increasing or decreasing the step rate.

9.4   A single-step program

Before writing some more-realistic stepping motor control programs, let us consider what is involved in generating a single-step pulse. Two I/O lines will be needed, one for the step pulse and another for the direction signal, and we shall assume that an 8080-type microprocessor is programmed to generate these signals. The I/O lines are two of the eight which constitute an I/O port. If the port address is FF, the lines could be assigned as follows:

Signal	Port address	Bit number
Direction	FF	D7
Step	FF	D0

The system used to verify the single-step and the other control programs has the following characteristics:

Motor: four-phase hybrid (permanent magnet) type.
Step angle, 7° 30′ (48 steps/revolution).
Maximum step rate, 300 steps/second.

Interface: SAA 1027
Minimum pulse width, 20 μs
Step initiated on the positive-going edge of the step pulse.

A single step is generated by sending a logic 1 to the step line (D0 of port FF), delaying for the minimum period of 20 μs, and then sending a logic 0 to the same output line. An algorithm for the single step program is:

1   Set direction line to logic 1 for counterclockwise direction and initialise the step line to logic 0.
2   Start pulse by sending a logic 1 to the step line.
3   Delay for a period of greater than 20 μs.
4   End pulse by sending a logic 0 to the step line.
5   Stop.

To reverse the direction of rotation the direction line would need to be initialised to logic 0 instead of logic 1.

Q9.3   Since the delay defining pulse width is fairly short, a simple delay routine in which a single-length register, register B, is loaded with the number 06 and then decremented to zero, has been used. The program is named STEP1 and is listed in Figure 9.4.

Notice however that the program may need to be modified if it runs in a system other than a Horizon. There are two reasons for this! First of all, although the 8085 and Z80 microprocessors will execute 8080 programs, they do not all execute instructions in the same number of clock cycles. Secondly, the master clock frequency in another system may very well not be the same as the Horizon clock frequency. The modification, if needed, will therefore amount to changing the number initially loaded into the register. Other than that though, the program which generates a step pulse is no different from the ones

Q9.2   that flash lamps on and off or start ADCs.

9.5   Generating a continuous sequence of step pulses

If the RET instruction at the end of STEP1 is replaced by an unconditional JMP to the CALL PULSE instruction, a continuous sequence of narrow (approximately 20-μs wide) pulses will appear on the step line. Almost certainly your stepping motor will not be able to keep up with the demanded step rate. Remember that if a motor on no-load is to be started from rest and then operated continuously at a fixed speed, that speed, or step rate, must be less than the maximum pull-in rate. What we will need in the program which drives the motor continuously is more time between step pulses.

Assume that our motor is to be driven at approximately 200

```
 1:
 2:
 3:                     ************************************************************
 4:                     *   PROGRAM NAME : STEP1                                   *
 5:                     *                                                          *
 6:                     *   MJM      19 11 80                                      *
 7:                     *                                                          *
 8:                     *   PROGRAM TO DRIVE A STEPPING MOTOR THROUGH ONE STEP     *
 9:                     *   AND THEN RETURN TO CP/M.                               *
10:                     *   STEPPING MOTOR CONNECTIONS ARE:                        *
11:                     *                            STEP      - D0 OF PORT FF     *
12:                     *                            DIRECTION - D7 OF PORT FF     *
13:                     *                                                          *
14:                     *                    PROGRAM STRUCTURE                     *
15:                     *                    '''''''''''''''''                     *
16:                     *   BEGIN                                                  *
17:                     *       SET DIRECTION BIT TO 1, STEP BIT TO 0              *
18:                     *       CALL PULSE SUBROUTINE                              *
19:                     *       RETURN TO CP/M                                     *
20:                     *   END                                                    *
21:                     ************************************************************
22:                     *
23:   0100                      ORG     0100H
24:                     *
25:   00FF =            MTRPRT: EQU     0FFH             ;MOTOR PORT ADDRESS
26:   0100 80           CCW:    DB      10000000B        ;COUNTER-CLOCKWISE
27:   0101 00           CW:     DB      00H              ;D7=0, CLOCKWISE.
28:                     *
29:   0102 3A0001       STEP1:  LDA     CCW              ;GET CCW CTRL. BYTE
30:   0105 D3FF                 OUT     MTRPRT           ;INITIALISE MTR + PORT
31:   0107 0606                 MVI     B,06H            ;SET-UP B FOR TIMING
32:   0109 CD0D01               CALL    PULSE            ;GENERATE ONE PULSE
33:   010C C9                   RET                      ;RETURN TO CP/M
34:                     *
35:                     ************************************************************
36:                     *   SUBROUTINE PULSE                                       *
37:                     *   ON ENTRY REGISTER A CONTAINS A DIRECTION BIT IN D7     *
38:                     *   ROUTINE CORRUPTS REGISTER B                            *
39:                     *                                                          *
40:                     *                    STRUCTURE                             *
41:                     *                    '''''''''                             *
42:                     *   BEGIN                                                  *
43:                     *       START PULSE                                        *
44:                     *       TCONS := 06H                 (* TIMING CONSTANT *) *
45:                     *       REPEAT                                             *
46:                     *           TCONS := TCONS - 1                             *
47:                     *       UNTIL TCONS := 0                                   *
48:                     *       END PULSE                                          *
49:                     *   END                                                    *
50:                     ************************************************************
51:                     *
52:   010D 3C           PULSE:  INR     A                ;D0 IN REG A = 1
53:   010E D3FF                 OUT     MTRPRT           ;START STEP PULSE
54:   0110 05           TIME:   DCR     B
55:   0111 C21001               JNZ     TIME             ;WAIT FOR TIME TO ELAPSE
56:   0114 3D                   DCR     A
57:   0115 D3FF                 OUT     MTRPRT           ;END STEP PULSE
58:   0117 C9                   RET
59:                     *
60:   0118                      END     STEP1
```

Figure 9.4 The STEP1 program

steps/second and that a step pulse is to be generated by the instruction sequence used in STEP1. The step pulse waveform is then a 20 µs pulse occurring at 5 ms intervals. For all practical purposes the pulse width is negligible compared with the total period so we can write the program algorithm as:

1 Initialise the step line to 0 and the direction line to 1 or 0 depending on the required direction of travel.
2 Generate a step pulse (subroutine PULSE).
3 Delay for approximately 5 ms.

Q9.8 4 Jump back to 2.

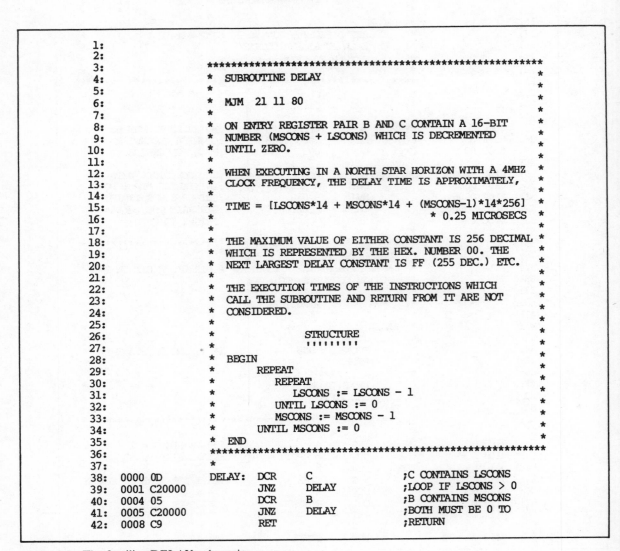

```
 1:
 2:
 3:          ***********************************************************
 4:          *  SUBROUTINE DELAY                                      *
 5:          *                                                        *
 6:          *  MJM  21 11 80                                         *
 7:          *                                                        *
 8:          *  ON ENTRY REGISTER PAIR B AND C CONTAIN A 16-BIT       *
 9:          *  NUMBER (MSCONS + LSCONS) WHICH IS DECREMENTED         *
10:          *  UNTIL ZERO.                                           *
11:          *                                                        *
12:          *  WHEN EXECUTING IN A NORTH STAR HORIZON WITH A 4MHZ    *
13:          *  CLOCK FREQUENCY, THE DELAY TIME IS APPROXIMATELY,     *
14:          *                                                        *
15:          *  TIME = [LSCONS*14 + MSCONS*14 + (MSCONS-1)*14*256]    *
16:          *                            * 0.25 MICROSECS           *
17:          *                                                        *
18:          *  THE MAXIMUM VALUE OF EITHER CONSTANT IS 256 DECIMAL   *
19:          *  WHICH IS REPRESENTED BY THE HEX. NUMBER 00. THE       *
20:          *  NEXT LARGEST DELAY CONSTANT IS FF (255 DEC.) ETC.     *
21:          *                                                        *
22:          *  THE EXECUTION TIMES OF THE INSTRUCTIONS WHICH         *
23:          *  CALL THE SUBROUTINE AND RETURN FROM IT ARE NOT        *
24:          *  CONSIDERED.                                           *
25:          *                                                        *
26:          *               STRUCTURE                                *
27:          *               '''''''''                                *
28:          *  BEGIN                                                 *
29:          *      REPEAT                                            *
30:          *         REPEAT                                         *
31:          *            LSCONS := LSCONS - 1                        *
32:          *         UNTIL LSCONS := 0                              *
33:          *         MSCONS := MSCONS - 1                           *
34:          *      UNTIL MSCONS := 0                                 *
35:          *  END                                                   *
36:          ***********************************************************
37:          *
38: 0000 0D     DELAY:  DCR    C          ;C CONTAINS LSCONS
39: 0001 C20000         JNZ    DELAY      ;LOOP IF LSCONS > 0
40: 0004 05             DCR    B          ;B CONTAINS MSCONS
41: 0005 C20000         JNZ    DELAY      ;BOTH MUST BE 0 TO
42: 0008 C9             RET               ;RETURN
```

Figure 9.5 The familiar DELAY subroutine

```
 1:
 2:
 3:             ***********************************************************
 4:             *   PROGRAM NAME : STEPON                                 *
 5:             *                                                         *
 6:             *   MJM   24 11 80                                        *
 7:             *                                                         *
 8:             *   PROGRAM TO GENERATE A CONTINUOUS SEQUENCE OF STEP     *
 9:             *   PULSES.                                               *
10:             *                                                         *
11:             *   SUBROUTINES PULSE AND DELAY ARE AS PREVIOUSLY         *
12:             *   LISTED                                                *
13:             *                                                         *
14:             *                      STRUCTURE                          *
15:             *                      ,,,,,,,,,                          *
16:             *   BEGIN                                                 *
17:             *       SET DIRECTION BIT TO 1, STEP BIT TO 0             *
18:             *       REPEAT                                            *
19:             *           GENERATE A STEP PULSE                         *
20:             *           DELAY FOR STEP PERIOD                         *
21:             *       UNTIL INFINITY                                    *
22:             *   END                                                   *
23:             ***********************************************************
24:             *
25:  0100                    ORG      0100H
26:             *
27:  0100 3A2701 STEPON: LDA      CCW
28:  0103 D3FF           OUT      MTRPRT           ;INITIALISE MOTOR
29:  0105 CD1101 AGAIN:  CALL     PULSE            ;GENERATE A STEP PULSE
30:  0108 018E06         LXI      B,PERIOD         ;SET-UP B FOR PERIOD
31:  010B CD1E01         CALL     DELAY            ;DELAY
32:  010E C30501         JMP      AGAIN            ;REPEAT INDEFINITELY
33:             *
34:  0111 010501 PULSE:  LXI      B,WIDTH          ;SET-UP B FOR WIDTH
35:  0114 3C             INR      A                ;MAKE D0 IN A = 1
36:  0115 D3FF           OUT      MTRPRT           ;START A PULSE
37:  0117 CD1E01         CALL     DELAY            ;DELAY FOR PULSE WIDTH
38:  011A 3D             DCR      A                ;MAKE D0 A 0
39:  011B D3FF           OUT      MTRPRT           ;END PULSE
40:  011D C9             RET                       ;RETURN TO MAIN PROG.
41:             *
42:  011E 0D     DELAY:  DCR      C                ;LSCONS:=LSCONS-1
43:  011F C21E01         JNZ      DELAY            ;LOOP IF LSCONS>0
44:  0122 05             DCR      B                ;ELSE MSCONS:=MSCONS-1
45:  0123 C21E01         JNZ      DELAY            ;BOTH MUST BE 0 TO
46:  0126 C9             RET                       ;RETURN
47:             *
48:             *   CONSTANTS
49:             *
50:  00FF =     MTRPRT: EQU      0FFH
51:  0127 80    CCW:    DB       10000000B
52:  0128 00    CW:     DB       00
53:  0105 =     WIDTH:  EQU      0105H            ;DEFINES PULSE WIDTH
54:  068E =     PERIOD: EQU      068EH            ;DEFINES PULSE PERIOD
55:             *
56:  0129               END      STEPON
```

Figure 9.6 The program STEPON

The 5 ms delay can be produced in the same way as the 20 μs delay was produced in STEP1 although, of course, a double-length register will be needed to hold the delay constant. The standard delay routine developed in Chapter 7 is re-used here and listed again in Figure 9.5 just to jog your memory.

The main program which calls this subroutine is called STEPON and is listed in Figure 9.6. When timing the pulse width, DELAY is called from PULSE, and then from the main program to time out the inter-pulse period. It is calculated that the numbers which approximately correspond with the required pulse width and period are 0105H and 068EH, respectively.

Q9.4, 9.5

9.6   Ramping applied to stepping motors

Ramping is the term used to describe the technique of accelerating a stepping motor early on in a stepping sequence, and then decelerating it before stopping or reversing the direction of travel. Special hardware called preset indexers, or just indexers, are available which produce this ramping drive. One type of indexer accepts a parallel digital input from a microprocessor, or other control system, which it interprets as the number of steps to be taken. Then, on command, the indexer generates the correct number of steps by first accelerating the motor to the highest speed attainable, maintaining this speed for as long as possible, and then decelerating the motor to finally stop after the prescribed number of steps have been taken. You will appreciate that this hardware is not simple and not inexpensive.

Another type of indexer accepts a pulse train which represents the maximum demanded speed. It controls the rate at which these pulses are passed on to the sequence generation logic so as to produce ramping. So long as the indexer passes on the same number of pulses as it has received, no pulses are lost and the drive is smooth.

In principle at least, it is not difficult to see how the action of an indexer could be imitated in software. Clearly the motor will step faster if the interval between pulses is reduced. Equally clearly, the motor will step slower if the interval is increased.

To illustrate this ramping procedure let us consider a program which accelerates the motor from rest to a speed of 300 steps/second, maintains maximum speed for a time, and then decelerates the motor. The direction of rotation will then be reversed and the cycle repeated.

The total number of pulses generated is 1,200 (25 revolutions) and it is arbitarily decided that acceleration and deceleration will be completed in 160 steps. At the beginning of every cycle the delay between successive pulses, if repeated, is chosen to equate with a constant step rate of 20 steps/second. Furthermore, using the standard delay formula, it is calculated that the delay constant should be 3894H for an approximate 20 steps/second and 04B4H for an approximate 300 steps/second. In the acceleration part of the cycle the number 0053H is subtracted from the current delay constant each time a step pulse is generated. After 160 subtractions the delay constant has been reduced to 04B4H.

The program is named RAMP and is listed in Figure 9.7. The mnemonics CURDEL, DELVAR and PCOUNT stand for current delay, delay variable and pulse count. CURDEL is the constant which fixes the pulse period and DELVAR is the number subtracted from or added to CURDEL during acceleration and deceleration. PCOUNT is the number of pulses generated in each phase of the RAMP program. All three of these program parameters are given symbolic names and declared in the data table so that they can be easily changed when experimenting with different acceleration/deceleration rates.

Q9.7

In thinking about this program it may have occurred to you that, using this technique, acceleration and deceleration are not constant. The reason for this is that, when approaching maximum speed during acceleration, the reduction in delay as a proportion of the current delay is much greater than the proportional reduction at low speed. If we could achieve linear acceleration then, at time t, the step rate would be given by,

$$\text{Step rate} = (\text{Step rate at } t = 0) + ft$$

where f is the acceleration in steps/second^2.

Linear acceleration means a linear (regular) increase in speed during the acceleration phase. However, speed, when measured in steps per second, is inversely proportional to period, and period is directly proportional to the delay constant. Therefore if we reduce the delay constant by the same amount between every step pulse we cannot hope to produce linear acceleration. To get some idea of what would be needed in a linear acceleration program we could write:

$$\text{Acceleration} = \frac{\text{Step rate at time } t - \text{Initial step rate}}{t} = f$$

$$= \frac{\dfrac{1}{\text{CURDEL}_t} - \dfrac{1}{\text{CURDEL}_0}}{t}$$

$$= \frac{1}{t}\left[\frac{\text{CURDEL}_0 - \text{CURDEL}_t}{\text{CURDEL}_0 \cdot \text{CURDEL}_t}\right]$$

Figure 9.7

```
 1:
 2:
 3:          *****************************************************
 4:          *   PROGRAM NAME : RAMP                              *
 5:          *                                                    *
 6:          *   MJM  1 12 80                                     *
 7:          *                                                    *
 8:          *   THIS PROGRAM ACCELERATES A STEPPING MOTOR FROM REST *
 9:          *   TO A SPEED OF 300 STEPS/SEC IN N1 STEPS, MAINTAINS *
10:          *   THAT SPEED FOR N2 STEPS AND THEN DECELERATES THE  *
11:          *   MOTOR TO REST IN A FURTHUR N1 STEPS. THE DIRECTION *
12:          *   OF ROTATION IS THEN REVERSED AND THE CYCLE REPEATED.*
13:          *   IT IS CALCULATED THAT THE FIRST STEP TAKEN, IF    *
14:          *   REPEATED, WOULD PRODUCE A CONSTANT STEP RATE OF   *
15:          *   20 STEPS/SEC.                                     *
16:          *   THE MINIMUM ROTATIONAL SPEED EQUATES APPROXIMATELY *
17:          *   WITH A DELAY CONSTANT OF 3894H AND THE MAXIMUM    *
18:          *   SPEED WITH 04B4H. DURING ACCELERATION AND         *
19:          *   DECELERATION THE DELAY CONSTANT IS REDUCED OR     *
20:          *   INCREASED BY DELVAR BETWEEN SUCCESSIVE PULSES     *
21:          *                                                    *
22:          *                      STRUCTURE                      *
23:          *                      '''''''''                      *
24:          *   BEGIN                                             *
25:          *       CURDEL=3894H  (MAX)                           *
26:          *       REPEAT                                        *
27:          *           PCOUNT:=N1                                *
28:          *           REPEAT    (*UNTIL MAX. SPEED REACHED *)   *
29:          *                                                    *
30:          *               GENERATE A PULSE                     *
31:          *               DELAY FOR CURDEL                     *
32:          *               CURDEL:=CURDEL - DELVAR              *
33:          *               (* SHORTER DELAY NEXT TIME THROUGH *) *
34:          *               PCOUNT:=PCOUNT - 1                   *
35:          *                                                    *
36:          *           UNTIL PCOUNT:=0                           *
37:          *           PCOUNT:=N2                                *
38:          *           REPEAT                                    *
39:          *                                                    *
40:          *               GENERATE A PULSE                     *
41:          *               DELAY FOR CURDEL                     *
42:          *               PCOUNT:=PCOUNT -1                    *
43:          *                                                    *
44:          *           UNTIL PCOUNT:=0                           *
45:          *           PCOUNT:=N1                                *
46:          *           REPEAT    (* UNTIL MIN. SPEED REACHED *)  *
47:          *                                                    *
48:          *               GENERATE A PULSE                     *
49:          *               DELAY FOR CURDEL                     *
50:          *               CURDEL:=CURDEL + DELVAR              *
51:          *               (* LONGER DELAY NEXT TIME THROUGH *)  *
52:          *               PCOUNT:=PCOUNT - 1                   *
53:          *                                                    *
54:          *           UNTIL PCOUNT:= 0                          *
55:          *           CHANGE DIRECTION                          *
56:          *       UNTIL INFINITY                                *
57:          *   END                                               *
58:          *****************************************************
59:          *
60: 0100                    ORG     0100H
```

Figure 9.7 continued

```
61:   0100 219438   RAMP:   LXI    H,DELCON    ;INITIALISE THE
62:   0103 228801           SHLD   CURDEL      ;CURRENT DELAY TO MAX
63:                 *
64:                 *   FIRST ACCELERATE THE MOTOR
65:                 *
66:   0106 11A000   BGN:    LXI    D,N1        ;INITIALISE PCOUNT
67:   0109 CD3D01   LOOP1:  CALL   STEP1       ;PULSE, THEN DELAY
68:   010C CD4901           CALL   ACCEL       ;REDUCE (CURDEL)
69:   010F CD5901           CALL   DEC20       ;DEC PCOUNT, TEST FOR 0
70:   0112 C20901           JNZ    LOOP1       ;FASTER IF PCOUNT<>0
71:                 *
72:                 *   MAX SPEED REACHED
73:                 *
74:   0115 117003           LXI    D,N2        ;REINITIALISE PCOUNT
75:   0118 CD3D01   LOOP2:  CALL   STEP1       ;PULSE, THEN DELAY
76:   011B CD5901           CALL   DEC20       ;DEC PCOUNT, TEST FOR 0
77:   011E C21801           JNZ    LOOP2       ;MAINTAIN SPEED
78:                 *
79:                 *   NOW DECELERATE
80:                 *
81:   0121 11A000           LXI    D,N1        ;REINITIALISE PCOUNT
82:   0124 CD3D01   LOOP3:  CALL   STEP1       ;PULSE, THEN DELAY
83:   0127 CD6001           CALL   DECEL       ;INCREASE (CURDEL)
84:   012A CD5901           CALL   DEC20       ;DEC PCOUNT, TEST FOR 0
85:   012D C22401           JNZ    LOOP3       ;SLOWER IF PCOUNT<>0
86:                 *
87:                 *   NOW CHANGE DIRECTION AND START AGAIN
88:                 *
89:   0130 3A8701           LDA    DIRC        ;GET CURRENT DIRECTION
90:   0133 EE80             XRI    80H         ;CHANGE MS BIT
91:   0135 328701           STA    DIRC        ;RESTORE DIRECTION
92:   0138 D3FF             OUT    MTRPRT      ;CHANGE DIRECTION
93:   013A C30601           JMP    BGN         ;START AGAIN
94:                 *
95:                 **********************************************************
96:                 *   SUBROUTINE STEP1                                     *
97:                 *   IMPLEMENTS THE FOLLOWING STRUCTURE STATEMENTS:-      *
98:                 *                GENERATE A PULSE                        *
99:                 *                DELAY FOR CURDEL                        *
100:                **********************************************************
101:                *
102:  013D CD6B01   STEP1:  CALL   PULSE       ;GENERATE A PULSE
103:  0140 2A8801           LHLD   CURDEL      ;GET CURRENT DELAY
104:  0143 4D               MOV    C,L         ;PUT LS BYTE INTO C
105:  0144 44               MOV    B,H         ;AND MS BYTE INTO B
106:  0145 CD7E01           CALL   DELAY       ;DELAY FOR CURDEL
107:  0148 C9               RET
108:                *
109:                **********************************************************
110:                *   SUBROUTINE ACCEL                                     *
111:                *   IMPLEMENTS THE STRUCTURE STATEMENT:-                 *
112:                *                CURDEL:=CURDEL - DELVAR                 *
113:                **********************************************************
114:                *
115:  0149 015300   ACCEL:  LXI    B,DELVAR    ;GET DELAY VARIABLE
116:  014C 2A8801           LHLD   CURDEL      ;GET CURRENT DELAY
117:  014F 7D               MOV    A,L         ;ISOLATE LS BYTE
118:  0150 91               SUB    C           ;SUBTRACT DELVAR LSBYTE
119:  0151 6F               MOV    L,A         ;RESTORE LS BYTE
120:  0152 7C               MOV    A,H         ;GET MS BYTE
```

(Continued)

Figure 9.7 continued

```
121:   0153 98              SBB    B            ;SUBTRACT DELVAR MSBYTE
122:   0154 67              MOV    H,A          ;RESTORE MS BYTE
123:   0155 228801          SHLD   CURDEL       ;RESTORE CURDEL
124:   0158 C9              RET                 ;AND RETURN
125:                  *
126:                  *******************************************************
127:                  *  SUBROUTINE DEC20                                   *
128:                  *  IMPLEMENTS THE STRUCTURE STATMENTS:-               *
129:                  *              PCOUNT:=PCOUNT - 1                     *
130:                  *          UNTIL PCOUNT:=0                            *
131:                  *  ON RETURN TO THE MAIN PROGRAM THE Z FLAG INDICATES *
132:                  *  WHETHER OR NOT PCOUNT IS 0.                        *
133:                  *******************************************************
134:                  *
135:   0159 1D       DEC20: DCR    E            ;DECREMENT LS BYTE
136:   015A C0              RNZ                 ;RETURN IF LS BYTE <> 0
137:   015B 15              DCR    D            ;ELSE DEC. MS BYTE
138:   015C 3EFF            MVI    A,0FFH       ;IF (D)=FF RETURN IS
139:   015E 92              SUB    D            ;MADE WITH Z = 1
140:   015F C9              RET                 ;OTHERWISE Z = 0
141:                  *
142:                  *******************************************************
143:                  *  SUBROUTINE DECEL                                   *
144:                  *  IMPLEMENTS THE STRUCTURE STATEMENT:-               *
145:                  *              CURDEL:=CURDEL + DELVAR                *
146:                  *******************************************************
147:                  *
148:   0160 015300    DECEL: LXI    B,DELVAR     ;GET DELAY VARIABLE
149:   0163 2A8801            LHLD   CURDEL       ;AND CURRENT DELAY
150:   0166 09               DAD    B            ;ADD THEM, RESULT TO HL
151:   0167 228801           SHLD   CURDEL       ;RESTORE CURDEL
152:   016A C9               RET                 ;AND RETURN
153:                  *
154:                  *  SUBROUTINE DELAY IS AS BEFORE. SUBROUTINE PULSE HAS
155:                  *  BEEN CHANGED SLIGHTLY BECAUSE A IS USED ELSEWHERE.
156:                  *
157:   016B 010501    PULSE: LXI    B,WIDTH      ;STE-UP B FOR WIDTH
158:   016E 3A8701            LDA    DIRC         ;GET DIRECTION BYTE
159:   0171 3C               INR    A            ;MAKE D0 A 1
160:   0172 D3FF             OUT    MTRPRT       ;START A PULSE
161:   0174 CD7E01           CALL   DELAY        ;DELAY FOR PULSE WIDTH
162:   0177 3D               DCR    A            ;D0 IN A = 0
163:   0178 D3FF             OUT    MTRPRT       ;END PULSE
164:   017A 328701           STA    DIRC         ;RESTORE DIRECTION BYTE
165:   017D C9               RET
166:   017E 0D       DELAY: DCR    C            ;LSCONS:=LSCONS-1
167:   017F C27E01           JNZ    DELAY        ;LOOP IF ;LSCONS>0
168:   0182 05               DCR    B            ;ELSE MSCONS:=MSCONS-1
169:   0183 C27E01           JNZ    DELAY        ;BOTH MUST BE 0 TO
170:   0186 C9               RET                 ;RETURN
171:                  *  CONSTANTS
172:   00FF =        MTRPRT: EQU    0FFH
173:   0187 80       DIRC:  DB     10000000B    ;COUNTERCLOCKWISE
174:   0105 =        WIDTH: EQU    0105H        ;PULSE WIDTH CONSTANT
175:   3894 =        DELCON: EQU    3894H        ;MINIMUM SPEED
176:   0053 =        DELVAR: EQU    0053H        ;DELAY VARIABLE
177:   0188          CURDEL: DS     2            ;CURRENT DELAY
178:   00A0 =        N1:    EQU    160D         ;PCOUNT FOR ACC/DECEL
179:   0370 =        N2:    EQU    880D         ;PCOUNT FOR CONSTANT
180:   018A          END    RAMP
```

Figure 9.7 The RAMP program

As t increases CURDEL$_t$ must reduce in such a fashion that the function given above remains constant. Further thought would undoubtedly yield a simpler expression and, eventually, a linear acceleration program could be written, but you will surely appreciate that it would not be a simple assembly-language program. Alternatively, of course, if we wanted to make the program easier, we could calculate all the values of CURDEL$_t$ before starting on the program and then use the calculated values as entries in a data table. The program would then only have to pick out the appropriate table entry at every step.

Both of these software solutions are beyond the scope of this text. For the time being we will reassure ourselves with the fact that at least we are aware of the problems involved in producing linear acceleration and deceleration of stepping motors. The more ambitious reader may consult the bibliography at the end of the chapter for ideas as to how to proceed from this point. We shall return to the problem in the next chapter.

Q9.6

When RAMP was used to drive the stepping motor system used throughout this series of experiments it gave a very graphic demonstration of resonance. You will recall that resonance occurs at certain step rates as a consequence of rotor overshoot at each new step position. The resonant frequency band is different for every type of motor but is usually evident at fairly low step rates (around 100 steps/second). When a motor is accelerated from below the resonant step band to a speed which is above it, the transition can be made successfully provided that the resonant band is narrow and/or acceleration is high. If these conditions are not satisfied the motor is seen to run erratically at some point in the acceleration/deceleration phases.

In the RAMP program the total number of pulses generated in one complete cycle, 2N1 + N2, is adjusted so that the motor completes 25 revolutions before changing direction. By attaching a pointer to the motor shaft it is possible to see whether every cycle begins and ends with the pointer in the same position. If the motor resonates at some step rate, this will not be the case and it will be possible to see this by watching the pointer.

The effect of resonance can be smoothed out by increasing the load inertia. If, when you run the RAMP program, you can see the resonance effect and your motor has sufficiently low torque, lightly press your finger on the end of the shaft and vary the pressure applied until resonance is eliminated. A better remedy, if you have some workshop facilities available, is to make up the little damper shown in Figure 9.8 and attach it to the motor. The pressure of the screw on the motor shaft increases the load inertia and, if properly adjusted, completely eliminates resonance.

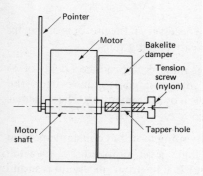

Figure 9.8 Simple mechanical damper used to eliminate the effect of resonance in low-torque stepping motors

References

SIGMA Stepping Motor Control Chip Set Data Catalogue, Unimatic Engineers Ltd, Granville Road, London NW2 (December 1979).

9.2　*SIGMA Stepping Motor Data Catalogue*, Unimatic (see ref. 9.1).

9.3　*Slo-syn Stepping Motor Data Catalogue* (1979).

9.4　*Microprocessor Control of Stepping Motors*, documentation accompanying the Bytronic Associates stepping motor system; Bytronic Associates, 88 Russell Bank Road, Sutton Coldfield, West Midlands B74 4RJ.

Bibliography

9.5　V.V. Athani, 'Universal step motor controller-indexer', *Microprocessors and Microsystems*, Vol. 4(7), (September 1980).

9.6　A. H. Al-Anbukky and G. A. Swadi, 'Microprocessor position control system', *ibid.*, Vol. 3(4), (May 1979).

Questions

9.1　Assuming that the full-step sequence given in Table 8.1 is stored as a table of numbers, write the structure for a program which reads a direction bit supplied by a switch connected to an input port and then picks out the appropriate table entry and sends it to the port connecting the motor. If the direction bit is a 1 the required direction of rotation is anti-clockwise. The motor is to be driven continuously.

9.2　Write a program similar to STEP1 which reads a direction bit (1 for anti-clockwise and 0 for clockwise) supplied on line D7 of input port FE, and then drives a stepping motor through one step in the indicated direction.

What changes to your program are necessary if the motor is driven by a negative-going, rather than a positive-going pulse?

9.3　Verify that 06 is a sufficiently large number to produce a delay of 20 µs when the number is loaded into a single-length register, the contents of which are reduced to zero by decrementing. The system is assumed to run at a clock frequency of 4 MHz.

9.4　Write a program which drives a stepping motor at constant speed in the direction indicated by the logic level supplied by a switch connected at line D7 of input port FE. The program should respond to a change of direction signal in the next step after the change has occurred.

9.5　The program STEPON uses two delay constants, one to define the step pulse width and another to define its period. Verify that the constants 0105H and 068EH are approximately correct for the delays 20 μs and 5 ms, respectively.

9.6 Discuss the problems presented when the prospect of linearly accelerating a stepping motor is contemplated. Why is acceleration and deceleration often necessary?

9.7 Write a program that drives a stepping motor through the following cycle:

1 Five revolutions clockwise at a speed of 50 steps/second.
2 Five revolutions in the same direction at 200 steps/second.
3 Five revolutions clockwise, again at a speed of 50 steps/second.
4 Then repeats the cycle with the direction reversed.

All speeds are approximate and the motor is to be driven continuously.

9.8 Delay routines could be implemented using the 16-bit arithmetic capability of the 8080. For example, the number −1 could be stored in register pair B,C or D,E and then repeatedly added to a number, the daily constant, stored in H,L. When H,L eventually contains 0, the delay time has elapsed. By referring to the 8080 instruction set, discuss how such a delay routine would work.

Chapter 10 High-level languages for microcomputer applications

Objectives of this chapter *When you have completed studying this chapter you should be able to:*

1 *Appreciate the need for a high-level language when developing microcomputer software.*
2 *Understand that there are disadvantages, as well as advantages, in using a high-level language.*
3 *Understand the difference between compiled and interpreted high-level languages.*
4 *Appreciate the use of some of the more common high-level languages.*
5 *Understand the way in which PASCAL and BASIC would be used to solve the same programming problem.*
6 *Appreciate that UCSD PASCAL is the most common PASCAL system for microcomputers and be aware of some of its features.*
7 *Understand that external assembly language subroutines can be linked with a UCSD PASCAL program.*
8 *Appreciate how the extra facilities of a high-level language overcome some of the difficulties of programming at assembly level.*
9 *Appreciate how UCSD PASCAL programs can be interrupted.*

10.1 The need for a high-level language

Consider the following problem. Two memory locations, X and Y, have been defined in an assembly language program as follows:

```
X:      DS      2
Y:      DS      2
```

X and Y each label one byte of a 16-bit number and, during the course of the program, it becomes necessary to swap over the numbers so that X and X + 1 contain twice the number previously stored at Y and Y + 1, and *vice versa*. The structure statements for this part of the program might be:

```
TEMP: = X        (*Copy contents of X into TEMP*)
   X: = 2*Y      (*Copy into X, two times Y*)
   Y: = 2*TEMP   (*Copy into Y, two times TEMP*)
```

When we come to write the assembler instructions which implement these statements, we need to know which byte is stored first, which registers we can use, and how to organise these registers for a 16-bit shift or double-length addition. Inevitably, in assembly language programming, we are closely involved with the microprocessor hardware.

Our task would be made much easier if we could disregard the hardware and just program in a series of structure statements. If this were possible, and the rest of the program could be written in the same way, there is no doubt that the logic of the finished program would be much clearer. There is equally no doubt that we could produce programs more quickly.

When other problems, such as the prospect of linearly accelerating a stepping motor, which we shied away from in the last chapter, are considered, the advantages are even clearer. If we could make the computer understand the statement

$$\texttt{SPEED: } = \frac{1}{\texttt{TIME}}$$

and program other complicated expressions without worrying about how these expressions will be evaluated, programming would be a much more manageable occupation.

What we are discussing here are utility programs which make it easier to write other programs. These utilities accept structure-like statements and translate them into machine instructions which the microprocessor can execute. They are called compilers or interpreters, depending upon how they do the translation, and the source code they process, the structure-like statements, constitute a programming language which is considerably more expressive (at a higher level) than machine language. There are many high-level languages, with their compilers and/or interpreters, and all of them

Q10.1   can be used in microprocessor systems.

10.2   The advantages and disadvantages of high-level languages (HLLs)

Because high-level language (HLL) programs are shorter and more understandable than equivalent assembly language programs, they are easier to maintain. Maintaining software, like maintaining hardware, is concerned with correcting faults as they arise. Intuitively, we think of software as being much more reliable than hardware because there is nothing to wear out. The point has already been made however, that all software is created with either actual or potential bugs in it. Debugging removes the obvious bugs, but if the program is not tested with every conceivable data combination or in every possible operating environment, there remains that lingering suspicion that a software fault could arise later. If it does the problem is often similar to those frustrating intermittent hardware faults which are so difficult to find.

The extra legibility of HLL programs helps in this respect because the suspected potential fault condition can be reproduced without, for example, worrying about the states of individual registers or flag bits. The program and its data are all that matters; you are separated from the hardware by the translation program.

Another, allied, advantage of HLL programs is that programmer productivity is improved. It is easier, and therefore quicker, to write in an HLL because the programmed statements have more in common with normal English than do assembler instructions. Consequently software production, as well as maintenance, costs are reduced.

Since writing programs is a highly labour-intensive occupation, the trend over the years has been for hardware to become relatively cheaper, and software, because of increased salaries and the fact that more ambitious projects were tackled, to become more expensive. The move towards the use of HLLs in microprocessor product development has accelerated in an effort to contain the rate of rising software production costs. The same point, you will remember, was made when recommending structured programming techniques – and for identical reasons.

Another advantage is concerned with program portability. An HLL program written to run on an 8080-based system should run on an M6800 system or a mini or mainframe computer with equal facility. The interface between the program and the hardware is the compiler (or interpreter) and although this will be tailored to a particular hardware configuration, this should make no difference to the HLL program. In practice of course, some changes are usually necessary as a program is moved from one machine to another. In most cases, however, these are minor changes to the program syntax – the underlying structure remains the same.

A disadvantage of HLLs is that they almost always occupy more memory than equivalent assembly language programs.* This is really a comment on the efficiency of the translation process, but is also affected by the skill of the programmer and the applicability of the language to the problem. All things being equal however, even the best compiler will generate at least 25% more code than a good assembly language programmer would produce. This has implications on the hardware costs and execution speeds because more memory will be needed and the program, since it is longer, executes more slowly.

*It has been reported that, in some circumstances, the language FORTH actually generates less code than its assembly language equivalent.

Another limitation of most HLLs is that they do not provide a means of programming instructions which control user peripherals. This facility is usually included as language extensions which of course, makes the program less portable.

All in all however, there is an inevitable move towards the use of HLLs in microcomputer applications and away from the use of assembly language. Indeed, some modern microprocessors are designed in such a way that they execute HLL programs more efficiently. This is in recognition of the fact that hardware and software have to work together to produce an efficient system so there is no point in producing advanced hardware if the software lags behind.

Q10.2

10.3 Compilers and interpreters

A compiler is a program which takes an HLL source code program and translates it into an equivalent set of machine language instructions, in much the same way that an assembler translates an assembly language program into machine code. At the end of the compilation the compiler is dismissed and the object code program reloaded and executed as a separate exercise.

An interpreter on the other hand is active in the system memory for as long as the program is running. It scans the lines of source code one-by-one, translates each into a set of equivalent machine instructions and then executes them. There is no identifiable object code program as there is in a compiler system, since object code only exist while a line is being interpreted. This means that when program loops are encountered, statements within the loop are re-interpreted in every loop transition. Consequently, interpreted language programs are quite slow to execute and the systems in which they run require extra memory to accommodate the interpreter.

Some modern interpreters compress the source code into a more compact form and then interpret this compressed code. The aim is to reduce the total amount of memory needed and speed-up program execution by interpreting pre-processed code rather than the original source code.

Interpreted languages are very often interactive in that they check the source code, as it is entered, for syntax errors and issue quite precise information about the nature of any error detected. During execution, also, they will stop and issue an error message when, for example, an unterminated loop has been found. Interactive languages of this sort are often said to be 'user friendly' because they provide so much help in getting a program working. This can however, be a disadvantage if it encourages the programmer to 'cobble' together programs which have not been properly planned, structured or documented. If these essential phases of program development become irritations which are secondary to the main business of typing commands into the interpreter, an advantage quickly becomes a disadvantage.

Compiled languages tend to feature much more cryptic error messages. When an error is detected during compilation, the compiler will usually stop and print an error number which is, hopefully, listed in the manual against a more precise error description. When a program compiles without error it is syntactically, if not logically, correct.

Run-time errors are described as fatal or non-fatal, the difference being that in the one case the program has, or is about to, run amok, and in the other that something less catastrophic, like an arithmetic overflow has occurred. Adequate debugging aids are not a feature of most HLLs. The most usual error correction procedure is to go through the source code listing until the error is brought to light. Another technique which is sometimes quite useful is to insert extra PRINT (or WRITE) statements at strategic points in the program **Q10.3** and remove them when the mistake has been corrected.

10.4 High-level languages

In general, new HLLs are introduced to satisfy a specific programming need. This need may be for a new language feature or a new source code style which reflects a more up-to-date programming philosophy. Most existing languages have some features which make them particularly applicable in solving a certain type of problem. If we were to attempt a review of all available programming languages our task would be difficult and inappropriate. Instead we shall briefly examine some of the better known languages.

FORTRAN (FORmula TRANslation)

This is the oldest and still, perhaps, the most widely used language for scientific and mathematical type computing. It is a compiled language in which the compiler produces efficient machine language programs and, as its name suggests, is particularly suited to applications in which mathematical functions are to be evaluated.

BASIC (Beginners All-purpose Symbolic Instruction Code)

This is a beginner's language. It is very popular in the personal computer (hobby) world but is not recommended for professional microcomputer developments. Most BASICs are interpreted but many compilers are now available. Although proposed as a beginner's language, it does much to encourage the production of unstructured, rambling programs and is probably the last language that a beginner should be encouraged to learn.

ALGOL (ALGOrithmetic Language)

This was developed around 1960 and was the forerunner of several ALGOL-like languages. It is a block-structured language in which code blocks are bracketed between the reserved words BEGIN and END to highlight and separate out individual program tasks. ALGOL variables are declared to be of a certain type which in the case of numeric variables, means that numbers are either INTEGER or REAL. (INTEGER variables have no fractional part.) BASIC makes no distinction between REAL and INTEGER numbers whereas FORTRAN variable names (labels) which began with the letters I, J, K, L, M or N are taken to be INTEGER identifiers and those which begin with any other letter are taken to be REAL identifiers. Incidentally, the distinction between REAL and INTEGER variables is not just arbitrary, it has implications for the way in which the numbers are stored, their format and the number of bits, and also in the way numbers may be manipulated. PL/1 is very similar to ALGOL and is important because it is supported by IBM, and PASCAL, which we shall discuss in more detail later, could be described as a second-generation ALGOL.

COBOL (COmmon Business Orientated Language)

This is best suited to applications arising in the data processing field. It deals efficiently with large text files in systems which handle a high volume of formatted input and output. Quite recently, COBAL compilers have been made available to run on microprocessor based systems used in business and commercial applications.

Others

In addition to those listed above, PL/M, MPL and PL/Z are HLLs introduced by the major microprocessor manufacturers, Intel, Motorola and Zilog, respectively, to run in their systems, and other languages such as CORAL and RTL/2 are said to be particularly suited to real-time applications in which the system should rapidly respond to service requests from peripherals. The expanding areas of pattern recognition and artificial intelligence has revived interest in an old language called LISP and newer languages which have recently received a great deal of attention are FORTH and the PASCAL-like **Q10.4**   language, ADA, and C.

10.5   HLLs for microprocessor applications

If we disregard those languages which are specific to only one microprocessor manufacturer, the most widely available languages for our engineering-type applications are PASCAL and BASIC. Obviously, in a few pages, we will not be able to study all the features of these languages, but we could usefully re-examine some of the programs used in previous chapters to see how they might appear in an HLL.

Consider for example the problem of comparing a number with an upper and lower limit. In PASCAL and BASIC, console I/O is very easy to program, so we shall look at two programs each of which accepts a number from the console, compares it with high limit and low limit values and then prints an appropriate message. One program will be written in PASCAL and the other in BASIC.

The PASCAL I/O statements are READ, or READLN, and WRITE, or WRITELN, respectively. The LN simply means that, on input, the value entered must be terminated in a carriage-return, line-feed (console RETURN key), and on output, the value or message written will be followed immediately by a carriage return, line-feed. (LN stands for a new LiNe.) In BASIC the corresponding statements are INPUT and PRINT.

The two programs are listed in Figures 10.1 and 10.2 with sample results. The first thing you will notice about the PASCAL version is that it is very like a program structure we would have written had we been asked to produce an assembly language program. The program has a name – COMPARE – and uses two constants HIGHLIMIT and LOWLIMIT. Note the way in which statements are terminated in a semi-colon. In the syntax of PASCAL programs, a semi-colon is a statement separator. Spaces and RETURNs have no special significance in this respect, other than to format the source code as we would wish. The program could, for instance, have been entered as one long string of characters and, provided that the statements are separated out by semi-colons and the odd space inserted after words like IF and VAR, it would work perfectly well. This is not a practice to adopt however, since we are trying to make our programs easier to read, not more difficult.

The single variable used in the program is given the name VALUE. It is declared as an INTEGER number (its type is INTEGER) by preceding the name by the reserved word VAR (variable) and following it with the word INTEGER. The main program block begins with the word BEGIN and ends in the word END. It, first of all, writes the message ENTER TRAIL VALUE on the console and then waits for the user to enter a number followed by RETURN. The number entered is assigned to the variable VALUE. The remainder of the program is just two IF-THEN-ELSE statements, one nested inside the other. The comparisons are made and then one of three messages are printed depending upon the outcome of those comparisons.

```
    PROGRAM COMPARE;

    (* A Pascal program to compare a number entered at the keyboard with
       fixed high and low limits, and print an appropriate message      *)

    CONST
         HIGHLIMIT = 204;                (* Decimal equivalent of 0CCH *)
         LOWLIMIT  = 51;                 (* Decimal equivalent of 033H *)
    VAR
         VALUE : INTEGER;


    BEGIN  (* The comparison *)
         WRITE ('ENTER A TRIAL VALUE ');
         READLN (VALUE);                 (* Read value then CRLF *)
         IF VALUE > HIGHLIMIT THEN
             WRITELN ('HIGH LIMIT EXCEEDED')
         ELSE
             IF VALUE < LOWLIMIT THEN
                  WRITELN ('LOW LIMIT EXCEEDED')
             ELSE
                  WRITELN ('VALUE IS OK');
    END.   (* Of comparison *)


    R


    Running...
    ENTER A TRIAL VALUE 205
    HIGH LIMIT EXCEEDED
    R


    Running...
    ENTER A TRIAL VALUE 204
    VALUE IS OK
    R


    Running...
    ENTER A TRIAL VALUE 100
    VALUE IS OK
    R


    Running...
    ENTER A TRIAL VALUE 51
    VALUE IS OK
    R


    Running...
    ENTER A TRIAL VALUE 50
    LOW LIMIT EXCEEDED
```

Figure 10.1   The UCSD PASCAL version of the comparison program

```
10  REM   BASIC PROGRAM TO COMPARE A NUMBER ENTERED AT THE KEYBOARD
20  REM   WITH FIXED HIGH AND LOW LIMITS, AND PRINT AN APPROPRIATE
30  REM   MESSAGE.
40  REM
50  LET  H = 204        \ REM - DECIMAL EQUIVALENT OF 0CCH
60  LET  L = 51         \ REM - DECIMAL EQUIVALENT OF 033H
70  INPUT "ENTER TRIAL VALUE ",V
80  IF V > H THEN 130
90  IF V < L THEN 160
100 PRINT "VALUE IS OK"
110 END
120 REM   HIGH LIMIT ALARM MESSAGE HERE
130 PRINT "HIGH LIMIT EXCEEDED"
140 GOTO 110
150 REM   LOW LIMIT ALARM MESSAGE HERE
160 PRINT "LOW LIMIT EXCEEDED"
170 GOTO 110
READY




RUN

ENTER TRIAL VALUE 205
HIGH LIMIT EXCEEDED
READY
RUN

ENTER TRIAL VALUE 204
VALUE IS OK
READY
RUN

ENTER TRIAL VALUE 100
VALUE IS OK
READY
RUN

ENTER TRIAL VALUE 51
VALUE IS OK
READY
RUN

ENTER TRIAL VALUE 50
LOW LIMIT EXCEEDED
READY
```

Figure 10.2   The North Star BASIC version of the comparison program

If we now turn our attention to the BASIC program, the most immediately obvious difference is that all lines are numbered and that comments are preceeded by the word REM, meaning remark. You will also notice that we can be far less explicit when choosing our variable and constant names. All we are allowed is a single letter followed, optionally, by a single digit. In the comparison part of the program we could have used a nested IF-THEN-ELSE statement provided that the whole statement can be contained in a single line. Since we cannot accomplish this, a single IF statement (with no ELSE) tests a logical expression ($V > H$ or $V < L$) and transfers control to the line number entered after the word THEN, if the condition is true.

Limitations like nested IF-THEN-ELSE statements being contained within a single line, and the lack of REPEAT-UNTIL and WHILE-DO statements, accounts for some of the disadvantages of BASIC when trying to produce structured programs. The PASCAL way of programming a multiway branch with a logical block of nested IF-THEN-ELSE statements, describes precisely the common-sense (human) way of arriving at a result given a set of qualifying conditions. It would be quite unusual to say: 'If the value is greater than the high limit then go somewhere else to find out how to deal with the situation', as we have to in this BASIC program. The logical flow of the argument is disrupted because we cannot read through the program without continually being directed to some other part of the listing. Consequently, even with all its simplicity, BASIC programs of any length are often as difficult to read as assembly language programs.

On the credit side, interpreted interactive BASIC is exceptionally user-friendly. Mistakes can be corrected very quickly by simply re-entering a line number with an alternative statement following it, and sections of a program can be run and program execution checked by requesting BASIC to type-out the current values of program variables. On balance however, the arguments against BASIC are considered to be more compelling than those for it, so we shall concentrate on PASCAL as the available microcomputer HLL of
Q10.5 choice.

10.6 UCSD PASCAL

The most popular implementation of PASCAL on microcomputers is the version originating from the University of California, San Diego (UCSD). This system has gained an acceptability with PASCAL users which compares with the position of CP/M in the broader field of microcomputer operating systems. It is based on the standard definition of PASCAL which was officially announced by Professor Niklaus Wirth in 1971, and set out in the book, *Pascal User Manual and Report* by Kathleen Jensen and Niklaus Wirth (Springer-Verlag, New York–Heidelberg–Berlin, 1975). UCSD PASCAL however, includes several features which were not in the original language definition, most notably a mechanism for driving user devices from a PASCAL program.

UCSD PASCAL is interesting in that it uses a compiler *and* an

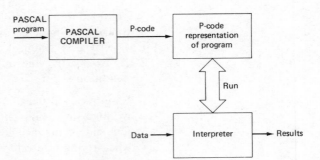

Figure 10.3   The UCSD PASCAL system

interpreter to translate user programs into machine language instructions. The compiler takes the PASCAL source code program and compiles, not to the machine code of the host machine, but to an intermediate level called P-code. This P, or pseudo, code will execute directly in a P or Pseudo machine, if such a machine existed. (The Western Digital, Pascal Microengine constructed from bit-slice microcomputer parts is the only hardware implementation of a P-machine known to the author.) In place of the hardware, the P-machine is simulated by an interpreter which acts on the compiler output to translate P-code into the N (native) code of the host machine.

The advantage of this technique is that implementing UCSD PASCAL on a new, different microcomputer is only a matter of rewriting the interpreter. The compiler and many of the system utilities are the same since these too are written in PASCAL and use the same interpreter as user programs.

Q10.6

10.7   Subroutines in PASCAL programs

There are two ways in which subroutines, or subprograms, are provided for in PASCAL. One type of subroutine is called a function and the other a procedure. Functions have a more restricted application than procedures becasuse they can only return a value to the main program. In other words, we could write a function-type subroutine to calculate some function of a variable, but we could not write a function to, say, generate a pulse. Considering this point further, function calls have the form:

```
Y: = SQRT(X)   (*Y becomes equal to √X̄*)
```

In a more general way we might say Y is a function of X. The particular function we are considering here is SQRT. Included somewhere in the PASCAL system software is a list of PASCAL statements headed:

```
FUNCTION SQRT (parameter);
```

This evaluates the square root of a parameter passed to it from the calling program. Towards the end of this list of statements will be the statement:

```
SQRT (parameter): = (the result)
END;        (*The SQRT function*)
```

When statement Y:=SQRT (X) is encountered in the main (calling) program, the current value of X is passed over to the SQRT function and on return the value of SQRT(X) is assigned to the variable Y. We say that the function SQRT returns a value.

There are several pre-declared functions, like SQRT, SIN, COS, etc., in PASCAL. These are 'pre-declared' in the sense that they are already included in the system library of subroutines and are automatically linked with your program should you call them. Any additional functions needed, such as TAN or CUBE, will have to be written as a separate, user-defined function.

Procedures are less restrictive than functions because they need not return a value. They are separately identifiable program modules which may be needed at several different points of a larger program, or simply written separately to improve the legibility of the main program. Figure 10.4 illustrates how functions and procedures could be used in PASCAL programs.

The subroutine (function) ALARMCODE is defined using the dummy parameter NUMBER. When it is called from the main program by the statement

```
CODE: = ALARMCODE (VALUE);
```

the current value of VALUE is substituted for NUMBER and the value returned (an integer number) is assigned to the variable CODE. This is then passed over to the PRINT procedure where it replaces the dummy variable FLAG, used when PRINT was defined. Notice that PRINT does not pass any information back to the main program; it just provides the facility for which it was created. In total, this program does precisely the same thing as the ones listed in Figures 10.1 and 10.2.

Q10.7

10.8 External functions and procedures

If our function ALARMCODE and procedure PRINT were of a sufficiently general nature, we might consider compiling and storing them with other useful functions and procedures, either separately or in our own user library. When they were needed in a later PASCAL

```
    PROGRAM SUBROUTINES;

    (* Illustrating how subroutines can be written into Pascal programs. *)

VAR
      VALUE, CODE : INTEGER;



    FUNCTION ALARMCODE (NUMBER : INTEGER) : INTEGER;
    (* This Function compares the value of an integer NUMBER with fixed limits
       and returns an integer result (indicated by the second ': INTEGER ')
       assigned to the label ALARMCODE.      *)

    (* ALARMCODE is 02 for a high alarm
                   01 for a low  alarm
            and 00 for    no     alarm.   *)

CONST
      HIGHLIMIT = 204;
      LOWLIMIT  = 51;
VAR
      CODENUMBER : INTEGER;              (* VAR NUMBER is defined in the heading *)

BEGIN
      CODENUMBER := 02;                  (* High alarm setting to start with *)
      IF NUMBER <= HIGHLIMIT THEN
      BEGIN    (* A Compound statement *)
            CODENUMBER := CODENUMBER - 1;        (* Its not a high alarm !*)
            IF NUMBER >= LOWLIMIT THEN
                 CODENUMBER := CODENUMBER - 1;  (* No alarm at all !      *)
      END;    (* Compound statement *)
      ALARMCODE := CODENUMBER;
END;    (* Return to the calling program with the code number in ALARMCODE *)



    PROCEDURE PRINT (FLAG : INTEGER);
    (* This little Procedure prints one of three messages depending on the value
       of an integer variable called FLAG which is passed to it from the calling
       program.                                                              *)

    BEGIN  (* Printing *)
              IF FLAG = 02 THEN WRITELN ('HIGH LIMIT EXCEEDED')
        ELSE IF FLAG = 01 THEN WRITELN ('LOW LIMIT EXCEEDED')
        ELSE                   WRITELN ('VALUE IS OK');
    END;   (* Printing *)



    BEGIN   (* The main program *)
        WRITE ('ENTER A TRIAL VALUE ');      READLN (VALUE);
        CODE := ALARMCODE (VALUE);
        PRINT (CODE);
    END.    (* The main program *)
```

Figure 10.4 The comparison program written using a Function and a Procedure in UCSD PASCAL

program we would simply declare them as external and subsequently link them with this new program. For example, the external declaration

```
FUNCTION ALARMCODE (NUMBER : INTEGER): INTEGER;
EXTERNAL;
```

informs the compiler that the function ALARMCODE which is called from this program but not defined here, will be linked with the main program before it is executed. The same technique was used, you will remember, when linking pre-assembled object code modules together in Chapter 6.

The real importance of EXTERNAL declarations from our point of view is that external subroutines need not be PASCAL programs. They could for instance be assembly language subroutines which control user-I/O devices – I/O drivers as they are called. These would need to be already assembled and a minimum requirement may be two subroutines, one of which sends an 8-bit number to a specified output port and another which reads an 8-bit number from an input port. We might choose to call these subroutines WRITEBIN and READBIN, respectively. WRITEBIN is better written as a procedure because it does not return a value, but READBIN will be a function. These would be declared in our main PASCAL program as

```
FUNCTION READBIN (PORTADDRESS: INTEGER): INTEGER;
EXTERNAL;

PROCEDURE WRITEBIN (PORTADDRESS, DATA : INTEGER);
EXTERNAL;
```

These declarations mean that:

1 Subroutine READBIN is passed an integer number (parameter) which is the address of a particular input port. (0 to 255). It returns a value (again 0 to 255) which is the number currently stored in the addressed input port register.
2 READBIN will be called from the main program with a statement like,

```
VALUE: = READBIN (255);
```

The port address is 255 (0FFH) and the value read from there will be returned from the function call and assigned to the main program variable, VALUE.
3 Subroutine WRITEBIN will be passed two parameters. Both will be integer numbers, the first identifying the output port address, and the second will be the value which must be written to the port.
4 WRITEBIN will be called from the main program by programming a statement such as

```
WRITEBIN (255, 22);
```

The number 22 (16H) will then be sent to output port number 255.

5   In both cases the subroutines are not defined in this PASCAL program, but will be linked with it before it is executed.

6   The variable names DATA and PORTADDRESS used in the declarations are just appropriate identifiers for actual parameters.

10.9   Parameter passing between PASCAL and assembly language programs

The success or otherwise of the READBIN and WRITEBIN subroutines depends on being able to pass parameters back and forth between calling and called programs. The UCSD PASCAL way of doing this is to use the stack. If we consider the WRITEBIN sub-routine first of all, entry is made with the stack organised as shown in Figure 10.5. The top two entries on the stack are the return address to the PASCAL program. This must be saved so that when the subroutine is finished, we return to the PASCAL program immediately after the point where the subroutine was called.

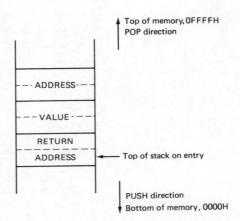

Figure 10.5   Stack organisation on entry to WRITEBIN

After that comes the two parameters passed from PASCAL to the subroutine. These are both 16-bit numbers with the second parameter, the value to send, above the first. In UCSD PASCAL all integer variables are 16-bit two's complement numbers, so integer parameters passed between a main program and a subroutine will take up two stack locations in an 8-bit system.

The READBIN function has one parameter passed to it, the input port address, and returns an integer value, the number read. The stack organisation on entry, and it is necessary organisation on exit, is shown in Figure 10.6.

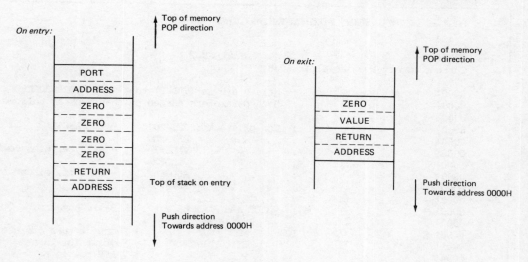

Figure 10.6 Stack organisation on entry to and exit from the READBIN function

It is fairly clear that alternative ways of passing parameters between PASCAL programs and user subroutines could have been devised. The method described here is the way the UCSD system designers solved the problem. We, the system users, need this information if we are to link our assembly language programs READBIN and WRITE-

Q10.8 BIN with a PASCAL program.

10.10   The WRITEBIN and READBIN subroutines

The assembly language listings for WRITEBIN and READBIN produced by the UCSD 8080 assembler are given in Figures 10.7 and 10.8. A complication arises when using the 8080 assembler because of the way port addresses are passed to the subroutines. When the port address is retrieved from the stack it must become the second byte of an OUT or IN instruction which either sends a value to a port or reads a value from it. Since the port address is a variable, it is not possible to specify both bytes of the IN/OUT instructions when the subroutines are first written. Consequently, we must build an OUT or IN instruction from information passed to the subroutine, at run time. Apart from this complication, and the fact that the assembler pseudo-ops are non-standard when compared with the Intel or CP/M equivalents, the subroutines are quite straightforward.

```
    PAGE -   1  WRITEBIN  FILE:SYSTEM.WRK.TEXT


    00000|                           .PROC    WRITEBIN,2
    Current memory available:    5048
    00000|                        ;
    00000|                        ;  Writes a byte (VALUE) to a port (PORTADDRESS).
    00000|                        ;  Both parameters passed on the stack as follows:-
    00000|                        ;
    00000|                        ;  Top of stack : RETADD1    - to PASCAL
    00000|                        ;                 RETADD2
    00000|                        ;                 VALUE1     - MS byte, discarded
    00000|                        ;                 VALUE2
    00000|                        ;                 ADDRESS1   - MS half, discarded
    00000|                        ;                 ADDRESS2
    00000|                        ;
    00000|                        ;  VALUE and ADDRESS are both 8-bit numbers.
    00000|                        ;
    00000| E1             BGN:     POP     H          ; Remove return address
    00001| 22 ****                 SHLD    RETADD     ; Save it for later
    00004| D1                      POP     D          ; VALUE now in E
    00005| C1                      POP     B          ; PORTADDRESS now in C
    00006| 79                      MOV     A,C        ; PORTADDRESS into A
    00007| 32 ****                 STA     SEND+1     ; Fill in byte 2 of OUT
    000A| 7B                       MOV     A,E        ; VALUE into A
    000B|                        ;
    000B|                        ;  Now build an OUT instruction
    000B|                        ;
    0008* 0C00
    000B| D3              SEND:    .BYTE   -45        ; -45D = D3H = 'OUT' op-code
    000C| 00                       .BYTE   0          ; PORTADDRESS will go here
    000D|                        ;
    000D|                        ;  VALUE now sent - tidy up.
    000D|                        ;
    000D| 2A ****                 LHLD    RETADD     ; Get RETADD back
    0010| E5                      PUSH    H          ; Put on top of stack
    0011| C9                      RET                ; Return to PASCAL
    0012|                        ;
    0012|                        ;  Define a 16-bit location for return address
    0012|                        ;
    000E* 1200
    0002* 1200
    0012| 0000           RETADD:  .WORD   0          ; Two bytes reserved
    0014|                        ;
    0014|                                 .END
```

Figure 10.7   The assembly language WRITEBIN procedure

In essence, all that WRITEBIN and READBIN do is to execute the equivalent assembly language instructions:

```
OUT    portaddress    - WRITEBIN
IN     portaddress    - READBIN
```

Finally notice how the two subroutines are headed. WRITEBIN is a procedure and is passed two parameters from the main program. This information is compressed into the statement,

```
PAGE -   1   READBIN    FILE:SYSTEM.WRK.TEXT


0000|                             .FUNC    READBIN,1
Current memory available:         5048
0000|                        ;
0000|                        ;   Reads a byte from a port address.
0000|                        ;   On entry, the stack is organised as follows:-
0000|                        ;
0000|                        ;   TOS : RETADD1        - To Pascal
0000|                        ;         RETADD2
0000|                        ;         ZEROBYTE        - These four zero bytes must removed
0000|                        ;         ZEROBYTE        - from the stack before you can get
0000|                        ;         ZEROBYTE        - at the port address which follows.
0000|                        ;         ZEROBYTE
0000|                        ;         ADDRESS1        - MS byte, discarded
0000|                        ;         ADDRESS2        - Actual port address
0000|                        ;
0000|                        ;   On exit, information must be stacked-up as follows:-
0000|                        ;
0000|                        ;   TOS : RETADD1
0000|                        ;         RETADD2
0000|                        ;         VALUE           - Returned from this Function.
0000|                        ;         ZEROBYTE
0000|                        ;
0000| E1                     BGN:    POP      H          ; Get return address
0001| 22 ****                        SHLD     RETADD     ; Save it for later
0004| E1                             POP      H          ; First two zero bytes gone
0005| E1                             POP      H          ; And the next two
0006| C1                             POP      B          ; Port address into C
0007| 79                             MOV      A,C        ; And now in A
0008| 32 ****                        STA      READ+1     ; Form second byte of IN
000B|                        ;
000B|                        ;   Now have to build an 'IN' instruction.
000B|                        ;
0009* 0C00
000B| DB                     READ:   .BYTE    -37        ; -37D = DBH = 'IN' op-code
000C| 00                             .BYTE    0          ; Address will go here
000D|                        ;
000D|                        ;   Value now read, tidy up the stack
000D|                        ;
000D| 5F                             MOV      E,A        ; 8-bit value into E
000E| 16 00                          MVI      D,00       ; Zero byte into D
0010| D5                             PUSH     D          ; Stack-up VALUE and zero
0011|                        ;
0011|                        ;   Now put return address on top of VALUE and ZERO.
0011|                        ;
0011| 2A ****                        LHLD     RETADD     ; Get return address back
0014| E5                             PUSH     H          ; Put it on top of the stack
0015| C9                             RET                 ; And go back to Pascal
0016|                        ;
0016|                        ;   Here make space for storing the return address
0012* 1600
0002* 1600
0016| 0000                   RETADD: .WORD    0          ; WORD is two bytes
0018|                        ;
0018|                                .END
```

Figure 10.8   The assembly language READBIN function

```
.PROC    WRITEBIN,2
```

READBIN, on the other hand, is a function and is passed only one parameter. Consequently it is headed

```
.FUNC    READBIN,1
```

10.11   Using WRITEBIN and READBIN in PASCAL programs

To test our elementary I/O drivers, a simple program which reads from an input port and writes the same number to an output port in a never-ending cycle, is perfectly adequate. Program TESTIO, which does this, is listed in Figure 10.9. When it runs, switches are connected

```
PROGRAM TESTIO;

(* Program to test the I/O drivers WRITEBIN and READBIN *)

VAR
      PORTADDRESS, VALUE : INTEGER;



FUNCTION READBIN (PORTNUMBER : INTEGER) : INTEGER;
EXTERNAL;

PROCEDURE WRITEBIN (PORTNUMBER, BYTE : INTEGER);
EXTERNAL;



BEGIN   (* The Test *)
      PORTADDRESS := 254;                      (* Equivalent of 0FEH *)
      REPEAT                                   (* Forever *)
            VALUE := READBIN (PORTADDRESS);    (* Read value from switches *)
            WRITEBIN (PORTADDRESS, VALUE);     (* Send same value to lamps *)
      UNTIL FALSE;
   END.   (* The Test *)
```

Figure 10.9   The PASCAL program to test READBIN AND WRITEBIN

Q10.9, 10.10

to the input port and lamps to the output port so that we can check that READBIN reads a changing digital input and WRITEBIN accepts the same.

10.12   Driving stepping motors from PASCAL programs

Continuously at constant speed in one direction

Only WRITEBIN will be needed when driving a stepping motor from a PASCAL program. As before, the motor is supplied with STEP and DIRECTION signals which account for only two of the eight available lines of an output port. Step pulses on the STEP line drives the motor in a clockwise or anti-clockwise direction depending on the logic level imposed on the DIRECTION line. A suitable program is listed in Figure 10.10. Two new PASCAL subroutines called PULSE and DELAY have been written to generate step pulses at various step rates (delay times).

Reversing the step direction is not a requirement in this program, but it will be in subsequent programs. It is for this reason that the motor is driven with a negative-going pulse, rather than the positive-going pulse used previously. A characteristic of the motor interface logic is that if the direction is changed when the STEP line is low, the motor, sometimes, takes an extra step in the wrong direction before the change takes effect. If the change is made with the STEP line high the transition always occurs smoothly. In this case any extra steps are not that important, but they could be if, for example, we were driving a machine tool from our stepping motor program.

The STEP and DIRECTION signal connections are made to lines D0 and D1, respectively, of output port number 254.

The only program statement which is not strictly necessary is the one which decrements the variable PULSECNT. This was added because this program was used to calibrate the delay routine. An oscilloscope was connected to the STEP line and the time between successive step pulses measured (very approximately) for various values of the variable TIME. The extra statement was included so that the loop which generates one step pulse would be the same in this, and any program which drives the motor through a limited number (PULSECNT) of steps.

Tentative results from this calibration test shows that the parameter passed to the delay routine, TIME, is related to the pulse period, measured in seconds, by the equation

$$\text{TIME} = (4{,}000 \times \text{Period}) - 8$$

You will appreciate that in HLL programs, it is all but impossible to estimate the pulse period by considering statement execution times as we have done before. Rearranging the equation gives

$$\text{TIME} = [4{,}000\,(1/\text{Step rate})] - 8$$

so that the step rate, in steps/second, is related to the delay constant TIME, by the formula

$$\text{Step rate} = 4{,}000/(\text{TIME} + 8)$$

So, for example, a step rate of 80 steps/second would result from a delay constant of 42.

Reversing the direction of rotation

In this program, STEP2, the motor is driven through two revolutions

```
PROGRAM STEP1;
(* Program to drive a stepping motor at a constant speed from Pascal *)

VAR
      PORTADDRESS, PULSECNT, VALUE, TIME : INTEGER;



(* Procedures called from the main program follow *)
PROCEDURE WRITEBIN (PORTNUMBER, BYTE : INTEGER);
EXTERNAL;


PROCEDURE DELAY (TIME : INTEGER);
(* Delay in here for a time proportional to the parameter TIME *)
BEGIN   (* Delay *)
      REPEAT
            TIME := TIME - 1;
      UNTIL TIME = 0;
END;    (* Of Delay *)



PROCEDURE PULSE;
(* Generates a negative-going pulse on D0 of PORTADDRESS. DIRECTION clockwise *)
VAR
      BINARY : INTEGER;
BEGIN
      BINARY := 0;
      WRITEBIN (PORTADDRESS, BINARY);
      DELAY (1);                          (* Short delay for pulse width *)
      WRITEBIN (PORTADDRESS, BINARY+1);
END;    (* Of pulse *)




BEGIN   (* Main program *)
      (* First set STEP line high, DIRECTION low, and the PULSE period *)
      VALUE := 01;                    (* STEP high, DIRECTION low *)
      TIME := 100;                    (* Time between pulses *)
      PORTADDRESS := 254;             (* Portaddress is 0FEH *)
      WRITEBIN (PORTADDRESS, VALUE);  (* Stepper initialised *)

         (* Now generate a continuous sequence of pulses *)
      REPEAT
          PULSE;
          DELAY (TIME);
          PULSECNT := PULSECNT - 1;    (* Needed for later *)
      UNTIL FALSE;
END.
```

Figure 10.10 The STEP1 program

```
        PROGRAM STEP2;
        (* This program drives a stepping motor through two revolutions in one direction
           and then two revolutions in the other. This cycle is repeated indefinitely at
           a speed of approximately 80 steps/second.                                    *)

        VAR
              PORTADDRESS, DIRECTION, PULSECNT, VALUE, TIME : INTEGER;



        (* Procedures used follow *)

        PROCEDURE WRITEBIN (PORTNUMBER, BYTE : INTEGER);
        EXTERNAL;

        PROCEDURE DELAY (TIME : INTEGER);
        BEGIN
              REPEAT
                    TIME := TIME - 1;
              UNTIL TIME = 0;
        END;

        PROCEDURE PULSE (DIRECTION : INTEGER);
        (* The parameter DIRECTION passed to this procedure is a 1 or a 0 for
           anti-clockwise or clockwise rotation.                              *)
        VAR
              BINARY : INTEGER;
        BEGIN
              BINARY := 2 * DIRECTION;              (* D0 = 0, D1 = DIRECTION *)
              WRITEBIN (PORTADDRESS, BINARY);
              DELAY(1);
              WRITEBIN (PORTADDRESS, BINARY+1);     (* D0 now a 1 *)
        END;



        BEGIN  (* STEP2 *)
              PORTADDRESS := 254;                   (* Output port 0FEH *)
              VALUE := 01;                          (* Initial direction CW, STEP line high *)
              WRITEBIN (PORTADDRESS, VALUE);        (* Initialise stepper *)
              TIME := 42;                           (* Speed approximately 80 steps/sec. *)
              DIRECTION := 0;                       (* Maintain CW rotation *)
              REPEAT                                (* Forever *)
                    PULSECNT := 96;                 (* Two revolutions *)
                    REPEAT                          (* Until two revolutions completed *)
                          PULSE (DIRECTION);        (* Generate a pulse *)
                          DELAY (TIME);
                          PULSECNT := PULSECNT - 1;
                    UNTIL PULSECNT = 0;
                    (* Now wait a bit, then change direction *)
                    DELAY (1000);
                    IF DIRECTION = 0 THEN DIRECTION := 1
                    ELSE                  DIRECTION := 0;
              UNTIL FALSE;
        END.   (* STEP2 *)
```

Figure 10.11 The STEP2 program

(PULSECNT = 96) at a constant speed of 80 steps/second and then the direction of rotation is reversed for a further two revolutions. This alternating cycle repeats indefinitely. The program is listed in Figure 10.11.

To bring about this change of direction a parameter labelled DIREC-TION is now passed to the procedure PULSE. DIRECTION is a 1 or 0 depending upon the intended direction of rotation. This bit is shifted one place left (by multiplying by 2) into the D1 position and then combined with the 0 to 1 change on the STEP line.

The timing of step pulses is not precisely the same as in the previous program but the difference is small enough to ignore in relation to the other approximations made.

Linear acceleration and deceleration of the motor

You may remember that this problem was considered in the previous chapter but rejected as a suitable assembly language programming exercise. Using a high-level language, however, the problem is not nearly so difficult.

From Newton's laws of motion, it can be shown that if a body is accelerated from an initial speed of u m s^{-1} at a uniform rate of f ms^{-2}, the final speed, v ms^{-1}, after s metres of travel is given by

$$v^2 = u^2 + 2fs$$

Relating this to our stepping motor problem, the speeds will be expressed in steps/second, the acceleration in steps/second^2 and the distance travelled in the number of steps taken. So, for example, if we wanted to accelerate a motor from an initial speed of 10 steps/second to a final speed of 150 steps/second in 5 revolutions (240 steps), the rate of acceleration would be,

$$f = (v^2 - u^2)/2s$$
$$= (150^2 - 10^2)/480 = 46.66 \text{ steps/second}^2$$

The initial speed will be set by the time between the first two step pulses. The time between subsequent pulses will be shorter so that when the 240th pulse is generated, the time between it and the 239th pulse will be the equivalent of the final velocity.

The problem with linearly accelerating the motor is calculating the individual times and then relating these to numbers passed to the delay routine. If we do the calculation between pulses, our calibration equation derived from the STEP1 results is no longer valid because we have some quite lengthy expressions to evaluate. However, there is no reason why, with the mathematical advantages provided by PASCAL, we should not calculate these times and convert them into delay parameters before the main, drive, part of the program is entered. We will, of course, need to store them somewhere accessible so that they can be retrieved and sent to the delay routine at the proper time.

An obvious way of storing numbers is in an array. If the concept of an array is unfamiliar to you, then just picture it as a row of boxes each of which contains a number. PASCAL, as in most things, is very precise about the way in which an array is defined. We must declare the array, just as we declare any other program variable, in a statement like,

```
DELAYS : ARRAY [1..UPPERBOUND] OF INTEGER;
```

The number of boxes in the array is given by the value of UPPER-BOUND and each box must, in this case, contain an integer number. We can access the number stored in each box by using an array subscript. The contents of the first box, for example, are referred to as DELAYS [1] (the subscript is 1) and the contents of the 42nd box as DELAYS [42].

Assuming that we could fill all the boxes with the proper numbers which define instantaneous speed during acceleration, accessing them will be a question of changing the statement

```
DELAY (TIME);
```

in STEP2 to

```
DELAY (DELAYS[PULSENUMBER]);
```

PULSENUMBER is a variable which, obviously, changes continually as the motor is driven. As it changes, reference is made to a different box in the array of boxes labelled DELAYS. The contents of successive boxes are therefore retrieved and passed to the delay routine to set the speed of rotation.

If we were using several arrays like DELAYS, it would be much more convenient to define a new data type which described the constitution of all of them. PASCAL allows us to do this with the TYPE declaration. For instance, we could say

```
TYPE
     DELAYARRAY = ARRAY [1...240] OF INTEGER;
```

and then

```
DELAYS, HOLDS, SPEEDS : DELAYARRAY;
```

Having told PASCAL about this new data type we are using, we can declare variables like DELAYS, HOLDS and SPEEDS to be of that type. The alternative would be to write

```
VAR
     DELAYS : ARRAY [1..240] OF INTEGER;
     HOLDS  : ARRAY [1..240] OF INTEGER;
     SPEEDS : ARRAY [1..240] OF INTEGER;
```

You will agree that using the TYPE declaration makes much more sense. Even if there is only one variable of type DELAYARRAY, the program is often clearer if the TYPE declaration is used.

The WORKOUTDELAYS procedure   Now that we know how to store these delay parameters and access them, we can concentrate on how to calculate them.

Let us assume that acceleration to maximum speed is achieved in a whole number of revolutions. We shall label that number SPEEDU-PREVS. It follows then, that the total number of pulses generated during acceleration (and deceleration) is the product of SPEEDU-PREVS and 48. Since the separation between the first two pulses generated sets the initial speed, acceleration to the final speed is completed in

```
(SPEEDUPREVS*48 - 2) steps
```

Consequently the acceleration in steps/second^2 is given by

$$\text{ACCELERATION} = \frac{(\text{FINAL})^2 - (\text{INITIAL})^2}{2*(\text{SPEEDUPREVS}*48 - 2)}$$

where the words FINAL and INITIAL refer to speeds.

At any point during the drive cycle, the number passed to the delay routine, N, is related to the instantaneous step rate by the equation

$$N = \frac{4000}{\text{STEP RATE}} - 8$$

N must be an integer (whole) number for the delay routine to work properly so we must round-off the evaluated expression to the nearest integer value before storing it in the array. For example, if we consider the initial speed and the delay parameter which produces it, the Pascal calculation is,

```
DELAYS [1] : = ROUND (4000/INITIAL - 8);
```

The pre-declared ROUND function takes the nearest whole number after the expression has been evaluated and stores it in the first box of the array. For an initial speed of 30 steps/second, then, the expression evaluates to 125.33 which is rounded-off to 125.

The numbers in the other boxes will be calculated from the speed on entry to a delay period and the necessary speed on exit to, eventually, achieve the FINAL speed at pulse number SPEEDUPREVS $\times$ 48. Figure 10.12 expresses the problem more precisely.

If we label the speed on entry as PRESENT and the speed on exit as NEXT, then NEXT is given by

$$\text{NEXT}^2 = \text{PRESENT}^2 + 2*f*1$$

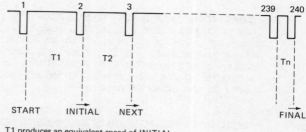

T1 produces an equivalent speed of INITIAL
T2 a speed of INITIAL + ΔV
Tn produces an equivalent speed of FINAL

Figure 10.12 Given an initial and final speed and the total number of pulses in which to accelerate, the WORKOUTDELAYS procedure calculates a series of numbers which are passed to the DELAY procedure to produce the required acceleration characteristics. This diagram assumes that acceleration to the FINAL speed is required in five revolutions

In PASCAL terms, this would be written as

```
NEXT: = SQRT(SQR(PRESENT) + 2*ACCELERATION);
```

Knowing the exit speed, we can calculate the delay parameter to realise that speed. In the step after that, NEXT becomes PRESENT so that we can calculate another speed and another delay parameter.

All of this is summarised in the procedure WORKOUTDELAYS which is listed in Figure 10.13. A self assessment exercise, for which no solution will be provided, would be to write an assembly language program which does the same thing as WORKOUTDELAYS. The PASCAL (HLL) program is concise, easy to understand and fairly easy to write and test. The same can very definitely not be said for the assembly language program.

One final point about WORKOUTDELAYS. There are no parameters passed to the procedure, but there is information passed back to the main program from it. In particular, the main program will need to know the numbers stored in the array DELAYS and the value of SPEEDUPREVS. By preceeding the procedure parameters by the word VAR, we are declaring them to be variable parameters rather than the value parameters used previously. This means that they can be changed in the procedure and their new values are accessible to any program which calls the procedure. Value parameters are the same on entry to and exit from a procedure.

For testing WORKOUTDELAYS several extra statements were added to produce the results printout shown in Figure 10.14. You will notice from this that, because the delay parameters are rounded-off to the nearest integer value, successive parameters are sometimes the

```
$
   PROCEDURE WORKOUTDELAYS (VAR SPEEDUPREVS : INTEGER;VAR DELAYS : DELAYARRAY);
   (* This procedure reads the INITIAL step rate, the FINAL step rate and the
      number of revolutions in which to accelerate. From this information the
      delay constants which will produce approximately linear acceleration and
      deceleration from INITIAL to FINAL in the prescribed number of steps, are
      calculated. These number are rounded-off to the nearest integer value and
      stored in the array DELAYS.                                              *)

   VAR
         INITIAL, FINAL, ACCELERATION, PRESENT, NEXT : REAL;
         PULSENO, TOTALPULSES : INTEGER;
   BEGIN
         WRITE ('INITIAL STEP RATE ?');
         READLN (INITIAL);
         WRITE ('FINAL STEP RATE   ?');
         READLN (FINAL);
         WRITE ('NUMBER OF REVOLUTIONS IN WHICH TO ACCELERATE - MAX IS 5 ?');
         READLN (SPEEDUPREVS);
         DELAYS[1] := ROUND (4000/INITIAL - 8);        (* First delay sets INITIAL *)
         TOTALPULSES := SPEEDUPREVS * 48;
         ACCELERATION := (SQR(FINAL) - SQR(INITIAL))/(2 * (TOTALPULSES - 2));
         PULSENO := 3;
         PRESENT := INITIAL;

         REPEAT (* Until the rest of the delays have been calculated *)
               NEXT := SQRT(SQR(PRESENT) + 2 * ACCELERATION);
               DELAYS[PULSENO - 1] := ROUND (4000/NEXT - 8);
               PRESENT := NEXT;
               PULSENO := PULSENO + 1;
         UNTIL PULSENO = TOTALPULSES + 1;

   END   (* Of delay calculation *);
   *
```

Figure 10.13   The WORKOUTDELAYS procedure

Q10.11

same. Linear acceleration is therefore even more approximate than we may have originally thought.

The main program   The program which calls WORKOUTDELAYS and the other procedures we have discussed is called RAMP. It accelerates the motor to a maximum speed, maintains that speed for 5 revolutions and then decelerates the motor. The direction of rotation is then reversed and the cycle repeated. The program is listed in Figure 10.15 and appears very similar to the structure of the RAMP program listed in the previous chapter. The difference is that our PASCAL program is more versatile, gives a much better approximation to linear acceleration and is more compact. Quite clearly it could be made even more versatile, perhaps by specifying a different number of steps (rather than revolutions) for acceleration, deceleration and constant speed. However, we have taken it as far as we need.

```
Running...
INITIAL STEP RATE ?10
FINAL STEP RATE    ?150
NUMBER OF REVOLUTIONS IN WHICH TO ACCELERATE - MAX IS 5 ?1


SPEED AT PULSE  2 = 1.00000E1 STEPS/SEC. DELAY CONSTANT BETWEEN PULSES  1 AND  2 IS 392
SPEED AT PULSE  3 = 2.42272E1 STEPS/SEC. DELAY CONSTANT BETWEEN PULSES  2 AND  3 IS 157
SPEED AT PULSE  4 = 3.27706E1 STEPS/SEC. DELAY CONSTANT BETWEEN PULSES  3 AND  4 IS 114
SPEED AT PULSE  5 = 3.95078E1 STEPS/SEC. DELAY CONSTANT BETWEEN PULSES  4 AND  5 IS 93
SPEED AT PULSE  6 = 4.52529E1 STEPS/SEC. DELAY CONSTANT BETWEEN PULSES  5 AND  6 IS 80
SPEED AT PULSE  7 = 5.03466E1 STEPS/SEC. DELAY CONSTANT BETWEEN PULSES  6 AND  7 IS 71
SPEED AT PULSE  8 = 5.49704E1 STEPS/SEC. DELAY CONSTANT BETWEEN PULSES  7 AND  8 IS 65
SPEED AT PULSE  9 = 5.92342E1 STEPS/SEC. DELAY CONSTANT BETWEEN PULSES  8 AND  9 IS 60
SPEED AT PULSE 10 = 6.32112E1 STEPS/SEC. DELAY CONSTANT BETWEEN PULSES  9 AND 10 IS 55
SPEED AT PULSE 11 = 6.69523E1 STEPS/SEC. DELAY CONSTANT BETWEEN PULSES 10 AND 11 IS 52
SPEED AT PULSE 12 = 7.04952E1 STEPS/SEC. DELAY CONSTANT BETWEEN PULSES 11 AND 12 IS 49
SPEED AT PULSE 13 = 7.38683E1 STEPS/SEC. DELAY CONSTANT BETWEEN PULSES 12 AND 13 IS 46
SPEED AT PULSE 14 = 7.70940E1 STEPS/SEC. DELAY CONSTANT BETWEEN PULSES 13 AND 14 IS 44
SPEED AT PULSE 15 = 8.01900E1 STEPS/SEC. DELAY CONSTANT BETWEEN PULSES 14 AND 15 IS 42
SPEED AT PULSE 16 = 8.31709E1 STEPS/SEC. DELAY CONSTANT BETWEEN PULSES 15 AND 16 IS 40
SPEED AT PULSE 17 = 8.60485E1 STEPS/SEC. DELAY CONSTANT BETWEEN PULSES 16 AND 17 IS 38
SPEED AT PULSE 18 = 8.88330E1 STEPS/SEC. DELAY CONSTANT BETWEEN PULSES 17 AND 18 IS 37
SPEED AT PULSE 19 = 9.15329E1 STEPS/SEC. DELAY CONSTANT BETWEEN PULSES 18 AND 19 IS 36
SPEED AT PULSE 20 = 9.41553E1 STEPS/SEC. DELAY CONSTANT BETWEEN PULSES 19 AND 20 IS 34
SPEED AT PULSE 21 = 9.67067E1 STEPS/SEC. DELAY CONSTANT BETWEEN PULSES 20 AND 21 IS 33
SPEED AT PULSE 22 = 9.91924E1 STEPS/SEC. DELAY CONSTANT BETWEEN PULSES 21 AND 22 IS 32
SPEED AT PULSE 23 = 1.01617E2 STEPS/SEC. DELAY CONSTANT BETWEEN PULSES 22 AND 23 IS 31
SPEED AT PULSE 24 = 1.03986E2 STEPS/SEC. DELAY CONSTANT BETWEEN PULSES 23 AND 24 IS 30
SPEED AT PULSE 25 = 1.06301E2 STEPS/SEC. DELAY CONSTANT BETWEEN PULSES 24 AND 25 IS 30
SPEED AT PULSE 26 = 1.08568E2 STEPS/SEC. DELAY CONSTANT BETWEEN PULSES 25 AND 26 IS 29
SPEED AT PULSE 27 = 1.10788E2 STEPS/SEC. DELAY CONSTANT BETWEEN PULSES 26 AND 27 IS 28
SPEED AT PULSE 28 = 1.12964E2 STEPS/SEC. DELAY CONSTANT BETWEEN PULSES 27 AND 28 IS 27
SPEED AT PULSE 29 = 1.15099E2 STEPS/SEC. DELAY CONSTANT BETWEEN PULSES 28 AND 29 IS 27
SPEED AT PULSE 30 = 1.17195E2 STEPS/SEC. DELAY CONSTANT BETWEEN PULSES 29 AND 30 IS 26
SPEED AT PULSE 31 = 1.19255E2 STEPS/SEC. DELAY CONSTANT BETWEEN PULSES 30 AND 31 IS 26
SPEED AT PULSE 32 = 1.21279E2 STEPS/SEC. DELAY CONSTANT BETWEEN PULSES 31 AND 32 IS 25
SPEED AT PULSE 33 = 1.23271E2 STEPS/SEC. DELAY CONSTANT BETWEEN PULSES 32 AND 33 IS 24
SPEED AT PULSE 34 = 1.25230E2 STEPS/SEC. DELAY CONSTANT BETWEEN PULSES 33 AND 34 IS 24
SPEED AT PULSE 35 = 1.27160E2 STEPS/SEC. DELAY CONSTANT BETWEEN PULSES 34 AND 35 IS 23
SPEED AT PULSE 36 = 1.29060E2 STEPS/SEC. DELAY CONSTANT BETWEEN PULSES 35 AND 36 IS 23
SPEED AT PULSE 37 = 1.30933E2 STEPS/SEC. DELAY CONSTANT BETWEEN PULSES 36 AND 37 IS 23
SPEED AT PULSE 38 = 1.32780E2 STEPS/SEC. DELAY CONSTANT BETWEEN PULSES 37 AND 38 IS 22
SPEED AT PULSE 39 = 1.34601E2 STEPS/SEC. DELAY CONSTANT BETWEEN PULSES 38 AND 39 IS 22
SPEED AT PULSE 40 = 1.36398E2 STEPS/SEC. DELAY CONSTANT BETWEEN PULSES 39 AND 40 IS 21
SPEED AT PULSE 41 = 1.38171E2 STEPS/SEC. DELAY CONSTANT BETWEEN PULSES 40 AND 41 IS 21
SPEED AT PULSE 42 = 1.39922E2 STEPS/SEC. DELAY CONSTANT BETWEEN PULSES 41 AND 42 IS 21
SPEED AT PULSE 43 = 1.41652E2 STEPS/SEC. DELAY CONSTANT BETWEEN PULSES 42 AND 43 IS 20
SPEED AT PULSE 44 = 1.43360E2 STEPS/SEC. DELAY CONSTANT BETWEEN PULSES 43 AND 44 IS 20
SPEED AT PULSE 45 = 1.45049E2 STEPS/SEC. DELAY CONSTANT BETWEEN PULSES 44 AND 45 IS 20
SPEED AT PULSE 46 = 1.46718E2 STEPS/SEC. DELAY CONSTANT BETWEEN PULSES 45 AND 46 IS 19
SPEED AT PULSE 47 = 1.48368E2 STEPS/SEC. DELAY CONSTANT BETWEEN PULSES 46 AND 47 IS 19
SPEED AT PULSE 48 = 1.50000E2 STEPS/SEC. DELAY CONSTANT BETWEEN PULSES 47 AND 48 IS 19
```

Figure 10.14   Results obtained from a modified WORKOUTDELAYS procedure

```
$
PROGRAM RAMP;
(* This program accelerates a stepping motor from an INITIAL speed to a FINAL
    speed in 'SPEEDUPREVS' number of revolutions. It maintains maximum speed
    for five revolutions and then decelerates to the INITIAL speed in a
    further 'SPEEDUPREVS' revolutions. The direction of rotation is then
    reversed and the cycle repeated indefinitely.                            *)

TYPE
     DELAYARRAY = ARRAY [1..239] OF INTEGER;
     (* Can store delays for a maximum of 5 revolutions *)
VAR
     DELAYS : DELAYARRAY;
     DIRECTION, PORTADDRESS, REVS, SPEEDUPCNT, PULSECNT, MIDDLECNT : INTEGER;

(* Procedures used by RAMP are :- *)
PROCEDURE WRITEBIN (PORTNUMBER, BYTE : INTEGER);
EXTERNAL;
PROCEDURE DELAY (TIME : INTEGER);
PROCEDURE PULSE (DIRECTION : INTEGER);
PROCEDURE WORKOUTDELAYS (VAR SPEEDUPREVS : INTEGER;VAR DELAYS : DELAYARRAY);


BEGIN (* Main RAMP program *)
     PORTADDRESS := 254;
     WRITEBIN (PORTADDRESS,1);           (* Initialise STEP line high *)
     WORKOUTDELAYS (REVS, DELAYS);       (* REVS updated in the procedure *)
     SPEEDUPCNT := REVS * 48;            (* Pulses to speed-up in *)
     DIRECTION := 0;                     (* Clockwise first *)
     PULSECNT := 1;
     REPEAT   (* The main loop indefinitely *)
          MIDDLECNT := 0;
          PULSE (DIRECTION);
          (* Note - this pulse is generated outside the first inner loop because
                    there is always one more pulse than there is space (delay)
                    between pulses.                                           *)

          REPEAT   (* Until maximum speed reached *)
               DELAY (DELAYS[PULSECNT]);
               PULSE (DIRECTION);
               PULSECNT := PULSECNT + 1;
          UNTIL PULSECNT = SPEEDUPCNT;

          REPEAT   (* Now maintain maximum speed for 5 revolutions *)
               DELAY (DELAYS [PULSECNT-1]);
               PULSE (DIRECTION);
               MIDDLECNT := MIDDLECNT + 1;
          UNTIL MIDDLECNT = 241;

          REPEAT   (* Now decelerate until INITIAL speed regained *)
               DELAY (DELAYS [PULSECNT-1]);
               PULSE (DIRECTION);
               PULSECNT := PULSECNT - 1;
          UNTIL PULSECNT = 1;

          (* Now wait a bit, change direction, and repeat *)

          DELAY (1000);
          IF DIRECTION = 0 THEN DIRECTION := 1
          ELSE                  DIRECTION := 0;
     UNTIL FALSE;
END.

*
```

Figure 10.15 The RAMP program

10.13 Interrupting UCSD PASCAL

The reasons why interrupt working is often desirable were discussed in Chapter 7 and are equally valid now that we are writing in a high level language. The HLL program should still respond to asynchronously occurring events while, in between interrupts, executing its main instruction sequence. To demonstrate this facility in UCSD PASCAL, the next program we shall study will be essentially the same as STEP2 but now it will be interrupted. Normally, it just drives a stepping motor two revolutions in one direction and then two in the other in an endless loop. When the interrupt occurs, the 8-bit output of an ADC is read, compared with a high and low limit and, if an alarm condition exists, a warning message is printed on the console. After that the main stepping motor drive program is re-entered.

The ADC is driven by the same one-minute timer circuit which was used in previous ADC experiments. The READY line of the ADC is connected to the interrupt input (STB) of input port FF and its digital output lines are connected to the main data lines of the same port. Since interrupts occur at one minute intervals we can maintain a real-time clock and update it as each value is read. The system hardware is shown in Figure 10.16.

Since it is a good idea to write as much of the program as possible in PASCAL, we have decided to read the value when the interrupt occurs, but only do the comparison when the motor is on the point of changing direction. The advantage of doing this is that we avoid the necessity of writing lengthy interrupt service routines. It also gives us an opportunity to introduce the Boolean data type which is featured in several HLLs.

Boolean variables can take on only two values, TRUE or FALSE, which correspond with logical 1 and logical 0, respectively. We can

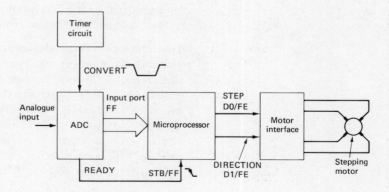

Figure 10.16 The hardware used with the program INTPASCAL

make assignments to Boolean variables such as,

    INTERRUPTED: = FALSE;

and test Boolean variables in conditional statements like,

    IF INTERRUPTED = TRUE THEN....

This is a useful facility because it means we can write our interrupt example program as follows:

```
REPEAT (*Forever*)
     INTERRUPTED: = FALSE; (*Initially and after interrupt*)
     REPEAT (*Until INTERRUPTED is TRUE*)
        Drive motor through two revolutions.
        Change direction.
     UNTIL INTERRUPTED;
     Now compare value with limits.
     Print alarm message if appropriate.
UNTIL FALSE; (*Return motor to drive loop*)
```

The interrupt service routine will do two things. First it will read the ADC output and assign the value read to the Pascal program variable VALUE, and then it will make the variable INTERRUPTED, TRUE, so that, after the direction has been changed, the program proceeds to work on the newly acquired VALUE before returning to drive loop. This second requirement will involve writing all '1s' into the variable INTERRUPTED.

Changing PASCAL program variables from a linked assembly language program is another new idea. The UCSD assembler provides a number of inter-program communications pseudo-ops, including the .PUBLIC directive which is used to identify PASCAL program variables which are accessible to linked assembly language programs. Figure 10.17 shows how this and the .DEF pseudo-op is used in the interrupt service routine called READ-VALUE. The .DEF declaration is the equivalent of the GLBL (global) statements used in earlier programs.

The interrupt service routine start address, ISR, is declared to be global because, just as when interrupts were used in programs which run under CP/M, our version of UCSD PASCAL does not allow code to be loaded directly into the restart area. We need a subroutine which moves a JMP ISR instruction to the restart area early on during program execution. This external procedure is called MOVE and is listed in Figure 10.18. It locates the ISR start address by defining ISR as an external global symbol and stores the complete JMP instruction at address 0008H which is RST 1.

Having dealt with the assembly language parts of the software, we can now turn our attention to the main PASCAL program. For the

```
              PAGE -   1  READVALU   FILE:SYSTEM.WRK.TEXT


.00001                              .PROC      READVALUE
Current memory available:           5048
.00001                              ;
.00001                              ; This is the interrupt service routine.
.00001                              ;
.00001                              .DEF       ISR          ; Defining ISR start address.
.00001                              
.00001                              .PUBLIC    INTERRUPTED,VALUE
.00001                              ;
.00001                              ; PUBLIC labels are defined in the Pascal program but
.00001                              ; accessible here.
.00001                              ;
.00001 E5                ISR:        PUSH      H            ; Save HL
.00011 F5                            PUSH      PSW          ; And A
.00021 DB FF             READ:       IN        0FFH         ; Read the value
.00041 6F                            MOV       L,A          ; LS 8 bits of value to L
.00051 26 00                         MVI       H,0          ; MS bits all zeros
.00071 22 0000                       SHLD      VALUE        ; Send it back, directly
.000A1 21 FFFF                       LXI       H,0FFFFH     ; Logical TRUE into
.000D1 22 0000                       SHLD      INTERRUPTED
.00101 F1                            POP       PSW          ; Restore registers
.00111 E1                            POP       H            ; Return add. on TOS
.00121 FB                            EI
.00131 C9                            RET
.00141
.00141                              .END

 PAGE -
```

Figure 10.17 The interrupt service routine which is executed when the main program, INTPASCAL, is interrupted

```
              PAGE -   1  MOVE       FILE:MOVE


.00001                              .PROC      MOVE
Current memory available:           5034
.00001                              ;
.00001                              ; Moves a JMP ISR instruction to Restart 1 address.
.00001                              ;
.00001                              .REF       ISR          ; External address REFerence
.00001
.00001 0008             RESTRT:      .EQU      8            ; Defines restart address
.00001
.00001 3E C3            BGN:         MVI       A,0C3H       ; JMP op-code
.00021 32 0800                       STA       RESTRT       ; Store it
.00051 21 0000                       LXI       H,ISR        ; ISR start address
.00081 22 0900                       SHLD      RESTRT+1     ; Into addresses 9 and 10
.000B1 DB FF                         IN        0FFH         ; Clear any pending intrpt
.000D1 FB                            EI
.000E1 C9                            RET                    ; RETADD still stacked
.000F1
.000F1                              .END
```

Figure 10.18 The external procedure that loads a JMP ISR instruction into address 0008H

```
$
PROGRAM INTPASCAL;
(* This an example of how a Pascal program can be interrupted. The main program
   is the same as STEP2. On interrupt a value is read from an ADC and the
   variable INTERRUPTED is made TRUE. When the motor stops, the 1-minute
   clock is updated and alarm message printed if the VALUE is out-of-limits.   *)


CONST
     HIGHLIMIT = 204;
     LOWLIMIT  = 51;
VAR
     HOURS, MINUTES, PULSECNT, VALUE,
     MOTORPORT, DATAPORT, DIRECTION  : INTEGER;
     INTERRUPTED : BOOLEAN;                     (* Its either TRUE or FALSE *)


(* Procedures used:- *)
PROCEDURE WRITEBIN (PORTADDRESS, BYTE : INTEGER);
EXTERNAL;
PROCEDURE MOVE;
EXTERNAL;                                       (* Moves JMP ISR instruction to RST 1 *)
PROCEDURE READVALUE;
EXTERNAL;                                       (* Passes back a value on interrupt *)
PROCEDURE UPDATECLOCK;                          (* Up-dates the RTC *)
PROCEDURE DELAY (TIME : INTEGER);               (* Delay routine *)
PROCEDURE PULSE (DIRECTION : INTEGER);          (* Generates a pulse in DIRECTION *)



BEGIN   (* Main Program *)
     HOURS := 0;
     MINUTES := 0;                              (* Initialise the clock *)
     MOTORPORT := 254;                          (* Stepper connected here *)
     DATAPORT  := 255;                          (* ADC connected here *)
     DIRECTION := 0;                            (* Clockwise initially *)
     WRITEBIN (MOTORPORT, 01);                  (* Set STEP line high *)

     MOVE;                                      (* Move JMP instruction to RST1 *)

     REPEAT  (* Forever *)
          INTERRUPTED := FALSE;                 (* Initially and after interrupt *)
          REPEAT  (* Until interrupted *)
               PULSECNT := 96;                  (* Two revolutions *)
               REPEAT  (* For 2 revolutions *)
                    PULSE (DIRECTION);
                    DELAY (42);                 (* Constant 80 steps/sec *)
                    PULSECNT := PULSECNT - 1;
               UNTIL PULSECNT = 0;
               DELAY (1000);                    (* Wait before direction change *)
               IF DIRECTION = 0 THEN DIRECTION := 1
               ELSE               DIRECTION := 0;
          UNTIL INTERRUPTED   (* Is TRUE. i.e. immediately after an interrupt *) *);

          (* After an interrupt do this ! *)
          UPDATECLOCK;
          IF VALUE > HIGHLIMIT THEN             (* Starting comparison *)
               WRITELN ('HIGH ALARM AT ',HOURS,':',MINUTES,' VALUE WAS ',VALUE)
          ELSE
          IF VALUE < LOWLIMIT THEN
               WRITELN ('LOW ALARM AT ',HOURS,':',MINUTES,' VALUE WAS ',VALUE);
     UNTIL FALSE;   (* Which means return to motor drive loop *)
END.
*
```

Figure 10.19   The main PASCAL program, INTPASCAL

most part, the program, which is listed in Figure 10.19 and called INTPASCAL, is clear. As before however, there are various other, different strategies we could have adopted and all of them would have been equally easy to accomodate in our high level language program. Not shown is the UPDATECLOCK procedure, but if you refer to the structure of the subroutine UPDATE given in Chapter 7 then, **Q10.12** essentially, you have the PASCAL code.

10.14 The role of assembly language routines in HLL programs

Given a free choice between programming in an HLL or assembler, most of us, with efficiency in mind, would choose the HLL. There are however, times when programming at least some of the code in assembly language is unavoidable. We have seen here, that there is no alternative to assembly language when writing I/O drivers and interrupt service routines to interface external devices with UCSD PASCAL.

On other occasions it may be necessary to make sections of code, once they have started executing, run as quickly as possible. Optimum speed is achieved by getting close to the microprocessor hardware which means programming in assembly language. There is still then a place for assembly language programs in modern system design but, for all the reasons given before, programming in a high level language is likely to be the future prospect for microprocessor development **Q10.13** engineers.

References

10.1   *North Star Pascal: Version 1 – System Reference Manual*, North Star Computers Inc., 2547 Ninth Street, Berkeley, Ca. 94710 (PAS-DOC Revision 2, 1979).

10.2   *North Star Systems Software Manual*, North Star Computers Inc., 2547 Ninth Street, Berkeley, Ca. 94710 (SOFT-DOC Revision 2.1, 1979).

10.3   R. W. Prowse and P. Van Santen, 'Microprocessors – their impact on the systems designer', *Electronics and Power*, Vol. 26(4), pp 305–9 (April 1980).

10.4   J. Handel, 'The new literacy: programming languages as languages', *Byte*, Vol. 6(3), pp 300–307 (March 1981).

10.5   R. A. Morris, 'Comparison of some high level languages', *ibid.*, Vol. 5(2), pp 128–39 (February 1980).

10.6   D. Moralee, 'High-level languages: a hardware-man's view', *Electronics and Power*, Vol. 27(2), pp 130–5 (February 1981).

10.7   R. Hokanson, 'Choosing a high-level language for micro-processor development systems', *Digital Design*, Vol. 9(2), pp 28–34 (February 1979).

10.8   J. S. James, 'FORTH conceptual introduction', *Conference Proceedings of the Sixth West Coast Computer Faire*, San Francisco, California 3–5 April 1981, pp 376–9.

10.9   R. Mateosian, 'Programming with free BASIC', *op cit*. ref 10.8, pp 398–401.

10.10 Special issue on the language FORTH, *Byte*, Vol. 5(8), (August 1980).

10.11 Special issue on the language LISP, *ibid.*, Vol. 4(8), (August 1979).

Questions

10.1   Briefly explain the need for a high level language when developing microprocessor software.

10.2   Summarise the advantages and disadvantages of HLLs.

10.3   Discuss the difference between compilers and interpreters when translating HLL programs into machine language instructions.

10.4   Briefly discuss some of the more common HLLs that run on microcomputers.

10.5   Discuss some of the advantages and disadvantages of BASIC as a microcomputer programming language and compare it with PASCAL.

10.6   Explain how UCSD PASCAL translates a source code program into machine code.

10.7   What is the difference between a PASCAL function and a procedure?

10.8   Discuss the way in which the stack is used in UCSD PASCAL to pass parameters between a PASCAL program and an external assembly language routine.

10.9   How could the READBIN function be used in a program which reads an 8-bit number from an ADC and then continues, as in the COMPARE program of Figure 10.1, to print an alarm message if the value is out-of-limits?

10.10 An external function called READADC returns the decimal equivalent of a 12-bit number read from the output of a 12-bit ADC. The 8 most significant bits are connected to the port labelled ADDRESS, and the 4 least significant bits are connected to the least significant 4 lines of ADDRESS + 1. Plan (but do not code) the assembly language program and show how it would be declared in the main PASCAL program. Show also how READBIN could be used to achieve the same end.

10.11 Suggest a form for the extra WRITE, or WRITELN, statements which were added to WORKOUTDELAYS to produce the printout of Figure 10.14.

10.12 Although the intention has not been to teach PASCAL programming in this chapter, write a procedure call UPDATECLOCK which updates a one-minute RTC when called.

10.13 Suggest tasks within an HLL program which are best written in assembly language, or for which there is no alternative to assembly language.

Appendix   Library file of console I/O routines

The library file listed below contains all the general purpose console
I/O routines which are used in the various ADC and DAC programs.

```
 1:
 2:
 3:                    *    PROGRAM NAME : CONSOL.LIB
 4:                    *    ======= ================
 5:                    *
 6:                    *    THIS FILE CONTAINS A NUMBER OF GENERAL PURPOSE CONSOL I/O
 7:                    *    ROUTINES WHICH CAN BE COMBINED WITH ANY CP/M SOURCE CODE
 8:                    *    FILE IN THE EDITOR.
 9:                    *
10:                    *    TO MAKE THE NECESSARY CONNECTION PUT THE 'ED' CHARACTER
11:                    *    POINTER AT THE END OF YOUR SOURCE CODE AND TYPE:
12:                    *
13:                    *            RCONSOL
14:                    *
15:                    *    THE WHOLE SET OF SUBROUTINES WILL BE ADDED TO YOUR FILE.
16:                    *    THE ONLY CONDITION IS THAT THIS FILE MUST BE ON THE MAIN
17:                    *    SYSTEM DISK AND MUST HAVE THE .LIB EXTENSION.
18:                    *
19:                    *    SUBROUTINE PRNLFT
20:                    *    =================
21:                    *
22:                    *    ON ENTRY TO THIS SUBROUTINE THE MOST SIGNIFICANT FOUR BITS
23:                    *    IN REGISTER A ARE ASSUMED TO CONTAIN A VALID BCD CHARACTER.
24:                    *    THIS CHARACTER IS PRINTED ON THE CONSOLE AND LEAST SIGNIFICANT
25:                    *    FOUR BITS ARE CORRUPTED.
26:                    *
27:                    *
28:                    *              STRUCTURE
29:                    *              '''''''''
30:                    *    BEGIN
31:                    *        ZERO RIGHT-HAND FOUR BITS
32:                    *        SHIFT REMAINING BITS FOUR PLACES RIGHT
33:                    *        CONVERT TO ASCII BY ADDING 30H
34:                    *        PRINT THE ASCII CHARACTER
35:                    *    END
36:                    *
37: 0000 E6F0          PRNLFT: ANI    0F0H              ; ZERO MS FOUR BITS
38: 0002 0F                    RRC
39: 0003 0F                    RRC                      ; SHIFT RIGHT FOUR PLACES
40: 0004 0F                    RRC
41: 0005 0F                    RRC
42: 0006 C630                  ADI    30H               ; CONVERT TO ASCII
43: 0008 47                    MOV    B,A               ; STORE IN B
44: 0009 CD2100                CALL   PCHAR             ; PRINT ASCII CHARACTER
45: 000C C9                    RET
```

```
 46:                   *
 47:                   *  SUBROUTINE PRNRGT
 48:                   *  ================
 49:                   *
 50:                   *  ON ENTRY TO THIS SUBROUTINE THE LEAST SIGNIFICANT FOUR
 51:                   *  BITS IN REGISTER A ARE A VALID BCD CHARACTER.
 52:                   *  THIS IS PRINTED ON THE CONSOLE - THE OTHER BITS ARE
 53:                   *  CORRUPTED.
 54:                   *
 55:                   *               STRUCTURE
 56:                   *               '''''''''
 57:                   *  BEGIN
 58:                   *      ZERO LEFT-HAND FOUR BITS
 59:                   *      CONVERT TO ASCII BY ADDING 30H
 60:                   *      PRINT ASCII CHARACTER
 61:                   *  END
 62:                   *
 63:  000D E60F        PRNRGT: ANI     0FH         ; ZERO LEFT-HAND FOUR BITS
 64:  000F C630                ADI     30H         ; CONVERT TO ASCII
 65:  0011 47                  MOV     B,A         ; STORE IN B
 66:  0012 CD2100              CALL    PCHAR       ; PRINT ASCII CHARACTER
 67:  0015 C9                  RET
 68:                   *
 69:                   *  SUBROUTINE NEWL
 70:                   *  ==============
 71:                   *
 72:                   *  THIS SUBROUTINE PRINTS A CARRAIGE RETURN-LINE FEED ON THE CONSOLE
 73:                   *
 74:                   *  REGISTERS A AND B ARE CORRUPTED.
 75:                   *
 76:                   *               STRUCTURE
 77:                   *               '''''''''
 78:                   *  BEGIN
 79:                   *      FETCH CARRAIGE RETURN ASCII CODE
 80:                   *      PRINT IT
 81:                   *      FETCH LINE-FEED ASCII CODE
 82:                   *      PRINT IT
 83:                   *  END
 84:                   *
 85:  0016 060D        NEWL:   MVI     B,0DH       ; ASCII FOR CARRAIGE-RETURN
 86:  0018 CD2100              CALL    PCHAR       ; PRINT IT
 87:  001B 060A                MVI     B,0AH       ; ASCII FOR LINE-FEED
 88:  001D CD2100              CALL    PCHAR       ; PRINT IT
 89:  0020 C9                  RET
 90:                   *
 91:                   *  SUBROUTINE PCHAR
 92:                   *  ================
 93:                   *
 94:                   *  CALLED FROM THE ABOVE ROUTINES TO SEND A CHARACTER TO THE CONSOLE
 95:                   *  WHICH, ON ENTRY, MUST BE IN THE B REGISTER.
 96:                   *
 97:                   *               STRUCTURE
 98:                   *               '''''''''
 99:                   *  BEGIN
100:                   *      REPEAT  (* UNTIL CONSOLE READY TO RECEIVE *)
101:                   *           READ STATUS BIT
102:                   *      UNTIL STATUS BIT = 1
103:                   *      SEND CHARACTER TO CONSOLE
104:                   *  END
105:                   *
106:                   *  PORT AND STATUS BIT ASSIGNMENTS FOR NORTH STAR
```

```
107:                              *
108:   0003 =        STATPT: EQU     03H              ; STATUS PORT NUMBER
109:   0002 =        CONSOL: EQU     02H              ; CONSOLE PORT NUMBER
110:   0001 =        STATBT: EQU     01H              ; STATUS BIT IS D0
111:                              *
112:   0021 DB03     PCHAR:  IN      STATPT           ; READ FROM STATUS PORT
113:   0023 E601             ANI     STATBT           ; CHECK STATUS BIT
114:   0025 CA2100           JZ      PCHAR            ; REPEAT UNTIL CONSOLE READY
115:   0028 78               MOV     A,B              ; TRANSFER ASCII TO A
116:   0029 D302             OUT     CONSOL           ; SEND TO CONSOLE
117:   002B C9               RET
118:                 *
119:                 *   SUBROUTINE MESP
120:                 *   ===============
121:                 *
122:                 *
123:                 *   THIS SUBROUTINE IS USED TO PRINT A CHARACTER STRING ON THE
124:                 *   CONSOLE. ON ENTRY THE START ADDRESS OF THE STRING MUST BE
125:                 *   CONTAINED IN THE D AND E REGISTER PAIR. ALSO, THE STRING
126:                 *   MUST END IN A NOP (00H).
127:                 *
128:                 *   REGISTERS A,B,D AND E ARE CORRUPTED.
129:                 *
130:                 *                      STRUCTURE
131:                 *                      '''''''''
132:                 *   BEGIN
133:                 *       READ THE FIRST CHARACTER
134:                 *       WHILE CHARACTER <> NULL DO
135:                 *       BEGIN
136:                 *           PRINT THE CHARACTER
137:                 *           READ NEXT CHARACTER
138:                 *       END
139:                 *   END
140:   002C 1A       MESP:   LDAX    D                ; GET FIRST CHARACTER
141:   002D FE00             CPI     00H              ; TEST FOR NULL
142:   002F C8               RZ                       ; END IF NULL
143:   0030 47               MOV     B,A
144:   0031 CD2100           CALL    PCHAR            ; PRINT CHARACTER
145:   0034 13               INX     D
146:   0035 C32C00           JMP     MESP             ; READ NEXT CHARACTER
147:                 *
```

Answers to Questions

1.1 A backing store is needed because it is just impractical to keep every user program module and utility in primary memory at the same time. This is particularly true when developing fairly large programs comprising separately tested subprograms which all have to be linked together. The backing store is somewhere to keep programs and data until they are needed.

Quite apart from the utilities that are used for developing assembly language programs, modern systems usually provide at least one high-level language compiler and/or interpreter (see Chapter 10), and sometimes, at extra cost, a range of useful program modules such as multiply/divide subroutines, floating point and other application packages. All these are supplied in some form of backing store either as part of, or separate from, the more essential software facilities. It has been said that if a cheap reliable backing storage system had not been invented, the pace of microprocessor development would not have been as great as it has been. Section 1.2 states the case for a backing store.

1.2 *(a)* 'Random access' means that the time to access data stored at any memory address is not a function of the address, but only a function of the system.

(b) Serial access memories have longer access times than random access memories because it depends on where in the serial system the required information is stored. A serial access system can be compared with a long, circular conveyor belt with only one loading/unloading point, and a random access system with an array of pigeon holes, all of which are within easy reach.

(c) Number of bytes $= 1,024/8 = 128$. With a 1 MHz clock rate, a bit entering one end of the shift register will emerge 1,024 clock periods later.

Time in the register $= 1,024$ μs.
Average access time $= 512$ μs.

1.3 Common sense dictates that the obvious factors are:

1 Length of tape.
2 Acceleration/deceleration time.
3 Maximum tape velocity.
4 Bit packing density related to reading speed.

Maybe you can suggest others.

1.4 One revolution takes 1/300 min = 200 ms. Therefore, the average time to locate one sector is 100 ms. The total time is therefore the seek time, T, plus 100 ms.

1.5 Width of recording band = 34/50 inch.
Capacity = $35 \times 10 \times 256$ bytes = 89.6 Kbytes.

1.6 Hard-sectored disks have sector index holes punched in the disk to mark each sector. Sector address information is read by detecting these holes. One extra hole marks sector 1. Soft-sectored disks do not have these holes. Instead, sector address information is stored on the disk much as any other information is stored. Figures 1.5 and 1.6 should make the distinction clear.

Soft-sectored disks are said to be capable of storing 23% less information than hard-sectored disks of the same size using the same recording technique (see reference 1.2 at the end of Chapter 1).

The answer to the second part of the question is: No! If you ever have to reorder disks for your system make sure that you order the correct kind.

1.7 The diagram below illustrates the difference between frequency and delay modulation.

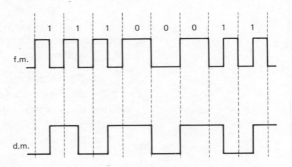

1.8 A file is a collection of data (information) stored on disk. Every file has a name and a unique start address – track number and sector number. Details of all the files on a disk are held in the disk directory. Apart from the name and start address, directory entries may include the length of the file, type information, creation date, etc.

1.9 An operating system is a program that runs whenever a user or utility program is not executing. It is the means by which a user gets access to the system resources. It should permit creation, deletion and modification of disk files, and also control of peripherals and everything else in the system. It could be called the system organiser, executive or supervisor, and it is a program.

1.10 Figure 1.8 shows a typical software development station. By this time the function of the individual components should be obvious, but refer to the text in this and earlier units if still in doubt.

A software development station differs from a microprocessor development system in that it does not have any facilities for in-circuit emulation (ICE). You will recall from earlier units that ICE modules permit debugging of microprocessor system hardware by effectively replacing the microprocessor in the system being debugged with a microprocessor in the development system. All the development system facilities are then available for debugging purposes as though they existed in the system being tested.

A software development station has all the software back-up of a proper MDS but none of the hardware. To partially compensate for this, it usually has a range of plug-in cards which allows user hardware to be driven from the system. Eventually however, if a dedicated system is required to control this hardware, the controlling program developed in the software development station will have to be committed to ROM or (E)PROM and the complete system debugged as a separate exercise. It is at this point that an MDS would be a useful tool.

1.11 To complete this exercise it will be necessary for you to consult the documentation for your operating system and then experiment with some of the available commands. Make sure that you have a back-up copy of the system disk before you start, however, and remember that time spent now will be well rewarded later.

2.1 The process is:

1 Enter new or unedited source code into the edit buffer (I or A).
2 Edit source code and then exit editor, saving edited source code in a disk file.
3 Assemble source code and look for assembler error messages.
4 If error messages are flagged, go to 1; otherwise continue.
5 LOAD object code file produced by the assembler to create a command (.COM) file.
6 Run debugger (DDT) with the command file and thoroughly check the program logic.
7 If logical errors are detected, correct in the debugger, if possible, and recheck. Then return to 1. If no errors then stop.

The flowchart of Figure 2.1 summarises the procedure more neatly.

2.2 To prepare source code for the assembler. The editor must maintain an edit buffer and provide a range of commands to make the necessary corrections to the source code.

2.3 The distinction is in the way they manipulate and interpret text. See Section 2.2 for a more complete answer.

2.4 One solution is:

```
SMVIL^ZMVAL<cr>
```

The point is that the string to be corrected must be unique. A command line such as

```
SMVI^ZMVA<cr>
```

would change the opcode mnemonic and not the error in the operand.

2.5 Because you always have a back-up version of the source code file just edited. This may be useful in the event that the newly edited file becomes corrupted or the latest corrections turn out to be unnecessary or themselves incorrect.

2.6 When a source code file exists, the command is

```
nA (append)
```

where *n* is the number of lines to be appended to text in the edit buffer. For entering new source code the command is

```
I (insert)
```

2.7 In the first case the edit prompt will appear when the <cr> is entered, and in the second case the editor will wait for more text or a CTRL-Z. Use the first form of the command when inserting text within a line, and the second when inserting more than one line.

2.8 The remainder of the table is shown in Table A.

Table A *Continuation of Table 2.3 in Question 2.8*

Command line	Action
4L1T	Move CP on 4 lines and type the line
1CIspace ^Z	Move CP on one character position and insert a space
STRE^ZTER	Substitute TER for the string TRE
FED^ZItab*Z0L1T	Find the character string ED. Insert after it a tab and then a star, then type the line

Table A – *continued*

2L1T	Move CP on two lines then type the line
1CItab^ Z0L1T	Move CP beyond the first star and insert a tab. Then type the line
FSTRUCTURE^ ZI.4tabs^ Z0L1T	Find the character string STRUC-TURE. Insert at that point a full-stop and then 4 tabs. Move CP to the start of the line and type the line
4L1T	Move on 4 lines and type the line
1CIspace^ ZF;^ ZItab^ Z0L1T	Move CP beyond the first star and insert a space. Now move CP to a position immediately after a semi-colon. Insert a tab there and then type the line
3L1CIthree spaces^ Z0L1T	Move CP on three lines and then one character position. Insert three spaces and then type the line
8L1T	Move on 8 lines and type the line
1CIspace^ ZFF^ ZItwo tabs^ Z0L1T	Move CP on one character position and insert a space. Now find the next F in the buffer. Insert two tabs and then type the line
FSA^ Z–1CIspace^ Z0L1T	Find the character string SA. Move CP between the S and A. Insert a space and type the line
SEU^ ZUE^ Z0L1T	Change the next occurrence of string EU to UE and then type the line
FM1^ Z–1C1D0L1T	Find the string M1. Move CP back one character position. Delete the next character and then type the line
FP^ Z–1CI;^ Z0L1T	Find the next P in the edit buffer. Move CP so that it is in front of it and insert a semi-colon after that point. Now type the line
4L1T	Move CP on 4 lines and type the line
FB^ ZItab^ Z0L1T	Find the next B in the buffer. Insert a tab after the B and then type the line
STIR^ ZTUR^ Z0L1T	Change the next occurrence of the string TIR to TUR. Then type the line
1L1K	Move CP on one line and then delete that line

(continued)

Table A – *continued*

3L1T	Move CP on three lines and type the line
F0ˆ ZIHˆ Z1LF0ˆ ZIH ˆZ 1L1F0ˆ ZIHˆ Z−2L3T	Find the next 0 in the buffer. Insert an H at that point. Move CP to the start of the next line and repeat the above operation. Move to the start of the next line and repeat again. Now move CP back two lines and type three lines to check these insertions. Note that repetitive commands like these can be written as Macros – a more advanced editor facility

2.9 The editor/user dialogue for this exercise is given in Figure A and the table compiled from this is given in Table B.

Table B *A solution for Question 2.9*

Error	Command line	Action
1 STRT preceded by a space	1D0L1T	Delete the first character – the space – then type the line
2 In the third line, the operand is O9 instead of 09	2LSO9ˆ Z09ˆ Z0L1T	Move CP on two lines, then substitute 09 for O9 and then type the line
3 The two lines between INR D and DCR D have been omitted	FDCRtabDˆ Z0L1T IGOON:tabMOVtabA,M tabCMPtabB	Find the DCRtabD and move CP back to the start of that line. Insert at that point the two missing lines
4 There is no JXYM opcode mnemonic. Delete the XY	5L1T 2C2D0L1T	Move CP on 5 lines to check that we have the correct line. Now move CP in two characters (tab and J), delete the next two characters and type the line
5 Semi-colon missing at the start of the previous line	−1L1T FIˆ Z−1CI;ˆ Z0L1T	Make sure we are at the correct line. Now find the next I. Move CP back one position and insert a semi-colon. Now type the line
6 B+A should be B,A	4L1T S+ˆ Z,ˆ Z0L1T	Move CP on 4 lines and type the line. Now substitute a comma for the plus sign and re-type the line
7 LOP should be LOOP	SLOPˆ ZLOOPˆ Z0L1T	Substitute LOOP for LOP and type the line
8 No END	−B I tabEND	Move CP to the end of the text and insert, on a new line, the word END at the first tab position

Note that your table may not be the same as above. We have used obvious command sequences to correct errors and so long as you are sure that your table would do the same, you may conclude that the question has been correctly answered.

```
        ED B:EDER.ASM
        *100A
        *B
        *1D0L1T
        STRT:   LXI     H,LIST          ;GET LIST STRT ADD.
        *2LSO9^Z09^Z0L1T
                MVI  ⌄  C,09H           ;INITIALISE ITEM COUNT
        *FDCR   D^Z0L1T
                DCR     D               ;DOESNT AFFECT CARRY
        *I
        GOON:   MOV     A,M             ;GET ITEM BACK
                CMP     B               ;AFFECTS ALL FLAGS
        *-3L4T
                INR     D               ;OTHERWISE INC D
        GOON:   MOV     A,M             ;GET ITEM BACK
                CMP     B               ;AFFECTS ALL FLAGS
                DCR     D               ;DOESNT AFFECT CARRY
        *5L1T
                JXYM    CON+1
        *2C2D0L1T
                JM      CON+1
        *-1L1T
                JNC     L1              IS. CARRY SET
        *FI^Z-1CI;^Z0L1T
                JNC     L1              ;IS CARRY SET
        *3L1T
        L1:     JP      CON+1
        *1L1T
        CON:    MOV     B+A             ;LARGEST TO B
        *S+^Z,^Z0L1T
        CON:    MOV     B,A             ;LARGEST TO B
        *SLOP^ZLOOP^Z0L1T
                JNZ     LOOP            ;LOOP IF NOT FINISHED
        *-B
        *I
                END
        *-3L3T
        LIST:   DS      0AH             ;ITEM LIST HERE
        *
                END
        *B
        *24SMOV^ZMOV^Z

        BREAK "#" AT V
        *B11T
        STRT:   LXI     H,LIST          ;GET LIST STRT ADD.
                MOV     B,M             ;FIRST ITEM TO B
                MVI     C,09H           ;INITIALISE ITEM COUNT
                INX     H               ;BUMP POINTER
        LOOP:   MOV     A,M             ;GET ITEM FROM LIST
                MVI     D,00H           ;CLEAR D
                XRA     B
                RLC                     ;CHECK FOR SAME SIGN
                JNC     GOON            ;JUMP IF SAME
                INR     D               ;OTHERWISE INC D
        GOON:   MOV     A,M             ;GET ITEM BACK
        *
```

Figure A The edit/user dialogue which corrects the listing of Figure 2.8 so that it appears as in Figure 2.9

3.1 *(a)* Symbolic addressing is used to describe the technique of assigning names to particular source code instructions and data declarations. An instruction can then be referenced by the name assigned to its address rather than its absolute hexadecimal address. Equally a data item can be accessed by referring to the contents of a named address. In this way instructions which reference symbolic addresses, e.g. JMP, CALL and LDA, are made more understandable.

(b) TABLE, LOOP and STRT are symbolic addresses whereas TWO is a name given to a data constant. TABLE is the address at which a block of ten (decimal) unassigned addresses begins, LOOP is the address occupied by the first byte of a two-byte MVI instruction and STRT is the address which contains the least significant half of another symbolic address, BGN.

3.2 If we consider a two-pass assembler, on the first pass a list of all the symbolic addresses and labels is compiled. Against each name the assembler fills in either the absolute address which corresponds with the symbolic address, or the constant value which is referred to by name elsewhere in the program. On pass two the assembler consults the list, called the symbol table, whenever a symbolic address or label is encountered in the operand field of a line of source code. In place of the symbolic address or label it substitutes the corresponding numeric symbol table entry.

3.3 One advantage has been mentioned in Answer 3.1 – symbolic addresses and labels make a program more readable. If the start of a program loop is labelled LOOP, then JMP LOOP is an explicit instruction. If LOOP is the absolute address 30CFH, then JMP 30CFH would have the same effect, but is clearly less explicit. Names often impart more meaning than numbers.

The second advantage arises when it becomes necessary to edit a source code file. The point is made in the text that all instructions after the change are very likely to have different addresses. Consequently, if absolute addresses are used, all references to the original addresses have to be changed even though the sense of the instruction is the same. If symbolic addresses are used, the assembler will take care of the fact that the actual addresses are different. All that happens is that the symbol table entries are different.

3.4 The symbol table for the arithmetic operators program is:

BGN1	0000H
LIST	0007H
LEND	000FH
BGN2	0010H
BGN3	0013H
NUMBR	000AH

3.5 A line of source code is written as:

Label: *Opcode* *Operand* *;Comment*

The label field is optional and is usually terminated in a colon. The opcode field must contain a valid 8080 opcode mnemonic or assembler directive. Most opcodes and pseudo-ops need an entry in the operand field. This entry can be an expression comprising one or more register identification letters, a numeric or string constant, a symbolic address or a combination of a symbolic address and register identifier. The assembler sorts out this operand field entry and generates the proper hexadecimal object code. The comment field begins with a semicolon and contains explanatory text which is for the benefit of a reader. The assembler ignores this field and so it need not be included.

3.6 A numeric constant is an 8- or 16-bit number which may be identified by a label but cannot change during the execution of the program. The base of the numbering system is indicated by attaching the letter B,O,D or H to the number. B stands for binary, O for octal (but Q is equally acceptable here), D for decimal and H for hexadecimal. The assembler checks that numbers are valid and assumes that, if no letter is used, the number is decimal. It would, for example, reject the numbers 3A, 638Q and 1010 1010H.

3.7 A string constant is a sequence of characters enclosed within apostrophes. The assembler stores the ASCII equivalent of each character when it encounters a string constant.

(a) Arithmetic operator precedence is:

Highest: *, / and MOD (Multiplication, division and integer division remainder)

Next: + and – (Addition and subtraction)

(b)

10 MOD 3 * 3	= 1*3	= 3
10 + 4 * 3 – 2	= 10 + 12 – 2	= 20
(10 + 4) * 3 – 2	= 42 – 2	= 40
(10 + 4) * (3 – 2)	= 14 $\times$ 1	= 14
13/2 + 13 MOD2	= 6 + 1	= 7

3.8 *(a)* The shift operators are SHR and SHL: A SHR B shifts A,B positions right; A SHL B shifts A,B positions left.

(b) MASK: 44H = 0100 0100

0100 0100 SHR 2 = 0001 0001 = 11H
0100 0100 SHL 2 = 0001 0000 = 10H
0100 0100 SHR 2 + 4 = 11H + 4 = 15H
0100 0100 SHL 1 – 40H = 88H – 40H = 48H

286 Microprocessor-based Systems: Level V

3.9 *(a)* The logical operator precedence is:

Highest:	NOT
Next:	AND
Lowest:	OR,XOR

(b) Note that the SHR and SHL operators have a higher priority than any of the logical operators.

MASK AND MASK SHR 2 = 0100 0100 AND 0001 0001 = 0000 0000

MASK AND NOT MASK = 0000 0000

MASK OR MASK SHR 2 = 0100 0100 OR 0001 0001 = 0101 0101

MASK XOR MASK SHR 2 = 0101 0101 (Same as OR in this case.)

MASK XOR MASK SHR 2 AND MASK SHL 2 Evaluates as

$$\text{MASK SHR 2} = 0001\ 0001$$
$$\text{MASK SHL 2} = 0001\ 0000$$
$$\text{MASK SHR 2 AND MASK SHL 2} = 0001\ 0000$$
$$\text{MASK XOR MASK SHR 2 AND MASK SHL 2} = 0101\ 0100$$

3.10 Standard directives are used to:

Define constants, e.g. EQU,SET.
Define data areas, e.g. DB,DW.
Reserve blocks of memory, DS.
Set the origin for assembly, ORG.

In addition there are pseudo-ops which are used to define macros and the various conditional assembly pseudo-ops.

3.11 The key difference is that pseudo-ops do not generate any object code whereas 'real' opcodes do. Pseudo-ops are assembler instruction mnemonics not microprocessor instruction mnemonics.

Several examples of pseudo-ops are given above, for example, DB, define a byte, and EQU, define a constant identifier, and we have already seen most of the 8080 'real' opcodes. For example, LDA, load register A with the contents of an address, and RLC, rotate contents of register A one bit position left. Both these mnemonics generate a byte of object code, the LDA assembles to 3AH (first byte of three-byte instruction) and RLC assembles to 07 (single-byte instruction).

3.12 Both SET and EQU are used to define constant names. The difference is that a name defined in an EQU statement cannot be redefined in the same program. The name and the number it identifies are entered in the symbol table when it is first encountered during assembly. If the same name is used to define a different number at a later stage in the program the assembler rejects it and both definitions are invalid. The SET directive however does not generate a symbol table entry in the accepted sense. It maintains the current value of the name separately, and just updates the current value when the name is later assigned to different value. The usefulness of being able to redefine constants with the SET directives is well illustrated in the conditional assembly example.

3.13 The technique used would be:

```
        ORG   3F47H
BUFFER: DS    127
```

Anything following this would be assembled at 3FC6H. (3F47H + 7FH)

3.14 The DB directive assigns values in the order they appear in the operand field, whereas the DW directive will treat the 'AB' as a 16-bit number and store its least significant byte ('B') at the lowest address. Therefore,

```
4142   MESSGE:   DB   'AB'
4241   ASCII :   DW   'AB'
```

3.15 The subroutine might be:

```
MESP:   LXI    D, MESSGE    ;start address to D,E
        LDAX   D            ;character to A
        CPI    '$'          ;is it dollar sign?
        RZ                  ;return if yes
        CALL   PCHAR        ;otherwise print character
        INX    D            ;update pointer
        JMP    MESP+3       ;and get next character
```

Assumptions:

Character must be in A to print it.

Only one message can be printed.

Message must terminate in $ so character string must be declared as

```
MESSGE:   DB   'AB'
          DB   '$'
```

or MESSGE string expanded to include the $.

3.16 The format of simple conditional assembly statement is:

```
IF      expression     ;evaluates to non-zero
  :
        instructions   ;assemble these instructions
  :
ENDIF                  ;end of instruction sequence
```

If the expression evaluates to zero the block of instructions is ignored.

Two examples of conditional assembly are given in the text and will not be repeated here. The first illustrates the use of conditional assembly as a debugging aid and second is an application which may be used by a manufacturer of microprocessor-controlled equipment which can be sold with various hardware/software options. Refer to the text if you do not recall these applications.

3.17 The easy way is:

```
IF COND1 AND COND2 AND NOT COND3
;assemble the instructions from this point to the
ENDIF
```

We could write:

```
    IF COND1
    IF COND2
    IF NOT COND3
    ;assemble
    ENDIF
    ENDIF
    ENDIF
```

3.18 Quite simply the file contents would be displayed as a list of hexadecimal characters. An F, for example, is stored as ASCII F and so on. If you have a CP/M-based system available, try typing a .HEX file and prove it for yourself.

As a consequence of the above, the answer to the second part of the question is: No. The ASCII characters have to be converted to binary (a .COM file) by another utility program. That program is the loader.

3.19 Error messages are an indication that something is wrong with the syntax of the source code program. As we have seen, an error in one part of a program can cause an error message in another, perfectly correct, part. Also one error can mask another in the same line. The error message identification letters give some idea of the nature of the error once the true source of the error has been tracked down. For example, in the latest revision of the CP/M manual (CP/M 2.2 1978) which we have, the following error messages are listed:

D	data error	– mistake in a data statement
E	expression error	– assembler cannot compute value of expression
L	label error	– perhaps duplicate label
N	not implemented	– trying to use an assembler facility which is not supported in the version, e.g. macros
O	overflow	– expression is too complicated to evaluate

P   phase error   – label has different value in pass 1 and
                                pass 2
R   register error   – register identifier is inappropriate
                                with this instruction
V   value error

In you look back at Figure 3.13 you will note that two of the three error messages, U and S, are not listed. We might hazard a guess that U stands for undefined since VALUE had been incorrectly defined, but what does S stand for?

The lesson is that there is something wrong with both DEC B instructions and the assembler manual may, or as in this case, may not, give some clue as to what precisely is wrong.

4.1   The common range of monitor commands include:

> Display a block of memory in hex. and ASCII.
> Display a single address for possible alteration.
> Fill a block of memory with a particular byte.
> Copy from one block of memory to another.
> Search a block of memory for a specific byte or byte string.

The extra facilities which a debugger must provide are:

> Examine and possibly modify the CPU registers.
> Disassemble the contents of a block of memory into assembler mnemonics.
> Execute a user program with breakpoints inserted.
> Trace program execution for a number of steps.

4.2   DDT converts the hexadecimal numbers to binary and loads these binary numbers into memory at the assembly addresses.

4.3   DDT inserts breakpoints by replacing the program byte at the breakpoint address with an RST 7 opcode. When program control reaches the breakpoint, the RST 7 instruction is executed so a CALL to 0038H occurs. At 0038H is an instruction which returns control to DDT. This means, of course, that RST 7 instructions cannot be used in your programs and also that DDT cannot be used to debug interrupt service routines which vector to 0038H.

4.4   We could imitate the action of the trace command by implementing the following algorithm:

1   Initialise a step counter.
2   Examine (X) the registers.
3   Go from the present setting of the program counter with a breakpoint at the next instruction address.

    4 Decrement the step counter.
    5 If not zero, go to step 2.
    6 Else, return to DDT.

4.5 The untrace command transfers control to a user program for a specified number of steps whereas the go command transfers control until a breakpoint at an absolute memory address is reached. The difference between them is that, if a program error prevents us reaching the breakpoint, there is no way of recovering apart from by rebooting the system and reloading. This could not happen with untrace because, even with the same program, control always returns to DDT.

5.1 The advantages of this design procedure relate mostly to the ease of testing and the ease of understanding programs. The advantages are explicitly stated in Section 5.2.

5.2 The four basic structures are:

    1 Sequence – Figure 5.2.
    2 The WHILE-DO structure – Figure 5.5.
    3 The REPEAT-UNTIL structure – Figure 5.5.
    4 The IF-THEN-ELSE structure – Figure 5.7.

They are described in the first four subsections of Section 5.3.

5.3 A suitable structure is:

```
BEGIN
        NUMBERCOUNT: = 0
        READ FIRST NUMBER FROM LIST.
        WHILE NUMBER <> 00H DO
        BEGIN
                NUMBERCOUNT: = NUMBERCOUNT+1
                READ NEXT NUMBER
        END
END
```

5.4 A structure for this program is:

```
BEGIN
        NUMBERCOUNT: = 0
        READ FIRST NUMBER FROM LIST
        REPEAT (*Until a 00H is read*)
                NUMBERCOUNT: = NUMBERCOUNT+1
                READ NEXT NUMBER
        UNTIL NUMBER = 0
END
```

5.5   The structure for this program will be:

```
BEGIN
        NUMBERCOUNT: = 0
        READ FIRST NUMBER FROM LIST
        IF NUMBER = 0 THEN
                    DO NOTHING
        ELSE
                    REPEAT (*Until 00H is read*)
                            NUMBERCOUNT: = NUMBERCOUNT+1
                            READ NEXT NUMBER
                    UNTIL NUMBER = 0
        ENDIF
END
```

Note the difference between this program and the program plan of Question 5.4.

5.6   The structures for versions 1 and 2 are given in Figure B. The first

```
*   VERSION 1 STRUCTURE.
*   '''''''''''''''''''''
*
*   BEGIN
*       PARTPROD := 0
*       IF MULTIPLIER = 0 THEN
*           END IF STATEMENT
*       ELSE
*           REPEAT
*               PARTPROD := PARTPROD + MULTIPLICAND
*               MULTIPLIER := MULTIPLIER -1
*           UNTIL MULTIPLIER = 0;
*       ENDIF
*       RESULT := PARTPROD;
*   END.
*
*
*   VERSION 2 STRUCTURE.
*   '''''''''''''''''''''
*
*   BEGIN
*       IF MULTIPLIER = 0 THEN
*           PARTPROD := MULTIPLIER (:= 0);
*       ELSE
*           PARTPROD := 0
*           REPEAT
*               PARTPROD := PARTPROD + MULTIPLICAND
*               MULTIPLIER := MULTIPLIER - 1
*           UNTIL MULTIPLIER = 0
*       ENDIF
*       RESULT := PARTPROD;
*   END.
*
B>
```

Figure B   Suggested structures for the alternative versions 1 and 2 of the multiplication program

```
              *   ANOTHER VERSION OF THE MULTIPLICATION BY REPEATED ADDITION PROGRAM
              *
              *                   STRUCTURE
              *                   '''''''''
              *   BEGIN
              *       PARTPROD := 0
              *       IF MULTIPLICAND = 0 THEN
              *           END IF STATEMENT
              *       ELSE
              *           INITIALISE MULTIPLICAND
              *           IF MULTIPLIER = 0 THEN
              *               END IF STATEMENT
              *           ELSE
              *               INITIALISE MULTIPLIER
              *               REPEAT
              *                   PARTPROD := PARTPROD + MULTIPLICAND
              *                   MULTIPLIER := MULTIPLIER -1
              *               UNTIL MULTIPLIER = 0
              *           NDIF
              *       NDIF
              *       RESULT := PARTPROD
              *   END.
              *
              *   REGISTER USAGE:
              *                   PARTIAL PRODUCT ACCUMULATED IN D
              *                   MULTIPLICAND IN C
              *                   MULTIPLIER IN B
              *                   REGISTER A CORRUPTED
              *
0100                  ORG     0100H
0100 AF      BGN:     XRA     A               ; CLEARS A
0101 57               MOV     D,A             ; (D) = INITIAL PARTPROD = 0
0102 3A2001           LDA     MCAND
0105 FE00    IF1:     CPI     0               ; MULTIPLICAND = 0 ?
0107 CA1B01           JZ      NDIF            ; IF YES, NDIF
010A 4F               MOV     C,A             ; ELSE, (C) = MULTIPLICAND
010B 3A2101           LDA     MPLIER
010E FE00    IF2:     CPI     0               ; MULTIPLIER = 0 ?
0110 CA1B01           JZ      NDIF            ; IF YES, NDIF
0113 47               MOV     B,A             ; ELSE, (B) = MULTIPLIER
0114 7A      REPT:    MOV     A,D             ; GET PARTPROD
0115 81               ADD     C               ; PARTPROD := PARTPROD + MULTIPLICAND
0116 57               MOV     D,A             ; RESTORE PARTPROD
0117 05               DCR     B               ; MULTIPLIER := MULTIPLIER - 1
0118 C21401   UNTIL:  JNZ     REPT            ; REPEAT UNTIL ZERO
011B 7A       NDIF:   MOV     A,D             ; GET PARTPROD
011C 322201           STA     RESULT          ; RESULT := PARTPROD
011F C9               RET
              *
              *   DATA AREA
              *
0120 03      MCAND:   DB      3               ; TRIAL VALUES FOR MCAND
0121 04      MPLIER:  DB      4               ; AND MULTIPLIER
0122         RESULT:  DS      1               ; DESTINATION OF RESULT
              *
0123                  END
0123
000H USE FACTOR
END OF ASSEMBLY
```

Figure C Multiplication program that tests for a zero multiplicand

structure is a standard REPEAT-UNTIL nested within an IF instruction with no ELSE. Version 2 is slightly more obscure in that the meaning of the statement

```
PARTPROD: = MULTIPLIER
```

is not immediately obvious. Version 3 does not easily fit into any of the standard structure definitions. The program was written from a flowchart and seemed quite a logical solution at the time. The contention is, however, that if the flowchart became detached from the listing, as it very well might, the program would be difficult to sort out. The structured version is virtually self-explanatory. Notice, however, that version 3 has one fewer instruction than version 1, the same number as version 2 and six fewer than the structured version. No doubt with a little effort, we could reduce the instruction count still further and make the program even more obscure.

5.7 A solution for this problem is given in Figure C.

5.8 A solution for this problem is given in Figure D.

5.9 A solution for this problem is given in Figure E.

5.10 A solution for this problem is given in Figure F.

5.11 A solution for this problem is given in Figure G.

5.12 The new main program is given in Figure H, PBIN is listed in Figure I and SPACE in Figure J.

6.1 LOAD operates on a .HEX file converting its contents to an executable, binary program. The result of a LOAD operation is a file with the .COM extension. LOAD is an example of an absolute loader. The addresses occupied by the program when it is eventually executed are those allocated during assembly. There is no possibility of the program being relocated so that it executes at any other address.

6.2 The need for relocation exists when programs are assembled and tested at one address but ultimately have to execute at another address which may not be available during testing. This could happen, for example, if the execution address is occupied by the debug program itself. Before the program, or program module, is committed to EPROM it has to be moved (relocated) so that it will execute at the proper address. Linking is required when a number of modules have to be linked together to make a complete program.

```
*       MULTIPLICATION PROGRAM WHICH CAN GENERATE A DOUBLE-LENGTH PRODUCT
*
*                       STRUCTURE
*                       '''''''''
*
*       BEGIN
*           PARTIAL PRODUCT (PARTPROD) :=`0
*           IF MULTIPLICAND = O THEN
*               END THIS IF STRUCTURE
*           ELSE
*               INITIALISE MULTIPLICAND
*               IF MULTIPLIER = 0 THEN
*                   END THIS IF STRUCTURE
*               ELSE
*                   INITIALISE MULTIPLIER
*                   REPEAT
*                       PARTPROD := PARTPROD + MULTIPLICAND
*                       MULTIPLIER := MULTIPLIER - 1
*                   UNTIL MULTIPLIER = 0
*               ENDIF
*           ENDIF
*           RESULT := FINAL PARTPROD
*       END.
*
*       REGISTER USAGE:
*                       DOUBLE LENGTH PARTIAL PRODUCT ACCUMULATED IN HL
*                       MULTIPLICAND IN E
*                       REGISTER D CONTAINS 0
*                       MULTIPLIER IN B
*                       REGISTER A IS CORRUPTED
*
0100                    ORG     0100H
0100 AF         BGN:    XRA     A               ; CLEAR A
0101 67                 MOV     H,A
0102 6F                 MOV     L,A             ; (HL) = INITIAL PARTPROD = 0
0103 3A2101             LDA     MCAND
0106 FE00      IF1:     CPI     0               ; MULTIPLICAND = 0 ?
0108 CA1C01             JZ      NDIF            ; IF YES THEN END IF
010B 5F                 MOV     E,A             ; ELSE INITIALISE MULTIPLICAND
010C 1600               MVI     D,00            ; AND CLEAR D
010E 3A2001             LDA     MPLIER
0111 FE00      IF2:     CPI     0               ; MULTIPLIER = 0 ?
0113 CA1C01             JZ      NDIF            ; IF YES THEN END IF
0116 47                 MOV     B,A             ; ELSE INITIALISE MULTIPLIER
0117 19        REPT:    DAD     D               ; PARTPROD := PARTPROD + MULTIPLICAND
               *
               * NOTE, (DE) ARE MULTIPLICAND EXPRESSED AS 16-BIT NUMBER
               *
0118 05                 DCR     B               ; MULTIPLIER := MULTIPLIER - 1
0119 C21701    UNTIL:   JNZ     REPT            ; REPEAT UNTIL ZERO
011C 222201    NDIF:    SHLD    RESULT          ; RESULT := FINAL PARTPROD
011F C9                 RET
               *
               * DATA AREA
               *
0120 FF        MPLIER:  DB      0FFH            ; TRIAL VALUES FOR MULTIPLIER
0121 FF        MCAND:   DB      0FFH            ; AND MULTIPLICAND
0122           RESULT:  DS      2               ; TWO LOCATIONS FOR RESULT
               *
               * RESULT STORED LEAST SIGNIFICANT BYTE FIRST
               *
0124                    END
0124
000H USE FACTOR
END OF ASSEMBLY
```

Figure D   A multiplication program that generates a double-length product

```
*       ALTERNATIVE VERSION OF THE ODD/EVEN PROGRAM.
*       ILLUSTRATES THE SECOND FORM OF THE IF-THEN-ELSE STRUCTURE
*
*                       STRUCTURE
*                       '''''''''
*       BEGIN
*           ODDS := 0
*           COUNT := 0
*           READ THE FIRST NUMBER IN THE LIST
*           WHILE NUMBER <> 0 DO
*           BEGIN
*               IF NUMBER IS EVEN THEN
*                   END THIS IF STATEMENT
*               ELSE
*                   ODDS := ODDS + 1
*               ENDIF
*               COUNT := COUNT + 1
*               READ NEXT NUMBER
*           END
*           ODDCNT := ODDS
*           EVNCNT := COUNT - ODDS
*       END
*
*       REGISTER USAGE:
*                       ODDS ACCUMULATED IN D
*                       COUNT ACCUMULATED IN E
*                       (HL) USED AS A LIST POINTER
*                       REGISTER A IS CORRUPTED
*
0100                    ORG     0100H
0100 AF        BGN:     XRA     A               ; CLEAR A
0101 57                 MOV     D,A             ; (D) = ODDS = 0
0102 5F                 MOV     E,A             ; (E) = COUNT = 0
0103 212301             LXI     H,LIST          ; SET LIST POINTER
0106 7E                 MOV     A,M             ; GET FIRST NUMBER
0107 B7        WHILE:   ORA     A               ; TEST FOR ZERO NUMBER
0108 CA1701             JZ      NDWHL           ; IF ZERO THEN NDWHL
010B E601               ANI     01H             ; NOT ZERO, TEST LS BIT
010D CA1101             JZ      ENIF            ; IF LSBIT = 0, NUMBER EVEN
0110 14        ODD:     INR     D               ; ELSE, ODDS := ODDS + 1
0111 1C        ENIF:    INR     E               ; COUNT := COUNT + 1
0112 23                 INX     H               ; POINT AT NEXT NUMBER
0113 7E                 MOV     A,M             ; READ IT
0114 C30701             JMP     WHILE           ; AND RE-TEST
0117 7B        NDWHL:   MOV     A,E             ; GET COUNT
0118 92                 SUB     D               ; SUBTRACT ODDS
0119 322201             STA     EVNCNT          ; EVNCNT := COUNT - ODDS
011C 7A                 MOV     A,D
011D 322101             STA     ODDCNT          ; ODDCNT := ODDS
0120 C9                 RET
*
*       DATA AREA
*
0121           ODDCNT:  DS      1
0122           EVNCNT:  DS      1
0123           LIST:    DS      255             ; MAX. EXTENT OF LIST
*
0222                    END
0222
000H USE FACTOR
END OF ASSEMBLY

A>
```

Figure E A solution for Question 5.9

```
                *  ANOTHER ALTERNATIVE VERSION OF THE ODD/EVEN PROGRAM.
                *  THIS TIME CATERING FOR A LIST OF UP TO 510 NUMBERS
                *
                *                  STRUCTURE
                *                  ''''''''''
                *  EXACTLY AS IN THE PREVIOUS FIGURE.
                *
                *  REGISTER USAGE:
                *              ODDS ACCUMULATED IN D
                *              COUNT ACCUMULATED IN BC
                *              (HL) USED AS A LIST POINTER
                *              REGISTER A IS CORRUPTED
                *
    0100                    ORG     0100H
    0100 AF     BGN:        XRA     A           ; CLEAR A
    0101 57                 MOV     D,A         ; (D) = ODDS = 0
    0102 47                 MOV     B,A
    0103 4F                 MOV     C,A         ; (BC) = COUNT = 0
    0104 212401             LXI     H,LIST      ; SET LIST POINTER
    0107 7E                 MOV     A,M         ; GET FIRST NUMBER
    0108 B7     WHILE:      ORA     A           ; TEST FOR ZERO NUMBER
    0109 CA1801             JZ      NDWHL       ; IF ZERO THEN NDWHL
    010C E601               ANI     01H         ; NOT ZERO, TEST LS BIT
    010E CA1201             JZ      ENIF        ; IF LSBIT = 0, NUMBER EVEN
    0111 14     ODD:        INR     D           ; ELSE, ODDS := ODDS + 1
    0112 03     ENIF:       INX     B           ; COUNT := COUNT + 1
    0113 23                 INX     H           ; POINT AT NEXT NUMBER
    0114 7E                 MOV     A,M         ; READ IT
    0115 C30801             JMP     WHILE       ; AND RE-TEST
    0118 79     NDWHL:      MOV     A,C         ; GET LSBYTE OF COUNT
    0119 92                 SUB     D           ; SUBTRACT ODDS
                *
                *  IF ODDS > LSBYTE OF COUNT A BORROW IS REQUIRED. THIS MUST BE
                *  IN B SINCE COUNT HAS BEEN GREATER THAN 255. AFTER THE SUB
                *  INSTRUCTION THE CORRECT DIFFERENCE MUST ALWAYS BE IN A.
                *
    011A 322301             STA     EVNCNT      ; EVNCNT := COUNT - ODDS
    011D 7A                 MOV     A,D
    011E 322201             STA     ODDCNT      ; ODDCNT := ODDS
    0121 C9                 RET
                *
                *  DATA AREA
                *
    0122        ODDCNT:     DS      1
    0123        EVNCNT:     DS      1
    0124        LIST:       DS      510         ; MAX. EXTENT OF LIST
                *
    0322                    END
    0322
    000H USE FACTOR
    END OF ASSEMBLY

    A>
```

Figure F   A solution for Question 5.10

Figure G

```
 1:
 2:
 3:                    *  DIVISION BY REPEATED SUBTRACTION
 4:                    *
 5:                    *  ON ENTRY:
 6:                    *        A 16-BIT DIVIDEND IS STORED IN ADDRESS DIVEND AND AN 8-BIT
 7:                    *        DIVISOR  IS STORED IN ADDRESS DIVSR.
 8:                    *  ON EXIT:
 9:                    *        THE QUOTIENT IS STORED IN QUOT
10:                    *        THE REMAINDER IN REMDR
11:                    *        ADDRESS OVFLOW CONTAINS 00 IF QUOTIENT AND REMAINDER ARE VALID
12:                    *                                 01 IF DIVISOR IS ZERO
13:                    *                                 02 IF DIVIDEND IS TOO LARGE OR DIVISOR
14:                    *                                    TOO SMALL TO GENERATE A PROPER 8-BIT
15:                    *                                    QUOTIENT.
16:                    *
17:                    *        WITH OVFLOW CONTAINING 01 OR 02 THE QUOTIENT AND REMAINDER ARE
18:                    *        BOTH SET TO ZERO.
19:                    *
20:                    *                STRUCTURE
21:                    *                '''''''''
22:                    *  BEGIN
23:                    *        REMAINDER := 0
24:                    *        PARTIAL QUOTIENT (PARTQUO) := 0
25:                    *        PARTIAL DIVIDEND (PARTDIVI) := DIVIDEND
26:                    *        INITIALISE DIVISOR
27:                    *        IF DIVISOR = 0 THEN
28:                    *             OVERFLOW := 1
29:                    *        ELSE
30:                    *             IF PARTDIVI >= 256 * DIVISOR THEN
31:                    *                  OVERFLOW := 2
32:                    *             ELSE
33:                    *                  OVERFLOW := 0
34:                    *                  REPEAT
35:                    *                       PARTQUO := PARTQUO + 1
36:                    *                       PARTDIVI := PARTDIVI -DIVISOR
37:                    *                  UNTIL PARTDIVI < 0
38:                    *                  PARTQUO := PARTQUO - 1
39:                    *                  REMAINDER := PARTDIVI + DIVISOR
40:                    *             ENDIF
41:                    *        ENDIF
42:                    *        QUOTIENT := PARTQUO
43:                    *  END.
44:                    *
45:                    *  REGISTER USAGE:
46:                    *                PARTQUO ACCUMULATED IN REGISTER B
47:                    *                DIVISOR IN E
48:                    *                PARTDIVI HELD IN HL REGISTER PAIR
49:                    *
50:   0100                   ORG     0100H
51:   0100 AF      BGN:      XRA     A
52:   0101 324301            STA     REMDR          ; REMAINDER := 0
53:   0104 47                MOV     B,A            ; (B) = PARTQUO = 0
54:   0105 2A3F01            LHLD    DIVEND         ; (HL) = DIVIDEND
55:   0108 3A4101            LDA     DIVSR
56:   010B 5F                MOV     E,A            ; (E) = DIVISOR
57:                    *
```

(Continued)

```
Figure G continued
58:                           *    INITIALISATION COMPLETE - CHECK FOR ZERO DIVISOR
59:                           *
60:   010C B7       IF1:      ORA    A            ; CHECK DIVISOR
61:   010D C21801             JNZ    ELSE1        ; IF NOT ZERO EXECUTE ELSE1
62:   0110 3E01               MVI    A,01
63:   0112 324401             STA    OVFLOW       ; IF ZERO, OVERFLOW := 1
64:   0115 C33A01             JMP    ENIF         ; EXIT IF
65:                           *
66:                           *    DIVISOR NOT ZERO - CHECK FOR POSSIBLE QUOTIENT OVERFLOW
67:                           *
68:   0118 7C       ELSE1:    MOV    A,H          ; MS BYTE OF PARTDIVI
69:   0119 BB                 CMP    E            ; COMPARE WITH DIVISOR
70:                           *
71:                           *    DIVISOR MUST BE GREATER THAN MS HALF OF DIVIDEND
72:                           *    I.E. 256 * DIVISOR > DIVIDEND
73:                           *    IF TRUE CMP WILL SET BORROW (CARRY) FLAG
74:                           *
75:   011A DA2501             JC     ELSE2        ; CY SET, EXECUTE ELSE CODE
76:   011D 3E02               MVI    A,02H
77:   011F 324401             STA    OVFLOW       ; IF ZERO, OVERFLOW := 2
78:   0122 C33A01             JMP    ENIF         ; EXIT IF
79:                           *
80:                           *    PROPER QUOTIENT AND REMAINDER CAN BE GENERATED - PROCEED
81:                           *
82:   0125 AF       ELSE2:    XRA    A
83:   0126 324401             STA    OVFLOW       ; OVERFLOW := 0
84:   0129 04       REPT:     INR    B            ; PARTQUO := PARTQUO + 1
85:   012A 7D                 MOV    A,L          ; LS HALF OF PARTDIVI
86:   012B 93                 SUB    E            ; SUBTRACT DIVISOR
87:   012C 6F                 MOV    L,A          ; RESTORE LS HALF OF PARTDIVI
88:   012D 7C                 MOV    A,H          ; MS HALF OF PARTDIVI
89:   012E DE00               SBI    0            ; SUBTRACT ANY BORROW
90:   0130 67                 MOV    H,A          ; PARTDIVI := PARTDIVI - DIVISOR
91:   0131 D22901   UNTIL:    JNC    REPT         ; REPEAT UNTIL PARTDIVI NEGATIVE
92:                           *
93:                           *    QUOTIENT NOW ONE TOO MANY, REMAINDER NEGATIVE, CORRECT
94:                           *
95:   0134 05                 DCR    B            ; PARTQUO := PARTQUO - 1
96:   0135 7D                 MOV    A,L          ; LS HALF OF PARTDIVI
97:   0136 83                 ADD    E            ; PARTDIVI := PARTDIVI + DIVISOR
98:   0137 324301             STA    REMDR        ; STORE REMAINDER
99:   013A 78       ENIF:     MOV    A,B
100:  013B 324201             STA    QUOT         ; QUOTIENT := FINAL PARTQUO
101:  013E C9                 RET
102:                          *
103:                          *    DATA AREA
104:                          *
105:  013F 9B12     DIVEND:   DW     4763
106:  0141 57       DIVSR:    DB     87
107:  0142          QUOT:     DS     1
108:  0143          REMDR:    DS     1
109:  0144          OVFLOW:   DS     1
110:                          *
111:  0145                    END

A>
```

Figure G   A solution for Question 5.17

```
 1:
 2:
 3:                         *   PROGRAM ADC4
 4:                         *   THIS PROGRAM READS AN 8-BIT VALUE FROM A DATA PORT AND THEN
 5:                         *   PRINTS THE EQUIVALENT VOLTAGE, IN THE RANGE 0 - 5VOLTS, ON
 6:                         *   THE CONSOLE.
 7:                         *
 8:                         *                   STRUCTURE
 9:                         *                   '''''''''
10:                         *   BEGIN
11:                         *       REPEAT
12:                         *           READ VALUE
13:                         *           PRINT BINARY EQUIVALENT OF VALUE
14:                         *           PRINT 10 SPACES
15:                         *           CONVERT VALUE TO A VOLTAGE
16:                         *           PRINT VOLTAGE
17:                         *       UNTIL INFINITY
18:                         *   END
19:                         *
20: 0100                          ORG     0100H           ; WILL RUN UNDER CP/M
21: 0100 CD1401      BGN:   CALL    READ            ; READ VALUE
22: 0103 CD1701             CALL    PBIN            ; PRINT BINARY
23: 0106 0E0A               MVI     C,10            ; INITIALISE SPACECOUNT
24: 0108 CD1801             CALL    SPACE           ; PRINT SPACES
25: 010B CD1501             CALL    CONV            ; CONVERT VALUE TO A VOLTAGE
26: 010E CD1601             CALL    PRINT           ; PRINT VOLTAGE
27: 0111 C30001             JMP     BGN             ; REPEAT INDEFINETLY
28:                         *
29:                         *   SUBROUTINE READ
30:                         *
31: 0114 C9         READ:  RET
32:                         *
33:                         *   SUBROUTINE CONV
34:                         *
35: 0115 C9         CONV:  RET
36:                         *
37:                         *   SUBROUTINE PRINT
38:                         *
39: 0116 C9         PRINT: RET
40:                         *
41:                         *   SUBROUTINE PBIN
42:                         *
43: 0117 C9         PBIN:  RET
44:                         *
45:                         *   SUBROUTINE SPACE
46:                         *
47: 0118 C9         SPACE: RET
48:                         *
49: 0119                          END

A>
```

Figure H   The new main program

```
 1:
 2:
 3:                         *   SUBROUTINE PBIN
 4:                         *   THIS SUBROUTINE PRINTS THE BINARY NUMBER STORED IN VALUE ON
 5:                         *   THE CONSOLE.
 6:                         *
 7:                         *                   STRUCTURE
 8:                         *                   '''''''''
 9:                         *   BEGIN
10:                         *       BITCOUNT := 8
11:                         *       INITIALISE VALUE
12:                         *       REPEAT
13:                         *           ISOLATE LEFTMOST BIT
14:                         *           IF BIT =0 THEN ASCII = 0
15:                         *           ELSE, ASCII = 1
16:                         *           ENDIF
17:                         *           PRINT ASCII
18:                         *           BITCOUNT := BITCOUNT - 1
19:                         *       UNTIL BITCOUNT := 0
20:                         *   END
21:                         *
22:                         *   REGISTER USAGE :
23:                         *               REGISTER C IS USED AS THE BIT COUNTER
24:                         *               REGISTERS A AND B ARE USED BY THE PCHAR ROUTINE
25:                         *               REGISTER D IS USED TO STORE THE BINARY
26:                         *
27:   0300                          ORG     0300H           ; PBIN ORIGIN
28:   0300 0E08        PBIN:        MVI     C,08H           ; (C) = BITCOUNT
29:   0302 3A1703                   LDA     VALUE
30:   0305 57                       MOV     D,A             ; INITIALISE VALUE
31:   0306 7A          REPT6:       MOV     A,D             ; GET BINARY
32:   0307 07                       RLC                     ; ISOLATE BIT IN CARRY
33:   0308 57                       MOV     D,A             ; SAVE BINARY AGAIN
34:   0309 0630                     MVI     B,30H           ; ASCII = 0
35:   030B D20F03                   JNC     PASCII          ; BIT = 0 PRINT ASCII 0
36:   030E 04                       INR     B               ; ELSE ASCII = 1
37:   030F CD8902      PASCII:      CALL    PCHAR           ; PRINT ASCII
38:   0312 0D                       DCR     C               ; BITCOUNT := BITCOUNT - 1
39:   0313 C20603      UNTIL6:      JNZ     REPT6           ; REPEAT UNTIL BITCOUNT = 0
40:   0316 C9                       RET
41:                         *
42:                         *   REDEFINE VALUE HERE FOR TESTING
43:                         *
44:   0317 FF          VALUE:       DB      0FFH
45:                         *
46:                         *   THE PCHAR ROUTINE WILL BE HOOKED UP BEFORE TESTING
47:                         *   ITS START ADDRESS IS 0289H
48:                         *
49:   0289 =           PCHAR:       EQU     0289H
50:                         *
51:                         *
```

A>

Figure I   The PBIN (print binary) subroutine

```
 1:
 2:
 3:                        *  SUBROUTINE SPACE
 4:                        *  PRINTS A NUMBER OF SPACES ON THE CONSOLE.
 5:                        *  THE ACTUAL NUMBER TO PRINT IS PASSED IN REGISTER C
 6:                        *
 7:                        *              STRUCTURE
 8:                        *              ''''''''''
 9:                        *  BEGIN
10:                        *      REPEAT
11:                        *          PRINT A SPACE
12:                        *          SPACECOUNT := SPACECOUNT - 1
13:                        *      UNTIL SPACECOUNT = 0
14:                        *  END
15:                        *
16:                        *  REGISTER USAGE:
17:                        *              REGISTER C CONTAINS THE SPACECOUNT ON ENTRY
18:                        *              REGISTERS A AND B ARE USED BY PCHAR
19:                        *
20:  0350                           ORG     0350H       ; SPACE ORIGIN
21:  0350 0620       SPACE:         MVI     B,' '       ; ASCII SPACE TO B
22:  0352 CD8902                    CALL    PCHAR       ; PRINT IT
23:  0355 0D                        DCR     C           ; SPACECOUNT := SPACECOUNT - 1
24:  0356 C25203                    JNZ     SPACE+2     ; REPEAT UNTIL FINISHED
25:  0359 C9                        RET
26:                        *
27:                        *  RE-DEFINE PCHAR START ADDRESS FOR TESTING
28:                        *
29:  0289 =           PCHAR:        EQU     0289H
30:                        *

A>
```

Figure J The SPACE (print spaces) subroutine

Linking and relocating is often a combined operation in modern systems. The Futuredata linker, for example, is called a linkage editor and it links and relocates program modules. Section 6.7 explains the need in greater detail.

6.3   The assembler which produces relocatable object code adds relocation information to the object code file. You can imagine it as marking all instructions which have to be changed if the program is subsequently relocated. This relocation information is read by the relocating loader and, when supplied with a module start address, the loader makes all the necessary changes to the object code as it is made absolute.

The object code produced by an absolute assembler cannot be relocated so the relocation information is missing from the object code file.

6.4 In general, all instructions which reference memory have to be changed. For example:

STA	store A directly
LDA	load A directly
SHLD	store HL directly
LHLD	load HL directly
JMP	all the jump instructions
CALL	and the call instructions

6.5 The main reason is that different kinds of program code and data can be easily formed into contiguous blocks and then, after relocating, if necessary, either committed to EPROM or assigned to read-write memory. Individual modules, when they are written, may contain a mix of variable data, fixed data, program code and general-purpose subroutine code. The use of different location counters allows these parts of every module to be picked out and formed into contiguous blocks.

6.6 Entry points are instructions or data in this module which are accessible to other modules when eventually modules are linked together. Intel refers to these addresses as PUBLIC (open to anyone), and Futuredata as GLBL (global). They are declared as,

```
PUBLIC    ENTRY1, ENTRY2, ENTRY3
  GLBL    ENTRY1, ENTRY2, ENTRY3
```

External address references are references to the addresses of instructions or data items which are used in this module but declared in another which is not present at assembly time. The Intel way of informing the assembler of external address references is to use the directive EXTRN, whereas Futuredata again uses the GLBL directive. Thus we might write:

```
EXTRN    SUB1, SUB2, VALUE
 GLBL    SUB1, SUB2, VALUE
```

and then use instructions like:

```
CALL    SUB1
LDA     VALUE
```

SUB1, SUB2 and VALUE are defined in another module so the assembler will not be able to properly assemble these instructions, but equally it will not flag an error message. It will mark the instructions in some way and leave it to the linker to make the external references absolute.

6.7 Software development aids such as relocating, linker loaders, are available to run on practically every modern system, but these only cover the software development stage of system development. The extra facilities which an MDS provides concern the integration of hardware and software in a standalone system. These are explained in the text but briefly they amount to the ability to gradually integrate hardware and software with the power of the MDS always providing support. Eventually, when the MDS has no further role to play, the standalone system will have been completely tested.

7.1 Representing each input as $1 = -5$ V and $0 = 0$ V, the table is as shown in Table C.

Table C

V_1	V_2	V_3	V_4	V_0, V
0	0	0	0	0
0	0	0	1	0.3125
0	0	1	0	0.625
0	0	1	1	0.9375
0	1	0	0	1.25
0	1	0	1	1.5625
0	1	1	0	1.875
0	1	1	1	2.1875
1	0	0	0	2.5
1	0	0	1	2.8125
1	0	1	0	3.125
1	0	1	1	3.4375
1	1	0	0	3.75
1	1	0	1	4.0625
1	1	1	0	4.375
1	1	1	1	4.6875

7.2 The resolution of a DAC is the change in analogue output voltage produced by a change in the least significant bit position of the digital input. In the previous question, for example, the resolution is 0.3125 V. Since, for a given dynamic range, the resolution is a function of the number of bits, it is very common to refer to DACs as having 8-, 10-, 12-, etc., bit resolutions.

In the case of an ADC, the resolution is the maximum change in analogue input which produces a change in the least significant bit position of the digital output. As with the DAC, the resolution of an ADC is usually given in terms of the number of bits in the digital output.

7.3 The program is named FORM2 and is listed in Figure K.

7.4 The sequence would be,

1000 – Try ½ scale. Too much, reject!

```
 1:
 2:
 3:              *   PROGRAM NAME FORM2
 4:              *   ==================
 5:              *
 6:              *   GENERATES A SAWTOOTH WAVEFORM AT AN OUTPUT PORT
 7:              *
 8:              *              STRUCTURE
 9:              *              '''''''''
10:              *   BEGIN
11:              *       AMPLITUDE := 0
12:              *       REPEAT
13:              *           SEND AMPLITUDE
14:              *           AMPLITUDE := AMPLITUDE + 1
15:              *       UNTIL INFINITY
16:              *   END.
17:              *
18:              *   OUTPUT PORT NUMBER IS FFH
19:              *
20: 00FF =       PORT:   EQU    0FFH
21:              *
22: 0100                 ORG    0100H          ; WILL RUN UNDER CP/M
23: 0100 AF      BGN:    XRA    A              ; AMPLITUDE = 0
24:              *
25: 0101 D3FF    REPT:   OUT    PORT           ; SEND AMPLITUDE
26: 0103 3C              INR    A              ; AMPLITUDE := AMPLITUDE + 1
27: 0104 C30101  UNTIL:  JMP    REPT           ; REPEAT UNTIL INFINITY
28: 0107                 END

A>
```

Figure K   A solution for Question 7.3

0100   – Try $\frac{1}{4}$ scale. Too little, retain!
0110   – Try $\frac{3}{8}$ scale. Too little, retain!
0111   – Try $\frac{7}{16}$ scale. Too much, reject!
0110   – All bits determined

Notice that a bit is rejected only if the DAC output is greater than the analogue input. If the two are exactly equal the bit will be retained at a 1.

7.5   The program is called SOFT2 and is listed in Figure L.

7.6   The usual way of deriving reasonably accurate figures is by trial and error. For example, we have to find values for MSCONS and LSCONS in the following formula:

$$T = (MSCONS \times 14) + (LSCONS \times 14) + (MSCONS - 1)(14 \times 256)\,0.25 \times 10^{-6}$$

If $T = 0.1$ s, then

$$0.4 \times 10^6 = (MSCONS \times 14 \times 257) + (LSCONS \times 14) - (14 \times 256)$$

```
 1:
 2:
 3:                    *    PROGRAM NAME SOFT2
 4:                    *    ====================
 5:                    *
 6:                    *    THIS PROGRAM IS A COUNTING TYPE CONVERSION ROUTINE.
 7:                    *    IT IMITATES, IN SOFTWARE, THE CONTROL LOGIC OF A COUNTING
 8:                    *    TYPE ADC.
 9:                    *
10:                    *
11:                    *              STRUCTURE
12:                    *              '''''''''
13:                    *    BEGIN
14:                    *        REPEAT
15:                    *             WAIT FOR A START SIGNAL (SUBROUTINE)
16:                    *             EXTINGUISH THE READY LAMP
17:                    *             VALUE := 0
18:                    *             REPEAT  (* UNTIL COMPARATOR OUTPUT = 1 *)
19:                    *                  SEND VALUE
20:                    *                  WAIT FOR COMPARATOR (SUBROUTINE)
21:                    *                  VALUE := VALUE + 1
22:                    *                  READ COMPARATOR OUTPUT
23:                    *             UNTIL COMPARATOR OUTPUT = 1
24:                    *             LIGHT THE READY LAMP
25:                    *        UNTIL INFINITY
26:                    *    END.
27:                    *
28:                    *    THE REGISTER USAGE AND I/O LINE ASSIGNMENTS, AS LISTED
29:                    *    IN THE PROGRAM SOFT1, ARE APPLICABLE HERE.
30:                    *
31:  00FF =     DATAPT: EQU      0FFH
32:  00FE =     CTRLPT: EQU      0FEH
33:  00FD =     STATPT: EQU      0FDH
34:                    *
35:  0100              ORG      0100H              ; RUNS UNDER CP/M
36:  0100 CD1C01  BGN:  CALL     START              ; WAIT FOR START SIGNAL
37:  0103 AF           XRA      A
38:  0104 D3FD         OUT      STATPT             ; CLEAR READY LAMP
39:  0106 47           MOV      B,A                ; (B) = VALUE = 0
40:                    *
41:  0107 78     REPT:  MOV      A,B
42:  0108 D3FF         OUT      DATAPT             ; SEND VALUE
43:  010A CD1E01       CALL     WAIT               ; WAIT FOR COMPARATOR
44:  010D 04           INR      B                  ; VALUE := VALUE + 1
45:  010E DBFE         IN       CTRLPT
46:  0110 E601         ANI      01H                ; CHECK COMPARATOR OUPUT
47:  0112 CA0701  UNTIL: JZ      REPT               ; REPEAT UNTIL TOO MUCH
48:                    *
49:  0115 3E01         MVI      A,01H
50:  0117 D3FD         OUT      STATPT             ; LIGHT READY LAMP
51:  0119 C30001       JMP      BGN                ; REPEAT UNTIL INFINITY
52:                    *
53:                    *    SUBROUTINES START AND WAIT ARE AS LISTED IN SOFT1 WHICH IS
54:                    *    GIVEN IN THE TEXT AS FIGURE 7.10
55:                    *
56:  011C FFFF   START: DW       0FFFFH             ; REDEFINE FOR THE BENEFIT
57:  011E FFFF   WAIT:  DW       0FFFFH             ; OF THE ASSEMBLER
58:                    *
59:  0120              END

A>
```

Figure L A solution for Question 7.5

Assuming that LSCONS has its maximum value, 256, then the expression simplifies to:

$$0.4 \times 10^6 = \text{MSCONS} \times 14 \times 257$$

from which

$$\text{MSCONS} = 400,000/(14 \times 257)$$
$$= 111.17$$

If we let MSCONS = 112, then LSCONS must be less than its maximum value. Substituting back for MSCONS:

$$400,000 = (112 \times 14 \times 257) + (\text{LSCONS} \times 14) - (14 \times 256)$$

Solving for LSCONS gives

$$\text{LSCONS} = 608/14 = 43.4$$

We cannot get precisely 0.1 s but could go above by making LSCONS equal to 44, or below by making it 43. The actual delay times would then be:

Above, with LSCONS = 44, MSCONS = 122, $T = 0.1000002$ s
Below, with LSCONS = 43, MSCONS = 112, $T = 0.0999985$ s

In both cases, the hexadecimal equivalent of MSCONS is 70H and LSCONS is 3EH or 3DH.

Repeating the above exercise for a time of 75 μs, initially gives a value for MSCONS of less than 1. This indicates that the required delay could be achieved by using a single-length register. Taking MSCONS equal to 1, LSCONS evaluates to 20.4.

If LSCONS = 21 (15H), total delay = 77 μs
If LSCONS = 20 (14H), total delay = 73.5 μs

7.7   A suitable subroutine would work as follows:

```
REPEAT  (*Until button released*)
        READ START
UNTIL START = 1
REPEAT  (*Until button pressed*)
        READ START
UNTIL START = 0
REPEAT  (*Until button released again*)
        READ START
UNTIL START = 1
```

7.8   The 8080 has a single INT input which is taken to a 1 when a peripheral demands service. The INTE flag within the 8080 must be set if this demand is to be satisfied. Assuming that INTE is set, the 8080 completes the instruction it is currently working on and then generates an $\overline{\text{INTA}}$ signal. At the peripheral this is used to force a restart instruction onto the data bus. When the processor executes the restart instruction it saves the program counter on the stack and then 'vectors' to the restart address number embedded in the restart code. After executing the interrupt service routine, a RET instruction restores the program counter to its pre-interrupt state and normal program execution resumes.

Since the interrupting peripheral actually informs the CPU of where to find its particular interrupt service routine, 8080 interrupts are often called vectored interrupts. The vector is the restart number supplied by the peripheral.

There are several quite elegant interrupt controller/generator chips which can be used in 8080 systems. The circuit diagram of Figure 7.19 shows a simple way of providing all that is needed.

7.9   The reason is that when a command is given to CP/M, the lower 256 bytes (00H to FFH) are used as a buffer area to set up file pointers which are needed to execute the command. For example, if we type the name of one of our .COM files, information about that file – where it is on the disk, how long it is, where the various segments of it are – is stored in this lower part of memory. If this information is corrupted during the loading process it will be impossible to complete the task. Consequently user interrupt service routines cannot be loaded directly into the restart area. Once CP/M has no further use for this memory, that is when loading is finished, it becomes available for general use. During execution, therefore, a subroutine like MOVE can fill in the restart area before any interrupts are enabled.

7.10   This program is called INT3 and is listed in Figure M.

7.11   A suggested program called INT4 is given in Figure N.

7.12   This program is called RTC and is listed in Figure O.

7.13   The program ADC4 will need to be modified in the following respects:

1   ADCINT will need to keep a running total of the number of alarm, or error, conditions. At the address labelled ALARM we must write:

```
CALL CNTERR  ;add 1 to the running
             ;total of alarms
```

When this instruction is executed it updates an error counter.

2   The error counter will be defined in the main program as

```
ERRCNT:  DS  2
```

```
 1:
 2:
 3:                           *   PROGRAM NAME INT3
 4:                           *   ================
 5:                           *
 6:   0100                        ORG     0100H
 7:   0100 F3         INT3:   DI                          ; DISABLE INTERRUPTS
 8:   0101 CD2501             CALL    MOVE                ; SET-UP THE RESTART ADDRESSES
 9:   0104 DBFF               IN      0FFH                ; CLEAR ANY PENDING ACKNOWLEDGE
10:                           *
11:   0106 3E01       REPT1:  MVI     A,01H
12:   0108 D3FF               OUT     0FFH                ; SWITCH ON THE LAMP
13:   010A DBFE       REPT2:  IN      0FEH                ; READ THE INPUT
14:   010C E601               ANI     01H                 ; TEST IT (D0 OF 0FEH)
15:   010E C20A01     UNTIL2: JNZ     REPT2               ; REPEAT UNTIL INPUT = 0
16:                           *
17:   0111 FB                 EI                          ; SWITCH ON THE INTERRUPTS
18:   0112 3E01               MVI     A,01H
19:   0114 324D01             STA     DIVIDR              ; FLASH RATE DIVIDER = 1
20:   0117 AF                 XRA     A
21:   0118 4F                 MOV     C,A                 ; MAKE (C) = RE-TRY = 0
22:                           *
23:   0119 CD4C01     REPT3:  CALL    FLASH               ; FLASH LAMP
24:   011C 79                 MOV     A,C
25:   011D FE00               CPI     00H                 ; TEST RE-TRY
26:   011F CA1901     UNTIL3: JZ      REPT3               ; REPEAT UNTIL RE-TRY = 1
27:   0122 C30601     UNTIL1: JMP     REPT1               ; REPEAT UNTIL INFINITY
28:                           *
29:   0125 3EC3       MOVE:   MVI     A,0C3H              ; JMP OP-CODE
30:   0127 320800             STA     0008H               ; INTO RESTART 1
31:   012A 321000             STA     0010H               ; AND RESTART 2
32:   012D 213A01             LXI     H,INTR1             ; SERVICE ROUTINE 1 START ADDRESS
33:   0130 220900             SHLD    0009H
34:   0133 214501             LXI     H,INTR2             ; SERVICE ROUTINE 2 START ADDRESS
35:   0136 221100             SHLD    0011H
36:   0139 C9                 RET
37:                           *
38:                           *   ENTERED WHEN ACKNOWLEDGE BUTTON OPERATED
39:                           *
40:   013A F5         INTR1:  PUSH    PSW                 ; SAVE ONLY WORKING REGISTER
41:   013B DBFF               IN      0FFH                ; CLEAR THIS INTERRUPT FLAG
42:   013D 3E08               MVI     A,08H
43:   013F 324D01             STA     DIVIDR              ; FLASH RATE DIVIDER = 8
44:   0142 F1                 POP     PSW                 ; RESTORE THE REGISTER
45:   0143 FB                 EI                          ; RE-ENABLE INTERRUPTS
46:   0144 C9                 RET
47:                           *
48:                           *   ENTERED WHEN RE-TRY PUSH BUTTON OPERATED
49:                           *
50:   0145 F5         INTR2:  PUSH    PSW                 ; SAVE THE ONLY WORKING REGISTER
51:   0146 DBFE               IN      0FEH                ; CLEAR THIS INTERRUPT FLAG
52:   0148 0E01               MVI     C,01H               ; MAKE RE-TRY = 1
53:   014A F1                 POP     PSW                 ; RESTORE REGISTER
54:   014B C9                 RET
55:                           *
56:                           *   USE SAME FLASH AND DELAY ROUTINES AS BEFORE
57:                           *
58:   014C C9         FLASH:  RET
59:   014D            DIVIDR: DS      1
60:                           *
```

Figure M   A solution for Question 7.10

Figure N

```
 1:
 2:
 3:                      *    PROGRAM NAME INT4
 4:                      *    ================
 5:                      *
 6:                      *    THIS PROGRAM WORKS AS FOLLOWS:
 7:                      *         1. IN ITS UN-INTERRUPTED STATE THE PROGRAM DOES NOTHING
 8:                      *            BUT HOLD THE LAMP OFF.
 9:                      *         2. WHEN AN ALARM CONDITION OCCURS, AN INTERRUPT IS
10:                      *            GENERATED WHICH CAUSES A LAMP TO FLASH.
11:                      *         3. ANOTHER PUSH-BUTTON IS CONNECTED TO A SECOND INTERRUPT
12:                      *            INPUT AND WHEN THIS IS PRESSED IT CANCELS THE FLASHING
13:                      *            LAMP AND RETURNS CONTROL TO THE MAIN PROGRAM.
14:                      *
15:                      *    IT IS AN EXAMPLE OF ONE INTERRUPT SERVICE ROUTINE INTERRUPTING ANOTHER
16:                      *
17:                      *                     STRUCTURE
18:                      *                     '''''''''
19:                      *    BEGIN
20:                      *         DISABLE INTERRUPTS
21:                      *         LOAD UP THE RESTART AREA
22:                      *         CLEAR ANY PENDING INTERRUPTS
23:                      *         ENABLE INTERRUPTS
24:                      *         REPEAT
25:                      *              DO NOTHING
26:                      *         UNTIL INFINITY
27:                      *    END
28:                      *
29:                      *    INTERRUPT SERVICE ROUTINE 1
30:                      *    ===========================
31:                      *
32:                      *    BEGIN   (* FLASH THE LAMP *)
33:                      *         CLEAR THIS INTERRUPT REQUEST
34:                      *         MAKE RE-TRY A 0
35:                      *         SELECT FAST FLASH RATE
36:                      *         ENABLE INTERRUPTS
37:                      *         REPEAT
38:                      *              FLASH LAMP
39:                      *         UNTIL RE-TRY = 1
40:                      *    END
41:                      *
42:                      *    INTERRUPT SERVICE ROUTINE 2
43:                      *    ===========================
44:                      *
45:                      *    BEGIN   (* CANCEL THE FLASHING *)
46:                      *         CLEAR THIS INTERRUPT REQUEST
47:                      *         MAKE RE-TRY = 1
48:                      *         ENABLE INTERRUPTS
49:                      *    END
50:                      *
51:  0100                     ORG     0100H
52:  0100 F3        INT4:     DI                        ; DISABLE INTERRUPTS
53:  0101 310010              LXI     SP,1000H          ; DEFINING MY OWN STACK THIS TIME
```

(Continued)

Figure N continued

```
54:   0104 CD1201           CALL   MOVE         ; PRIME THE RESTART AREA
55:   0107 DBFF             IN     0FFH         ; CLEAR ANY PENDING INTERRUPT REQUESTS
56:   0109 DBFE             IN     0FEH
57:   010B FB               EI
58:                    *
59:   010C AF       REPT1:  XRA    A
60:   010D D3FF             OUT    0FFH         ; KEEP THE LAMP OFF
61:   010F C30C01  UNTIL1:  JMP    REPT1        ; UNTIL INFINITY
62:                    *
63:   0112 3EC3     MOVE:   MVI    A,0C3H       ; JMP OP-CODE
64:   0114 320800           STA    0008H        ; INTO RESTART 1
65:   0117 321000           STA    0010H        ; AND RESTART 2 ADDRESSES
66:   011A 212701           LXI    H,INTR1
67:   011D 220900           SHLD   0009H        ; COMPLETE RESTART 1
68:   0120 213A01           LXI    H,INTR2
69:   0123 221100           SHLD   0011H        ; AND RESTART 2 AREAS
70:   0126 C9               RET
71:                    *
72:   0127 DBFF     INTR1:  IN     0FFH         ; CLEAR THIS INTERRUPT REQUEST
73:   0129 AF               XRA    A
74:   012A 4F               MOV    C,A          ; (C) = RE-TRY = 0
75:   012B 3C               INR    A
76:   012C 324301           STA    DIVIDR       ; FLASHING AT THE FAST RATE
77:   012F FB               EI                  ; ENABLE INTERRUPTS
78:   0130 CD4201  REPT2:   CALL   FLASH        ; FLASH THE LAMP
79:   0133 79               MOV    A,C
80:   0134 FE00             CPI    00H          ; TEST RE-TRY FOR 0
81:   0136 CA3001  UNTIL2:  JZ     REPT2        ; REPEAT UNTIL RE-TRY = 1
82:   0139 C9               RET                 ; THEN RETURN
83:                    *
84:   013A F5       INTR2:  PUSH   PSW          ; SAVE REGISTER A
85:   013B DBFE             IN     0FEH         ; CLEAR THIS INTERRUPT REQUEST
86:   013D 0E01             MVI    C,01H        ; MAKE RE-TRY = 1
87:   013F F1               POP    PSW
88:   0140 FB               EI                  ; RE-ENABLE INTERRUPTS
89:   0141 C9               RET
90:                    *
91:                    *  SAME FLASH AND DELAY ROUTINES AS BEFORE
92:                    *
93:   0142 C9       FLASH:  RET
94:   0143          DIVIDR: DS     1
95:                    *
96:                    *
97:   0144                  END
```

Figure N   A solution for Question 7.11

Figure O

```
 1:
 2:
 3:                  *    PROGRAM NAME : RTC
 4:                  *    =================
 5:                  *
 6:                  *    A REAL TIME CLOCK UP-DATE AND DISPLAY PROGRAM
 7:                  *
 8:                  *    UP-DATES OCCUR AT ONE MINUTE INTERVALS
 9:                  *
10:                  *                  STRUCTURE
11:                  *                  '''''''''
12:                  *    BEGIN
13:                  *        DISABLE INTERRUPTS
14:                  *        FILL UP THE RESTART AREA
15:                  *        CLEAR ANY CURRENT INTERRUPT REQUESTS
16:                  *        MINS := 0
17:                  *        HOURS:= 0
18:                  *        ENABLE INTERRUPTS
19:                  *        REPEAT
20:                  *             DO NOTHING
21:                  *        UNTIL INFINITY
22:                  *
23:                  *    RTC INTERRUPT SERVICE ROUTINE
24:                  *    =============================
25:                  *
26:                  *    BEGIN
27:                  *        SAVE ALL THE REGISTERS
28:                  *        CLEAR THE RTC INTERRUPT REQUEST LINE
29:                  *        MINS := MINS + 1
30:                  *        CONVERT MINS TO BCD
31:                  *        IF MINS = 60 THEN
32:                  *            MINS := 0
33:                  *            HOURS := HOURS + 1
34:                  *            CONVERT HOURS TO BCD
35:                  *            IF HOURS = 24 THEN
36:                  *                 HOURS := 0
37:                  *            ELSE
38:                  *                 DO NOTHING
39:                  *            ENDIF
40:                  *        ELSE
41:                  *            DO NOTHING
42:                  *        ENDIF
43:                  *        PRINT "RUNTIME = "
44:                  *        READ HOURS AND MINS
45:                  *        PRINT HOURS
46:                  *        PRINT ':'
47:                  *        PRINT MINS
48:                  *        START A NEW LINE
49:                  *        RESTORE ALL THE REGISTERS
50:                  *        ENABLE INTERRUPTS
51:                  *    END
52:                  *
53:    0100                  ORG     0100H
54:    0100 F3       MAIN:   DI                        ; DISABLE INTERRUPTS
55:    0101 DBFF             IN      0FFH              ; CANCEL THE INTERRUPT REQUEST
56:    0103 CD1201           CALL    MOVE              ; SET UP THE RESTART AREA
57:    0106 AF               XRA     A                 ; ZERO INTO A
58:    0107 325A01           STA     MINS              ; MINS := 0
```

(Continued)

Figure O continued

```
59:  010A 325B01           STA     HOURS           ; HOURS := 0
60:  010D FB               EI                      ; SWITCH ON THE INTERRUPTS
61:                 *
62:  010E 7F       PARK:   MOV     A,A             ; DO NOTHING
63:  010F C30E01           JMP     PARK            ; UNTIL INFINITY
64:                 *
65:  0112 3EC3     MOVE:   MVI     A,0C3H          ; JMP OP-CODE
66:  0114 320800           STA     0008H           ; INTO RESTART 1 ADDRESS
67:  0117 211E01           LXI     H,RTC           ; RTC START ADDRESS
68:  011A 220900           SHLD    0009H           ; INTO 0009 AND 000A
69:  011D C9               RET
70:                 *
71:  011E F5       RTC:    PUSH    PSW             ; SAVE THE REGISTERS
72:  011F C5               PUSH    B
73:  0120 D5               PUSH    D
74:  0121 E5               PUSH    H
75:  0122 DBFF             IN      0FFH            ; CANCEL THE INTERRUPT REQUEST
76:  0124 3A5A01           LDA     MINS
77:  0127 C601             ADI     01H
78:  0129 27               DAA                     ; CONVERT MINS TO BCD
79:  012A 325A01           STA     MINS            ; MINS := MINS + 1
80:  012D FE60     TST60:  CPI     60H             ; TEST FOR 60 MINS
81:  012F C24801           JNZ     DISPLY          ; IF NOT DISPLAY TIME
82:  0132 AF               XRA     A
83:  0133 325A01           STA     MINS            ; IF 60, MINS := 0
84:  0136 3A5B01           LDA     HOURS
85:  0139 C601             ADI     01H
86:  013B 27               DAA                     ; CONVERT HOURS TO BCD
87:  013C 325B01           STA     HOURS           ; HOURS := HOURS + 1
88:  013F FE24     TST24:  CPI     24H             ; TEST FOR 24 HOURS
89:  0141 C24801           JNZ     DISPLY          ; IF NOT, DISPLAY TIME
90:  0144 AF       /       XRA     A               ; IF 24, HOURS := 0
91:  0145 325B01           STA     HOURS
92:                 *
93:  0148 115C01   DISPLY: LXI     D,MESS          ; GET MESSAGE START ADDRESS
94:  014B CD6701           CALL    MESP            ; PRINT THE MESSAGE
95:  014E CD6901           CALL    PRNTIME         ; SUBROUTINE DEFINED IN THE TEXT
96:  0151 CD6801           CALL    NEWL            ; THEN A NEW LINE
97:  0154 E1               POP     H               ; RESTORE THE REGISTERS
98:  0155 D1               POP     D
99:  0156 C1               POP     B
100: 0157 F1               POP     PSW
101: 0158 FB               EI                      ; RE-ENABLE INTERRUPTS
102: 0159 C9               RET
103:                *
104: 015A          MINS:   DS      1               ; MINUTES SAVED HERE
105: 015B          HOURS:  DS      1               ; AND HOURS HERE
106: 015C 52554E5449 MESS: DB      'RUNTIME = '
107: 0166 00       TERM:   NOP                     ; MESSAGE TERMINATOR
108:                *
109:                *     EXTERNALS - MESP AND NEWL DEFINED IN CONSOL.LIB, AND PRNTIME
110:                *                 LATER IN THE TEXT.
111:                *
112: 0167 C9       MESP:   RET
113: 0168 C9       NEWL:   RET
114: 0169 C9       PRNTIME: RET
115:                *
116: 016A                  END
```

Figure O A solution for Question 7.12

and initialised to zero immediately after the clock is initialised.

3   The error counter will hold BCD numbers, much like MINS and HOURS hold BCD numbers, allowing for a maximum error count of 9999. If this is not enough then there is something drastically wrong with the system.

4   We shall need another interrupt service routine, called STATUS, which is executed when the STATUS button is pressed. This is listed in Figure P. The subroutine PERROR called from STATUS is listed in Figure Q.

5   Subroutine CNTERR which up-dates ERRCNT is given in Figure R.

Typical results from the modified ADC4 are shown in Figure S.

7.14   A diagram is given in Figure T.

7.15   Sample and hold circuits are needed when the analogue input of an ADC is changing more quickly than the ADC can complete a conversion. We will not repeat the explanation given in the text, but briefly, if the analogue input changes by more than the analogue equivalent of the least significant bit during the conversion time, then a sample and hold circuit is needed.

7.16   A suitable program would be,

```
PCHAN:   LDA      CHANNL      ;get channel number (BCD)
         CALL     PRNRGT
         RET
```

7.17   The FNDLMT subroutine is listed in Figure U.

8.1   Stepping motors are digital devices. Given a suitable motor interface circuit, a step pulse drives the motor shaft through a precise angular displacement known as the step angle. If the shaft is mechanically coupled with a leadscrew, this angular displacement translates into a fixed linear, or longitudinal, displacement which depends on the step angle and the pitch of the leadscrew. If a series of pulses is supplied, the final displacement is directly proportional to the total number of pulses received. In rotational systems the constant of proportionality is just the step angle, and in linear systems it is the pitch of the leadscrew divided by the number of steps/revolution.

The main advantage of stepping motors in position-control systems therefore arises because determining position from a datum is simply a question of counting pulses – no feedback control information is needed.

8.2   Variable reluctance, permanent magnet and hybrid types.

```
 1:
 2:
 3:                         *    STATUS BUTTON INTERRUPT SERVICE ROUTINE
 4:                         *    ====================================
 5:                         *
 6:                         *    THIS INTERRUPT SERVICE ROUTINE IS PART OF THE MODIFIED ADC4.
 7:                         *    WHEN THE STATUS BUTTON IS PRESSED IT REPORTS ON THE NUMBER
 8:                         *    OF ALARM CONDITIONS (ERRORS) WHICH HAVE BEEN DETECTED.
 9:                         *
10:                         *                  STRUCTURE
11:                         *                  '''''''''
12:                         *    BEGIN
13:                         *         SAVE THE REGISTERS
14:                         *         CLEAR THIS INTERRUPT REQUEST
15:                         *         PRINT 'REPORTING AT '
16:                         *         PRINT THE CURRENT RUN-TIME
17:                         *         PRINT 'TOTAL ERROR COUNT SO FAR IS '
18:                         *         PRINT THE ERROR COUNT
19:                         *         PRINT A CARRAIGE RETURN-LINE FEED
20:                         *         RESTORE THE REGISTERS
21:                         *         RE-ENABLE INTERRUPTS
22:                         *    END
23:                         *
24:   0000 F5              STATUS: PUSH   PSW              ; SAVE THE REGISTERS
25:   0001 C5                      PUSH   B
26:   0002 D5                      PUSH   D
27:   0003 E5                      PUSH   H
28:   0004 DBFE                    IN     0FEH             ; CLEAR THIS INTERRUPT REQUEST
29:   0006 112100                  LXI    D,MESS3          ; MESSAGE 3 START ADDRESS
30:   0009 CD4700                  CALL   MESP             ; PRINT 'REPORTING AT
31:   000C CD4900                  CALL   PRNTIME          ; PRINT THE CURRENT RUNTIME
32:   000F 112F00                  LXI    D,MESS4          ; MESSAGE 4 START ADDRESS
33:   0012 CD4700                  CALL   MESP             ; PRINT MESSAGE 4
34:   0015 CD4A00                  CALL   PERROR           ; PRINT CURRENT ERROR COUNT
35:   0018 CD4800                  CALL   NEWL             ; THEN A NEW LINE
36:   001B E1                      POP    H                ; RESTORE THE REGISTERS
37:   001C D1                      POP    D
38:   001D C1                      POP    B
39:   001E F1                      POP    PSW
40:   001F FB                      EI                      ; RE-ENABLE INTERRUPTS
41:   0020 C9                      RET                     ; AND RETURN
42:                         *
43:                         *    MESSAGES HERE ARE
44:                         *
45:   0021 5245504F52MESS3:  DB     'REPORTING AT ',00H
46:   002F 204552524FMESS4:  DB     ' ERROR COUNT SO FAR IS ',00H
47:                         *
48:                         *    EXTERNAL ADDRESS REFERENCES ARE,
49:                         *
50:   0047 C9              MESP:   RET                      ; DEFINED IN CONSOL.LIB
51:   0048 C9              NEWL:   RET                      ; LIKEWISE
52:   0049 C9              PRNTIME: RET
53:   004A C9              PERROR: RET                      ; A NEW SUBROUTINE
54:                         *
55:   004B                         END
```

Figure P Part of the extra code that has to be added to ADC4 to satisfy Question 7.13

```
 1:
 2:
 3:                         *  SUBROUTINE PERROR
 4:                         *  ==================
 5:                         *
 6:                         *  PRINTS OUT THE TOTAL ERROR COUNT TO DATE WHEN REPORTING ON
 7:                         *  THE ERROR STATUS
 8:                         *
 9:                         *                STRUCTURE
10:                         *                '''''''''
11:                         *  BEGIN
12:                         *      GET ERROR COUNT (4 BCD CHARACTERS)
13:                         *      PRINT FIRST
14:                         *      PRINT SECOND
15:                         *      PRINT THIRD
16:                         *      PRINT FOURTH (LEAST SIGNIFICANT)
17:                         *  END
18:                         *
19:    0000 2A1400    PERROR: LHLD    ERRCNT        ; (L)=LS HALF, (H)=MS HALF
20:    0003 7C                MOV     A,H           ; GET FIRST TWO
21:    0004 CD1600            CALL    PRNLFT        ; PRINT FIRST
22:    0007 7C                MOV     A,H
23:    0008 CD1700            CALL    PRNRGT        ; PRINT SECOND
24:    000B 7D                MOV     A,L
25:    000C CD1600            CALL    PRNLFT        ; PRINT THIRD
26:    000F 7D                MOV     A,L
27:    0010 CD1700            CALL    PRNRGT        ; PRINT LAST
28:    0013 C9                RET
29:                    *
30:                    *  ADDRESSES DEFINED ELSEWHERE ARE:
31:                    *
32:    0014            ERRCNT: DS      2
33:    0016 C9         PRNLFT: RET
34:    0017 C9         PRNRGT: RET
35:                    *
36:    0018                    END
```

Figure Q   The PERROR subroutine that is called from STATUS

```
 1:
 2:
 3:                    *    SUBROUTINE CNTERR
 4:                    *    ================
 5:                    *
 6:                    *    THIS SUBROUTINE UPDATES THE ERROR COUNTER WHENEVER AN ALARM
 7:                    *    CONDITION IS DETECTED
 8:                    *
 9:                    *                    STRUCTURE
10:                    *                    '''''''''
11:                    *    BEGIN
12:                    *        GET ERROR COUNT
13:                    *        LS HALF := LS HALF + 1
14:                    *        CONVERT BACK TO BCD
15:                    *        MS HALF := MS HALF + 0 + (CARRY)
16:                    *        CONVERT BACK TO BCD
17:                    *        RESTORE THE ERROR COUNTER
18:                    *    END
19:                    *
20:   0100                        ORG     0100H           ; INCLUDED FOR DEBUGGING ONLY
21:   0100 2A1101       CNTERR: LHLD    ERRCNT          ; (L)=LS HALF, (H)=MS HALF
22:   0103 7D                   MOV     A,L
23:   0104 C601                 ADI     01H             ; LS HALF := LS HALF + 1
24:   0106 27                   DAA                     ; CONVERT TO BCD
25:   0107 6F                   MOV     L,A
26:   0108 7C                   MOV     A,H
27:   0109 CE00                 ACI     00H             ; ADD ANY CARRY TO MS HALF
28:   010B 27                   DAA                     ; CONVERT TO BCD
29:   010C 67                   MOV     H,A
30:   010D 221101               SHLD    ERRCNT          ; RESTORE ERROR COUNTER
31:   0110 C9                   RET
32:                    *
33:   0111             ERRCNT: DS      2
34:                    *
```

Figure R   The CNTERR subroutine that is called from the modified ADC4 whenever an alarm condition is detected

```
LOW ALARM AT 01:55-MEASURED VALUE WAS 0.75
REPORTING AT 01:55 ERROR COUNT SO FAR IS 0013
HIGH ALARM AT 02:31-MEASURED VALUE WAS 4.03
HIGH ALARM AT 02:32-MEASURED VALUE WAS 4.10
LOW ALARM AT 02:50-MEASURED VALUE WAS 0.94
REPORTING AT 02:51 ERROR COUNT SO FAR IS 0016
```

Figure S   Typical result from the modified ADC4

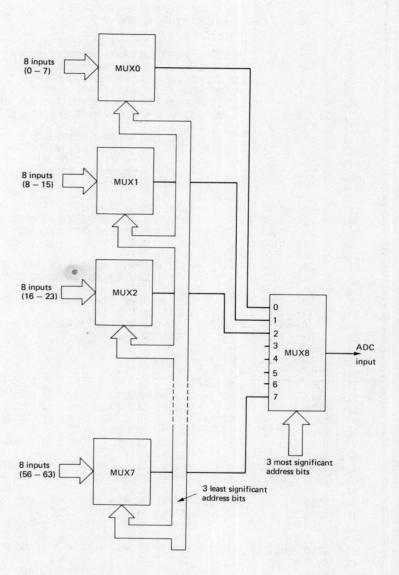

Figure T A system for connecting 64 analogue inputs to a data-acquisition system

Figure U

```
 1:
 2:
 3:                    *    SUBROUTINE   FNDLMT
 4:                    *    ==================
 5:                    *
 6:                    *    THIS SUBROUTINE MAY BE NEEDED IN MULTI-CHANNEL SYSTEMS IN WHICH
 7:                    *    SEVERAL DIFFERENT TRANSDUCERS ARE USED AND EACH MEASURES A
 8:                    *    SYSTEM PARAMETER WHICH HAS DIFFERENT HIGH AND LOW LIMITS. THE
 9:                    *    PROBLEM IS TO LOCATE THE CORRECT LIMIT VALUES, WHICH MAY BE
10:                    *    STORED ANYWHERE IN MEMORY, AND PUT THEM IN 'HLMT' AND 'LLMT' SO
11:                    *    THAT COMP HAS THE APPROPRIATE LIMITS TO WORK WITH.
12:                    *
13:                    *    WE ASSUME THAT IN EACH LIMIT SET THE LOW LIMIT VALUE IS STORED
14:                    *    FIRST.
15:                    *
16:                    *                    STRUCTURE
17:                    *                    '''''''''
18:                    *    BEGIN
19:                    *        TRIAL SET NO. = 7
20:                    *        GET CHANNEL (AND HENCE APPROPRIATE) SET NUMBER
21:                    *        POINT AT ADDRESS OF TRIAL SET
22:                    *        WHILE TRIAL SET NO. <> REQUIRED SET NO. DO
23:                    *        BEGIN
24:                    *            POINT AT ADDRESS OF THE NEXT SET
25:                    *            TRIAL SET NO. := TRIAL SET NO. - 1
26:                    *        END
27:                    *        GET RELEVANT LOW LIMIT VALUE
28:                    *        STORE IN 'LLMT'
29:                    *        GET RELEVANT HIGH LIMIT VALUE
30:                    *        STORE IN 'HLMT'
31:                    *    END
32:                    *
33:    0100                        ORG      0100H
34:    0100 0607       FNDLMT:  MVI      B,07H              ; FIRST TRY FOR LIMIT7
35:    0102 3A3F01              LDA      CHANNL             ; GET CHANNEL NUMBER
36:    0105 211F01              LXI      H,LMTADD           ; POINT AT LIMIT ADDRESS TABLE
37:    0108 B8         TRYAGN:  CMP      B                  ; COMPARE TRIAL WITH ACTUAL
38:    0109 CA1201              JZ       GOTIT              ; IF THE SAME, YOU'VE GOT IT
39:    010C 23                  INX      H                  ; POINT TO NEXT ADDRESS
40:    010D 23                  INX      H
41:    010E 05                  DCR      B                  ; TRY FOR THENEXT SET
42:    010F C30801              JMP      TRYAGN             ; AND TRY AGAIN
43:                    *
44:    0112 5E         GOTIT:   MOV      E,M                ; GET LS HALF OF LIMIT ADDRESS
45:    0113 23                  INX      H
46:    0114 56                  MOV      D,M                ; GET MS HALF OF LIMIT ADDRESS
47:    0115 1A                  LDAX     D                  ; GET LOW LIMIT
48:    0116 324101              STA      LLMT               ; AND STORE
49:    0119 13                  INX      D
50:    011A 1A                  LDAX     D                  ; GET HIGH LIMIT
51:    011B 324001              STA      HLMT               ; AND STORE
52:    011E C9                  RET                         ; LIMITS CORRECTLY STORED
53:                    *
54:    011F 2F01       LMTADD:  DW       LIMIT7
55:    0121 3101                DW       LIMIT6
56:    0123 3301                DW       LIMIT5
57:    0125 3501                DW       LIMIT4
58:    0127 3701                DW       LIMIT3
59:    0129 3901                DW       LIMIT2
```

(Continued)

```
Figure U continued
60:   012B 3B01               DW      LIMIT1
61:   012D 3D01               DW      LIMIT0
62:                     *
63:                     *  NOTE LIMIT VALUES COULD BE ANYWHERE IN MEMORY, THEY NEED
64:                     *  NOT BE IN CONSECUTIVE ADDRESSES
65:                     *
66:   012F 01       LIMIT7: DB      01H              ; ASSUMED LOW LIMIT FIRST
67:   0130 10               DB      10H              ; THEN HIGH LIMIT
68:   0131 02       LIMIT6: DB      02H
69:   0132 20               DB      20H
70:   0133 03       LIMIT5: DB      03H
71:   0134 30               DB      30H
72:   0135 04       LIMIT4: DB      04H
73:   0136 40               DB      40H
74:   0137 05       LIMIT3: DB      05H
75:   0138 50               DB      50H
76:   0139 06       LIMIT2: DB      06H
77:   013A 60               DB      60H
78:   013B 07       LIMIT1: DB      07H
79:   013C 70               DB      70H
80:   013D 08       LIMIT0: DB      08H
81:   013E 80               DB      80H
82:                     *
83:                     *  EXTERNAL ADDRESS REFERENCES
84:                     *
85:   013F 03       CHANNL: DB      03H              ; FOR TESTING
86:   0140         HLMT:   DS      1
87:   0141         LLMT:   DS      1
88:                     *
89:   0142                 END
```

Figure U   The FNDLMT subroutine

8.3   The variable reluctance motor has a different number of rotor and stator teeth. In one step position two (or more) pairs of stator/rotor teeth are aligned by virtue of the electromagnetic pull exerted on the rotor teeth by the energised stator windings (phase). Other pairs of teeth are misaligned by the step angle. When the energisation is switched to a different stator phase, the rotor is pulled around through the step angle so that different pairs of teeth are aligned. One step pulse is therefore converted into a different pattern of stator excitation by the motor interface circuit.

8.4   This is the torque present when the motor is switched off. If it exists, it does so because the motor incorporates some form of permanent magnet.

8.5   Briefly, this device comprises a rotor which is magnetised along its length and has gear-like constructions machined at each end. There are 50 teeth on each gear-wheel and they are offset by 180°. The stator has 8 poles with 5 teeth protruding from each pole. When the stator excitation is changed, the combination of rotor construction and its magnetic orientation, and the way in which the rotor and stator teeth become magnetically meshed, causes the rotor to step through 1/200th of a revolution.

8.6   *Static torque*   When the rotor is completely aligned with the stator field the motor does not produce any torque. To develop torque, the rotor must be displaced from its equilibrium magnetic position. The torque which is then produced is a function of the displacement angle and its maximum value is called the holding torque.

Dynamic torque   This is the torque developed by a stepping motor at a particular step rate. It is a measure of the ability of the motor to drive a load at a particular speed. The dynamic torque reduces as the speed increases.

Maximum pull-in rate   This is the maximum speed which a motor at rest can achieve without loosing steps. It is related to the demanded (pull-in) torque which the motor can develop at the pull-in rate. The greater the motor load (and therefore demanded torque) the lower the maximum pull-in rate.

Maximum pull-out rate   This is the maximum speed which a motor can achieve when gradually accelerated, without loosing steps.

Slew range   This is the difference between the pull-in and pull-out rates at a particular torque. When a motor is running at some speed within this range, it cannot be stopped or reversed abruptly, without loosing steps.

Resonance   This is a phenomenon which occurs at or around a particular step rate (and maybe more than one), in which the motor action ceases to be synchronised with the incoming step pulses. Damping, much like adding resistance to an L-C-R circuit, improves the situation.

Mechanical and electrical data for a particular machine is usually presented in the following way:

(Sigma) motor number – 20–2215D200– E04
Torque (dynamic) at 50 steps/s – 22 oz.in/0.16 N.m
Holding torque – 27 oz.in/0.19 N.m
Detent torque – 1.5 oz.in/0.01 N.m
Rotor inertia – 0.30 $oz.in^2/10^{-3}kg.m^2$
Weight – 0.8 lb/0.36 kg
Phase resistance – 1.4 Ω
Phase inductance – 1.25 mH $\pm$ 20%

The torque/speed information is usually given in the form of a performance curve similar to the one shown in Figure V. The dips in the curve are potential resonance areas. The two dotted curves show

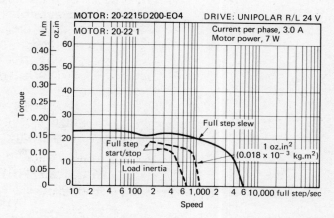

MOTOR: 20-2215D200-EO4   DRIVE: UNIPOLAR R/L 24 V

Figure V Typical torque/speed curves for a 200 steps/revolution hybrid stepping motor. *(Reproduced with permission from the Sigma catalogue)*

the pull-in torque/pull-in speed relationship for two different load inertias and the boldface curve would, in the UK, be called the pull-out torque/speed curve. It is from information in this form that a system designer must decide whether a particular motor is powerful enough for the application in mind.

8.7 Stepping a stepping motor from one step position to the next involves switching a d.c. supply from one set of stator windings to another. Since the windings are inductive, it takes time for the rated current, and therefore the rated torque, to be achieved. If the switching speed is changing so fast that the rated current is never achieved then the torque developed must be less than maximum. Obviously, this will get worse as the switching speed is increased.

The torque/speed curve can be improved by either adding resistance in series with the inductive stator windings to reduce the time constant (L/R), or by using a chopper drive circuit which causes the stator current to build up very rapidly. This second method is used for high-speed operation of stepping motors.

9.1 A suitable structure would be:

```
BEGIN
     Establish table:  FIRST   = 09
                       SECOND  = 10
                       THIRD   = 06
                       LAST    = 05
     Set POINTER = FIRST
```

```
                    Send (POINTER) to establish start position.
                    REPEAT  (*Forever*)
                        Read DIRECTION
                        IF DIRECTION = 0 THEN  (*Go down the table*)
                            IF POINTER <> LAST THEN
                                POINTER = POINTER+1
                            ELSE
                                POINTER = FIRST
                            ENDIF
                        ELSE  (*DIRECTION = 1, CCW*)
                            IF POINTER <> FIRST THEN
                                POINTER = POINTER-1
                            ELSE
                                POINTER = LAST
                            ENDIF
                        ENDIF
                        Send (POINTER) to motor
                        DELAY
                    Until infinity
            END
```

9.2 A program called STEP2 is listed in Figure W. The only changes needed to make this program generate a negative-going pulse are:

1   The constants CW and CCW should now be 01 and 10000001B, respectively, so that the step line starts off high.
2   The INR A and DCR A instructions in subroutine PULSE should be interchanged. To start a pulse execute DCR A and to end it execute a INR A.

9.3 Since there are 14 clock cycles in the decrement-jump non-zero loop, the formula for calculating delays for a single-register delay routine is:

$$T = \text{CONSTANT} \times 14 \times 0.25 \ \mu s$$

Therefore when CONSTANT = 6,

$$T = 6 \times 14 \times 0.25 \ \mu s = 21 \ \mu s$$

9.4 This program is called STEP4 and is listed in Figure X.

9.5 Using the standard formula, the width is

$$T = [(1 \times 14) + (5 \times 14)]0.25 \ \mu s = 21 \ \mu s$$

and the period

$$T = [(6 \times 14) + (142 \times 14) + (5 \times 256 \times 14)]0.25 \ \mu s$$
$$= 4.998 \ ms$$

```
  1:
  2:
  3:                              *    PROGRAM NAME : STEP2
  4:                              *
  5:                              *    THIS PROGRAM DRIVES A STEPPING MOTOR THROUGH ONE STEP
  6:                              *    IN THE DIRECTION READ FROM A DIRECTION SWITCH, AND
  7:                              *    THEN RETURNS CONTROL TO CP/M.
  8:                              *    STEPPING MOTOR CONNECTIONS ARE:
  9:                              *                         STEP      - D0 OF PORT FF
 10:                              *                         DIRECTION - D7 OF PORT FF
 11:                              *    THE DIRECTION SWITCH CONNECTION IS:
 12:                              *                                   - D7 OF PORT FE
 13:                              *
 14:                              *                    STRUCTURE
 15:                              *                    '''''''''
 16:                              *    BEGIN
 17:                              *        READ DIRECTION BIT
 18:                              *        IF DIRECTION BIT = 1 THEN
 19:                              *             DRIVE = CCW
 20:                              *        ELSE
 21:                              *             DRIVE = CW
 22:                              *        ENDIF
 23:                              *        PULSE MOTOR
 24:                              *        RETURN TO CP/M
 25:                              *    END
 26:                              *
 27: 0100                              ORG      0100H
 28:                              *
 29: 0100 DBFE         BGN:    IN       DIRPRT         ; READ DIRECTION BIT
 30: 0102 E680                 ANI      80H            ; TEST IT
 31: 0104 CA0D01               JZ       ELSE           ; DIRECTION = 0, MEANS CW
 32: 0107 3A2301               LDA      CCW            ; OTHERWISE ITS CCW
 33: 010A C31001               JMP      REST
 34: 010D 3A2401        ELSE:   LDA      CW
 35: 0110 D3FF          REST:   OUT      MTRPRT         ; INITIALISE DIRECTION LINE
 36: 0112 0606                  MVI      B,06H          ; INITIALISE FOR TIMING
 37: 0114 CD1801                CALL     PULSE          ; PULSE THE MOTOR
 38: 0117 C9                    RET                     ; RETURN TO CP/M
 39:                      *
 40:                      *  SAME PULSE SUBROUTINE AS BEFORE IS USED !
 41:                      *
 42: 0118 3C           PULSE:  INR      A
 43: 0119 D3FF                 OUT      MTRPRT         ; START A PULSE
 44: 011B 05           TIME:   DCR      B
 45: 011C C21B01               JNZ      TIME           ; WAIT FOR TIME TO ELAPSE
 46: 011F 3D                   DCR      A
 47: 0120 D3FF                 OUT      MTRPRT         ; END PULSE
 48: 0122 C9                   RET
 49:                      *
 50:                      *  PROGRAM DATA
 51:                      *
 52: 00FF =            MTRPRT: EQU      0FFH           ; MOTOR PORT ADDRESS
 53: 00FE =            DIRPRT: EQU      0FEH           ; SWITCH PORT ADDRESS
 54: 0123 80           CCW:    DB       10000000B      ; COUNTERCLOCKWISE
 55: 0124 00           CW:     DB       0              ; CLOCKWISE
 56:                      *
 57: 0125                      END
```

Figure W The program STEP2

```
 1:
 2:
 3:                    *    PROGRAM NAME : STEP4
 4:                    *
 5:                    *    THIS PROGRAM DRIVES A STEPPING MOTOR CONTINUOUSLY IN
 6:                    *    THE DIRECTION READ FROM A DIRECTION SWITCH.
 7:                    *    MOTOR AND DIRECTION SWITCH CONNECTIONS ARE AS IN STEP2.
 8:                    *
 9:                    *              STRUCTURE
10:                    *              '''''''''
11:                    *    BEGIN
12:                    *        REPEAT
13:                    *            READ DIRECTION BIT
14:                    *            IF DIRECTION BIT = 1 THEN DRIVE = CCW
15:                    *            ELSE                     DRIVE = CW
16:                    *            ENDIF
17:                    *            PULSE MOTOR
18:                    *            DELAY FOR PULSE PERIOD
19:                    *        UNTIL INFINITY
20:                    *    END
21:                    *
22:     0100                      ORG     0100H
23:                    *
24:     0100 DBFE      BGN:   IN      DIRPRT          ;READ DIRECTION BIT
25:     0102 E680             ANI     80H             ;TEST IT
26:     0104 CA0D01           JZ      ELSE            ;DIRECTION = 0, MEANS CW
27:     0107 3A3401           LDA     CCW             ;OTHERWISE ITS CCW
28:     010A C31001           JMP     REST
29:     010D 3A3501     ELSE:  LDA     CW
30:     0110 D3FF       REST:  OUT     MTRPRT          ;INITIALISE DIRECTION LINE
31:     0112 CD1E01            CALL    PULSE           ;GENERATE A STEP PULSE
32:     0115 018E06            LXI     B,PERIOD        ;SET-UP B FOR PERIOD
33:     0118 CD2B01            CALL    DELAY           ;DELAY
34:     011B C30001            JMP     BGN             ;REPEAT INDEFINITELY
35:                    *
36:     011E 010501     PULSE: LXI     B,WIDTH         ;SET-UP B FOR WIDTH
37:     0121 3C                INR     A               ;MAKE D0 IN A = 1
38:     0122 D3FF              OUT     MTRPRT          ;START A PULSE
39:     0124 CD2B01            CALL    DELAY           ;DELAY FOR PULSE WIDTH
40:     0127 3D                DCR     A               ;MAKE D0 A 0
41:     0128 D3FF              OUT     MTRPRT          ;END PULSE
42:     012A C9                RET                     ;RETURN TO MAIN PROG.
43:                    *
44:     012B 0D         DELAY: DCR     C               ;LSCONS:=LSCONS-1
45:     012C C22B01            JNZ     DELAY           ;LOOP IF LSCONS>0
46:     012F 05                DCR     B               ;ELSE MSCONS:=MSCONS-1
47:     0130 C22B01            JNZ     DELAY           ;BOTH MUST BE 0 TO
48:     0133 C9                RET                     ;RETURN
49:                    *
50:                    *    CONSTANTS
51:                    *
52:     00FF =         MTRPRT: EQU     0FFH
53:     00FE =         DIRPRT: EQU     0FEH            ;SWITCH PORT ADDRESS
54:     0134 80        CCW:    DB      10000000B
55:     0135 00        CW:     DB      00
56:     0105 =         WIDTH:  EQU     0105H           ;DEFINES PULSE WIDTH
57:     068E =         PERIOD: EQU     068EH           ;DEFINES PULSE PERIOD
58:                    *
59:     0136                   END
```

Figure X The program STEP4

9.6   Briefly stated, the problem is:

1   For linear acceleration, the speed increases at a uniform (linear) rate.

2   We increase speed by reducing the time between step pulses.

3   Speed $= 1/$time, therefore for linear acceleration we have to uniformly increase the number $1/$time.

4   We can calculate speed easily enough, but calculating the required reciprocal of speed, and from that a delay constant, is not so easy.

Acceleration is necessary when the required speed is greater than the pull-in rate. You will recall that, for a given motor load, i.e. required motor torque, the pull-in rate is the maximum speed at which a motor can be started from rest.

9.7   The program called CYCLE, which drives the motor with a negative-going step pulse, is listed in Figure Y.

9.8   Assuming that register pair BC contains –1 (0FFFFH), the DAD B instruction will reduce the number in H,L by 1. A carry is always generated except when H,L contains 0. The Z flag is not affected at all by this instruction. Consequently, if H,L contains 5 on entry to the delay routine, the first five additions of –1 will generate a carry but the sixth will not. Our new delay routine will therefore take the form:

```
DELAY:   DAD   B       (11)
         JC    DELAY  (10)
         RET
```

If H,L contains zero on entry, the loop is executed once, and if it contains 65535 (0FFFFH) the loop is executed 65,536 times. The maximum delay is therefore:

$$65,536 \times 22 \times 0.25 \ \mu s = 0.36 \ s$$

The clock cycles for the two instructions in the loop are the equivalent Z80 figures since we have assumed that the program will run in a Z80-based North Star Horizon.

10.1   The need for a high-level language becomes evident when programming all but the most modest problems. Such languages enable you to tackle the problem directly without worrying about which CPU registers are available at a particular point in the program.

10.2   Following on from the previous answer, the advantages of an HLL are, briefly:

1   Programming is easier.

Figure Y

```
 1:
 2:
 3:                    *   PROGRAM NAME : CYCLE
 4:                    *
 5:                    *   THIS PROGRAM DRIVES A STEPPING MOTOR THROUGH THE FOLLOWING
 6:                    *   CYCLE:
 7:                    *          5 REVOLUTIONS AT SLOW (50 STEPS/SEC) SPEED
 8:                    *          5 REVOLUTIONS AT HIGH (200 STEPS/SEC) SPEED
 9:                    *          5 REVOLUTIONS AT SLOW SPEED AGAIN
10:                    *          CHANGE DIRECTION AND REPEAT
11:                    *
12:                    *   MOTOR PORT CONNECTIONS ARE AS BEFORE.
13:                    *   MOTOR DRIVE PULSE IS NEGATIVE-GOING
14:                    *
15:                    *                 STRUCTURE
16:                    *                 '''''''''
17:                    *   BEGIN
18:                    *       INITIALISE STEP LINE HIGH, DIRECTION CW
19:                    *       SPEED = SLOW
20:                    *       REPEAT
21:                    *           DRIVE FOR 5 REVOLUTIONS
22:                    *           SPEED = FAST
23:                    *           DRIVE FOR 5 REVOLUTIONS
24:                    *           SPEED = SLOW
25:                    *           DRIVE FOR 5 REVOLUTIONS
26:                    *           IF DIRECTION = CCW THEN DIRECTION := CW
27:                    *           ELSE                    DIRECTION := CCW
28:                    *           ENDIF
29:                    *       UNTIL INFINITY
30:                    *   END
31:                    *
32:    0100                      ORG      0100H
33:                    *
34:    0100 3A5401     BGN:      LDA      CW
35:    0103 D3FF                 OUT      MTRPRT         ; STEP=1, DIRECTION=CW
36:    0105 213B17               LXI      H,SLOW
37:    0108 225501               SHLD     PERIOD         ; SPEED = SLOW
38:                    *
39:    010B CD3101     LOOP:     CALL     DRIVE          ; DRIVE FOR 5 REVS
40:    010E 218E06               LXI      H,FAST
41:    0111 225501               SHLD     PERIOD         ; SPEED = FAST
42:    0114 CD3101               CALL     DRIVE          ; DRIVE AGAIN
43:    0117 213B17               LXI      H,SLOW
44:    011A 225501               SHLD     PERIOD         ; SPEED = SLOW
45:    011D CD3101               CALL     DRIVE
46:                    *
47:    0120 E680                 ANI      80H            ; TEST CURRENT DIRECTION
48:    0122 CA2B01               JZ       NOWCCW         ; IF CW THEN MAKE IT CCW
49:    0125 3A5401               LDA      CW             ; ELSE MAKE IT CW
50:    0128 C32E01               JMP      NDIF
51:    012B 3A5301     NOWCCW:   LDA      CCW
52:    012E C30B01     NDIF:     JMP      LOOP           ; DIRECTION CHANGED, REPEAT
53:                    *
54:                    *   SUBROUTINE DRIVE
55:                    *
56:                    *   DRIVES A STEPPING MOTOR FOR 5 REVOLUTIONS
57:                    *
58:                    *                 STRUCTURE
59:                    *                 '''''''''
```

Figure Y continued

```
60:                      *     BEGIN
61:                      *         INITIALISE PULSECNT = 240
62:                      *         REPEAT
63:                      *             GENERATE A DRIVE PULSE
64:                      *             DELAY FOR FAST OR SLOW PERIOD
65:                      *             PULSECNT := PULSECNT - 1
66:                      *         UNTIL PULSECNT = 0
67:                      *     END
68:                      *
69:   0131  16F0         DRIVE:  MVI   D,PLSCNT      ; INITIALISE PULSECNT
70:   0133  210501       MORE:   LXI   H,WIDTH
71:   0136  3D                   DCR   A
72:   0137  D3FF                 OUT   MTRPRT        ; START A PULSE
73:   0139  CD4A01               CALL  DELAY         ; DEFINE WIDTH
74:   013C  3C                   INR   A
75:   013D  D3FF                 OUT   MTRPRT        ; END PULSE
76:   013F  2A5501               LHLD  PERIOD
77:   0142  CD4A01               CALL  DELAY         ; DEFINE SPEED
78:   0145  15                   DCR   D             ; PULSECNT := PULSECNT - 1
79:   0146  C23301               JNZ   MORE
80:   0149  C9                   RET
81:                      *
82:                      *   STANDARD DELAY ROUTINE FOLLOWS
83:                      *
84:   014A  2D           DELAY:  DCR   L
85:   014B  C24A01               JNZ   DELAY
86:   014E  25                   DCR   H
87:   014F  C24A01               JNZ   DELAY
88:   0152  C9                   RET
89:                      *
90:                      *   PROGRAM DATA
91:                      *
92:   00FF  =            MTRPRT: EQU   0FFH
93:   0153  81           CCW:    DB    10000001B
94:   0154  01           CW:     DB    1
95:   0105  =            WIDTH:  EQU   0105H
96:   068E  =            FAST:   EQU   068EH
97:   173B  =            SLOW:   EQU   173BH
98:   0155               PERIOD: DS    2
99:   00F0  =            PLSCNT: EQU   240D
100:                     *
101:  0157                       END
```

Figure Y   The program CYCLE

2   Programmer productivity is improved because programs can be produced more quickly.

3   HLL programs are easier to understand.

4   As a consequence of 2 and 3 above, software production and maintenance costs are reduced.

5   HLL programs are portable, or at least more portable than assembly language programs.

The disadvantages are that HLL programs almost always occupy more memory than equivalent assembly language programs, and that language extensions, such as the method by which I/O drivers are included, are different in every system supporting the language.

10.3   Basically, the difference is that a compiler produces an executable object code program but an interpreter does not. The interpreter is always in memory when the user program is running and generates object code on a line-by-line basis. In other words, the interpreter will have to go through the same translation process every time the program runs. Compilation on the other hand is a once-for-all operation. Refer back to the text for a fuller explanation of the difference.

10.4   The most common languages are given in the text. Summarising the characteristics of each in a few words:

FORTRAN	– is a mathematically orientated language
ALGOL	– is a block-structured algorithmic language
COBOL	– is a business-orientated language
BASIC	– is a beginner's language
PASCAL	– is very much like ALGOL
PL/M	– is Intel's 8080/8085/8086 HLL
MPL	– is Motorola's equivalent of PL/M
PL/Z	– is the Zilog equivalent
LISP	– is good for artificial intelligence applications (see ref. 10.11)
FORTH	– is a 'threaded code' language – very compact (see ref. 10.10)

There are others, but those mentioned, together with assembly language, probably account for the vast majority of code written for microcomputers.

10.5   The problem with BASIC is that there is nothing in the language which forces a programmer to design programs in a logical manner. Admittedly, rules can be self-imposed [10.9], but they seldom are. As a result, BASIC programs are often littered with GOTO statements which direct the reader to some other part of the listing. BASIC is a victim of its own simplicity. It has a restricted vocabulary which is quick and easy to learn, but very restrictive. It is popular in the personal computing world where the exhilaration of seeing a program work properly for the first time is seldom tempered by the need to make the program understandable to others. It is only fair to point out, however, that opinions vary on the merits or otherwise of BASIC.

The discipline of PASCAL, which some would say stifles programming 'flair', forces a programmer to design programs in a logical way. It is the HLL realisation of our structure statements which were proposed as a better method of documenting programs than flowcharts. It includes all the classical control constructs, like WHILE DO and REPEAT-UNTIL, and has precisely set-out rules regarding program syntax and the ways in which variables can be used. Like everything else though, it does have disadvantages but these are, mostly, features which stop you doing something which was perfectly legal in the language you used before PASCAL. If your previous language was BASIC, this may be an advantage.

10.6 The point here is that UCSD PASCAL uses a compiler to compile down to P-code, and an interpreter to interpret the P-code at run-time (see Figure 10.3). This means that if, for example, UCSD PASCAL runs on an 8080-based machine, there is no 8080 object code which can be committed to ROM or EPROM and then plugged into a dedicated 8080 system. There are PASCAL compilers which produce ROMable object code, but UCSD PASCAL is not one of them.

10.7 Briefly:

1 A function always returns a value whereas a procedure may return one or more values, but need not.
2 A function is always passed a value (parameter) to work on whereas a procedure may be passed parameters but could equally well be an independent code block.

10.8 The stack is organised differently depending on whether the call is to a function or a procedure. Figures 10.5 and 10.6 illustrate the difference.

10.9 The main body of the program could be written as,

```
ADCPORT: = 254;
REPEAT
     VALUE: = READBIN (ADCPORT);
     IF VALUE > HIGHLIMIT THEN
          WRITELN ('HIGH LIMIT EXCEEDED')
     ELSE
          IF VALUE < LOWLIMIT THEN
               WRITELN ('LOW LIMIT ALARM')
UNTIL FALSE;
```

10.10 The maximum value which can be read is 4095 decimal, which can be contained in a PASCAL INTEGER variable. Two IN instructions will be needed to read the 8 most significant bits and then the least significant 4 bits. Because of the way the 4 least significant bits are connected to the system, and assuming that two IN instructions can be built as shown in READBIN, the plan could be:

```
$
PROGRAM TEST;
TYPE
     DELAYARRAY = ARRAY [1..239] OF INTEGER;
VAR
     DELAYS : DELAYARRAY;
     REVS   : INTEGER;



PROCEDURE WORKOUTDELAYS (VAR SPEEDUPREVS : INTEGER;VAR DELAYS : DELAYARRAY);

VAR
     INITIAL, FINAL, ACCELERATION, PRESENT, NEXT : REAL;
     PULSENO, TOTALPULSES : INTEGER;
BEGIN
     WRITE ('INITIAL STEP RATE ?');
     READLN (INITIAL);
     WRITE ('FINAL STEP RATE   ?');
     READLN (FINAL);
     WRITE ('NUMBER OF REVOLUTIONS IN WHICH TO ACCELERATE - MAX IS 5 ?');
     READLN (SPEEDUPREVS);
     WRITELN;
     WRITELN;         (* Three blank lines between the input data and the table *)
     WRITELN;
     DELAYS[1] := ROUND (4000/INITIAL - 8);        (* First delay sets INITIAL *)
     WRITE ('SPEED AT PULSE  2 = ',INITIAL,' STEPS/SEC. ');
     WRITELN ('DELAY CONSTANT BETWEEN PULSES  1 AND  2 IS ',DELAYS[1]);
     TOTALPULSES := SPEEDUPREVS * 48;
     ACCELERATION := (SQR(FINAL) - SQR(INITIAL))/(2 * (TOTALPULSES - 2));
     PULSENO := 3;
     PRESENT := INITIAL;

     REPEAT (* Until the rest of the delays have been calculated *)
          NEXT := SQRT(SQR(PRESENT) + 2 * ACCELERATION);
          DELAYS[PULSENO - 1] := ROUND (4000/NEXT - 8);
          WRITE ('SPEED AT PULSE ',PULSENO:2,' = ',NEXT,' STEPS/SEC. ');
          WRITE ('DELAY CONSTANT BETWEEN PULSES ',PULSENO-1:2);
          WRITELN (' AND ',PULSENO:2,' IS ',DELAYS[PULSENO - 1]);
          PRESENT := NEXT;
          PULSENO := PULSENO + 1;
     UNTIL PULSENO = TOTALPULSES + 1;

END   (* Of delay calculation *);



BEGIN
     WORKOUTDELAYS (REVS, DELAYS);
END.
*
```

Figure Z The modified WORKOUTDELAYS procedure which prints results

Read the 8 most significant bits	(IN ADDRESS)
Store in register D	(MOV D,A)
Read LS 4 bits	(IN ADDRESS+1)
Store in E	(MOV E,A)
Clear A	(XRA A)
Shift (D) so that the LS 4 bits in D finish in the MS 4 bits of A, with MS 4 bits of D = 0.	(Subroutine)
Combine with LS 4 bits of VALUE	(ADD E)
Put back in E	(MOV E,A)
Put D and E on the stack	(PUSH D)
Return to PASCAL	

The form of the external function declaration will be,

```
FUNCTION READADC (ADDRESS:INTEGER):INTEGER;
EXTERNAL;
```

Alternatively we could use READBIN twice and add the results. For example:

```
MSVALUE: = READBIN (ADDRESS);
LSVALUE: = READBIN (ADDRESS+1);
VALUE   : = LSVALUE + MSVALUE;
```

We have the choice but the second method is probably easier.

10.11 The procedure was actually tested with a one-line main program. It is listed in Figure Z with the added WRITE/WRITELN statements marked. Incidentally, the ':2' after the variable identifier PULSENO indicates that two character positions are allocated on the printout for this variable. It is included just to get the required print format.

10.12 The procedure is listed in Figure AA.

10.13 I/O drivers, interrupt service routines and any code section which must run at maximum speed.

```
$
PROCEDURE UPDATECLOCK;
(* Up-dates a RTC whenever a one-minute interrupt occurs *)

BEGIN
     MINUTES := MINUTES + 1;
     IF MINUTES = 60 THEN
     BEGIN
          MINUTES := 0;
          HOURS := HOURS + 1
     END;
     IF HOURS = 24 THEN HOURS := 0;
END;
*
```

Figure AA   Procedure UPDATECLOCK

Index